Future Trends and US National Security

Lt Col John T. Ackerman, PhD, Editor
USAF, Retired

Col Kathleen Mahoney-Norris, PhD, Editor
USAFR, Retired

Air University Press
Air Force Research Institute
Maxwell Air Force Base, Alabama

January 2015

Project Editor
Belinda L. Bazinet

Copy Editor
Sandi D. Davis

Cover Art, Book Design, and Illustrations
L. Susan Fair
Daniel Armstrong

Composition and Prepress Production
Nedra Looney

Print Preparation and Distribution
Diane Clark

AIR FORCE RESEARCH INSTITUTE

AIR UNIVERSITY PRESS

Director and Publisher
Allen G. Peck

Editor in Chief
Oreste M. Johnson

Managing Editor
Demorah Hayes

Design and Production Manager
Cheryl King

Air University Press
155 N. Twining St., Bldg. 693
Maxwell AFB, AL 36112-6026
afri.aupress@us.af.mil

http://aupress.au.af.mil/
http://afri.au.af.mil/

Library of Congress Cataloging-in-Publication Data

Future trends and US national security / Lt Col John T.
Ackerman, PhD, editor, USAF, Retired ; Col Kathleeen
Mahoney-Norris, PhD, editor, USAFR, Retired.
    pages cm
Includes bibliographical references and index.
ISBN 978-1-58566-242-5
 1. National security—United States—Forecasting.
 2. Military art and science—Forecasting. 3. Twenty-first
century—Forecasts. I. Ackerman, John T., 1956– II. Mahoney-
Norris, Kathleen.
   UA23.F885 2014
   355'.033073—dc23
                              2014016190

Published by Air University Press in January 2015

Disclaimer

AIR FORCE RESEARCH INSTITUTE

Contents

Illustrations

Figure

CONTENTS

Table

About the Authors

Lt Col John T. Ackerman, PhD, USAF, retired, is an assistant professor of Political Science at Ashford University. Before this new position, he was an associate professor of national security studies at the USAF's Air Command and Staff College (ACSC) and the International Security Studies course director for the ACSC Department of Distance Learning. A retired Air Force lieutenant colonel, Dr. Ackerman has held assignments in intercontinental ballistic missile operations and training and has taught professional military education courses to both company grade and field grade officers. Dr. Ackerman holds a PhD in political science from the University of Alabama and master's degrees in political science, military operational art and science, and information systems management. His research efforts have included exploration into the relationships between sustainability and security, the international relations implications of global climate change, and the impact of selected strategic trends on national security. Dr. Ackerman is published in multiple journals, including *Technology*, *Strategic Studies Quarterly*, *Air and Space Power Journal*, *Joint Forces Quarterly*, and *Journal of Peace Research*.

Lt Col Amanda S. Birch, USAFR, is the commander (individual mobilization augmentee), 4th Civil Engineer Squadron, Seymour Johnson AFB, North Carolina. Colonel Birch is a distinguished graduate of the USAF Academy, where she earned bachelor of science degrees in mechanical engineering and engineering sciences with a French minor. She holds a master of science degree in mechanical engineering from the Massachusetts Institute of Technology where she was a National Science Foundation Graduate Research Fellow. She earned a master of military operational art and science as a distinguished graduate of ACSC. Colonel Birch is also a distinguished graduate of Squadron Officer School and a licensed professional engineer. Her previous assignments include expeditionary engineering at the Air Staff and Air Forces Central Command; civil engineer operations flight commander at Andrews AFB, Maryland; chief of base development at Elmendorf AFB, Alaska; and executive officer at the Air Force Research Laboratory Munitions Directorate, Eglin AFB, Florida.

Lt Col Jack Donahue, USAF, is currently assigned as a systems acquisition manager with the US Special Operations Command, MacDill AFB, Florida. He has served in several space acquisition positions, including the Education with Industry Program at Honeywell Space Systems, Inc., Clearwater, Florida, as a member of the Space Guidance and Navigation Product Qualification Development Team. He also served as the Delta IV mission manager for the first operational, largest-ever Air Force heavy-lift rocket mission worth $800 million at the Headquarters Space and Missiles Center, Los Angeles AFB, California. Colonel Donahue holds a bachelor's degree in aviation management from Embry-Riddle Aeronautical University, a master's degree in human resources development from Webster University, and a master's degree in military operational art and science from ACSC.

Lt Col Lourdes M. Duvall, USAF, is the commander, 6th Intelligence Squadron, Osan AB, Republic of Korea. Colonel Duvall is a distinguished graduate of the USAF Academy, where she earned a bachelor of science degree in political science. She holds a master's degree in public policy from Harvard University's Kennedy School of Government and a master of military operational art and science degree as a distinguished graduate of ACSC. Her previous assignments include unit, wing, numbered air force, Air Staff, and Joint Staff positions, as well as serving on the faculty of ACSC in the Department of International Security and Military Studies.

Maj Kelvin S. Fan, Singapore Air Force, was awarded the Singapore Armed Forces (SAF) overseas scholarship and read economics at Cambridge University. He went on to graduate with a master's degree in international and developmental economics from Yale University. He is a ground-based air defense officer by training and has also attended the Air Defense Artillery School in Fort Bliss, Texas. His other published articles include "Will China Attack Taiwan" and "Social Capital: Cultivating This Vital Element for the 3rd Generation SAF" in the SAF's *Pointer* magazine.

Maj Yvonne Carrico Gurnick, USAF, retired, served in the Air Force from 1998 to 2009 as a C-130 pilot. Her master's thesis, "The USAF and Alternative Jet Fuel: How to Fuel the Future of Airpower," was born out of an interest in aviation as well as the environmental, political, and military implications of US dependence on petroleum. She was honored to receive both the Future Trends Studies Research Award and the Lieutenant General John M. Nowak Award for Logistics from Air University (AU) in 2009. Ms. Gurnick currently lives in Clovis, New Mexico, with her husband.

Lt Col Christopher S. Kean, USAF, is the commander of Detachment 10, Training Support Squadron, for Air Combat Command. He is a senior navigator and flies as an electronic warfare officer aboard the RC-135S Cobra Ball, operating out of Offutt AFB, Nebraska. Colonel Kean holds a bachelor of science in engineering sciences from the USAF Academy, a master of arts in French language, literature, and civilization from Middlebury College, and a master of arts in military operational art and science from AU. He has served as an exchange officer to the Canadian Forces School of Aerospace Studies in Winnipeg, Manitoba, where he was the chief of Electronic Warfare Training, and taught French to cadets at the USAF Academy, achieving the academic rank of assistant professor. Colonel Kean has served, flown, and commanded aerial reconnaissance missions worldwide and is a distinguished graduate of ACSC.

Cdr David C. Kneale, US Navy Reserve, began his military officer and naval aviator career as an instructor pilot flying the P-3C based at Naval Air Station (NAS) Whidbey Island, Washington, followed by a tour as an instructor pilot at NAS Pensacola, Florida, flying the T-34C. After a brief stint as an airline pilot and selected reservist, he joined the Navy Reserve's full-time support program. Upon completion of a tour in the C-130T based at NAS Washington, he received his master's degree via the Air Force's ACSC 2008–9 in-residence program, during which time this research was conducted. He has since served at US Central Command in Tampa, Florida, and is currently assigned to US Africa Command in Stuttgart, Germany, where he has served as a Joint Operations Center operations officer and as a member of the combatant commander's special staff. He hails from South Onondaga, New York, and earned his commission and a bachelor of science degree in mechanical engineering from the Rochester Institute of Technology in New York.

Col Kathleen Mahoney-Norris, PhD, US Air Force Reserve (USAFR), retired, is a professor of national security studies at ACSC and currently directs the research program for ACSC's accredited online master's degree. She is an international relations specialist with a PhD in international studies from the University of Denver. Her research and teaching interests focus on national security issues, civil-military relations, military education, democratization and human rights, and Latin American security issues. Dr. Mahoney-Norris's latest publication is *Human Security in a Borderless World.* She has also coedited *Democratization and the Protection of Human Rights: Challenges and Contradictions,* along with various journal articles and book chapters. Dr. Mahoney-Norris retired from the Air Force Reserve with over 26 years of service as an intelligence officer and political-military affairs officer. She is a graduate of the National War College with a master of science degree in national security strategy.

Lt Col Kelly L. Varitz, USAF, is deputy chair for operations for ACSC Distance Learning at Maxwell AFB, Alabama. She assists in managing distance learning operations supporting over 11,000 nonresident ACSC students worldwide. Colonel Varitz integrates technical innovations to improve professional military education for midcareer officers and civilians. She also acts as an adjunct instructor, advising resident students conducting master's-level air, space and cyberspace power studies. Colonel Varitz entered the Air Force in June 1993 and served in various positions in the communications computer systems career field. In 1996 she entered the officer corps and has served in a variety of command and control and communications information positions at squadron, headquarters, agency, and joint levels. She has deployed in support of Operations Southern Watch, Desert Fox, Enduring Freedom, and Iraqi Freedom.

Preface

The study of the future is always a work in progress as the forecasts and prognostications are never entirely correct or valid.[1] Constant adjustments and refinements to ongoing investigations and even new inquiries into fresh and previously undetected topics are an integral component of future studies. Nevertheless, the study of the future is critical as it helps prepare us for uncertainties, revealing potential challenges not identified before the analytical effort began. This type of analysis is particularly valuable when it comes to assessing challenges to national security.

The collection of papers in this book represents an effort to address a number of current and future trends that have national and international security implications, some of which could adversely affect US national security. In fact, the recent report from the National Intelligence Council (NIC), *Global Trends 2030: Alternative Worlds*, underscores several trends that the authors in this anthology analyze. For example, our book includes a chapter that discusses two potential game changers from the NIC report—the "governance gap" and the "role of the United States"—and evaluates the US government's use of mercenaries.[1] Additionally, the chapter scrutinizes an NIC megatrend involving demographic patterns and their potential to create a "demographic arc of instability" in western Europe.[2] Another chapter investigates the ramifications of the megatrend of "individual empowerment" in complex military command and control environments.[3] Furthermore, three chapters evaluate a combination of the NIC megatrend of the "food, water, energy nexus" with select game-changing new technologies.[4] Finally, another chapter investigates potentially game-changing new technologies in the space realm.[5]

The authors are military professionals from the United States and its allies. They completed their research while students at ACSC in either the in-residence or the online master's degree program.

The student authors come from the US Air Force, the US Navy, and the US Army. In addition, an international officer from Singapore contributed a chapter.

These essays were written by Air Command and Staff College students in academic year 2009–2010. They reflect the events and conditions that were current at that time.

The editors' purpose in publishing this diverse analysis is three-fold. First, the book would be an excellent reader for any of the professional military education schools throughout the Department of Defense and for civilian institutions that offer security-focused courses. It could be employed extensively in various international security, international relations, war and politics, defense policy, military history, war fighting, and, naturally, futures-oriented courses. Second, the book is a vehicle to present the top-level scholarship produced by ACSC students (and other AU scholars) to a wider community; in fact, several of the projects here have won research awards. The editors' third objective in producing this work is to stimulate research and discussion of future studies and global security issues. The prospect for US national security depends upon the type of insightful and far-reaching investigation and analysis offered here by the best and the brightest military officers.

Notes

All notes appear in shortened form. For full details, see the appropriate entry in the bibliography.

1. NIC, *Global Trends* 2030, ii, 48–58, and 98–106.
2. Ibid., ii, 20–29, and 98–106.
3. Ibid., ii, 8–14.
4. Ibid., ii, 30–37, and 83–97.
5. Ibid.

Chapter 1

Introduction

Dr. John T. Ackerman and Dr. Kathleen Mahoney-Norris

The study of the future is difficult and dynamic but extraordinarily valuable. Multiple forces have significant influences over how the future unfolds. Political, social, economic, technological, environmental, and military trends create enormous pressures that drive the patterns and currents that shape the future. Even as our world has become more complex, the study of the future has become sophisticated, and new methodologies have evolved to help examine, innovate, and evaluate both potential futures and the decisions that will impact these futures.[1] Unsurprisingly, some of the new futures research methods are highly quantitative while others are wholly qualitative. Yet all of the research methods share the same goal of expanding what we know about the present to help us understand what the future may bring.

The Air Command and Staff College (ACSC) student master's research theses in this book are thoughtful, credible, and, in several cases, award-winning attempts to develop future visions. These creative future visions offer insights into long-range strategies, policies, and plans that will augment and prepare US national security policy for a spectrum of uncertain futures. Optimally, these future trends papers will essentially "enhance anticipatory consciousness," and their true value will be measured not by how accurate they are but by their "usefulness in planning and opening minds to consider new possibilities and changing the policy agenda."[2] Clearly, the purpose of these papers is to help us make better decisions today by enabling us to "anticipate opportunities and threats and consider how to address them. And strategically it is better to anticipate, rather than just respond to change."[3]

This volume contains seven ACSC student theses that employ a variety of respected futures research methods. Each paper explains the method chosen and why it was chosen. Methodologies vary from impact analysis to scenario-planning processes to relevance tree analysis. All of the papers address a key theme, examining how emerging trends will affect the security of the United States and/or our allies. Additionally, a few basic philosophical assumptions that permeate most futures research underpin all these cases:

1. You cannot know the future, but a range of possible futures can be known.

2. The likelihood of a future event or condition can be changed by policy, and policy consequences can be forecasted.

3. Gradations of foreknowledge and probabilities can be made; we can be more certain about the sunrise than about the rise of the stock market.

4. No single method should be trusted; hence, cross-referencing methods improve foresight.

5. Humans will have more influence on the future than they did in the past.[4]

Futures research is part art and part scientific research. Gen John Shaud, USAF, retired, former director of the Air Force Research Institute, wrote that "the inherent difficulty of anticipating the future does not negate the need to understand the trends that are shaping and influencing it. Failing to look forward may prove more detrimental than an inaccurate prediction. This is particularly true for the Air Force, with its strong ties to technological developments."[5]

The important images of the future crafted by the researchers in this text can help us deal with the complexity and speed of change that render precise decision making more and more difficult. The futuristic images offered give us a glimpse into what may be possible and desirable and, most importantly, should serve as a catalyst for an enhanced security dialogue on how we should prepare for the plausible and desirable.

All of the papers are the product of environmental scanning, which has been described as "the practice of searching both the internal and external environments of an organization, looking for threats, opportunities, and early warning signs."[6] We offer a short synopsis of each chapter below to spark the reader's interest and to ignite dialogue on the selected research topic.

Chapter 2 begins the discussion with a topic that has a long, well-studied, and fascinating history but, simultaneously, a less clear future. Historically, mercenaries have been, and continue to be, integral to traditional war fighting. The "outsourcing" of combat capability goes hand in hand with the outsourcing of combat support activities such as military research and development, combat equipment production, and even food support services. In the United States, defense contractors such as Boeing, General Dynamics, and Halliburton have financially benefited from recent efforts to privatize many military processes. However, a new trend is the development of the modern-day private military company (PMC).

The new PMCs have business goals that include not only the more traditional development of peacetime-centric hardware/support products but also combat equipment, training, and lethal combat services. Not surprisingly, the largest employer of PMCs in the world is the US government (USG), which has been outsourcing a variety of combat requirements. This has resulted in what Maj Kelvin S. Fan describes as the "mercenarizing" of the USG.

Fan applies impact analysis research methods to examine the current and future growth of mercenaries into a global business phenomenon. He approaches this impact analysis from a unique angle as he does not investigate the cost-effectiveness, lethality, or overall legality of modern PMCs. Instead, he qualitatively investigates the potential effect PMCs are having—and could continue to have—on US national security. He adopts a position that if the new PMCs serving the USG are left unregulated, they will have a negative effect not only on the ability of the US security establishment to attain critical defense strategy objectives but also on the US ability to promote freedom abroad, establish justice and human dignity, and support the spread of democracy internationally.

Fan supports his thesis with three main arguments. First, he admits that military privatization is not new but demonstrates that the overall scale and scope are growing briskly. The new PMCs are providing more lethal combat services than ever before. Second, as the scale and scope of military privatization have increased, many unforeseen second- and third-order consequences that could harm key long-term US strategic security goals—and perhaps ultimately overall military effectiveness—have also increased. Last, Fan contends that the ongoing lack of clear regulatory policies, operational transparency, and firm lines of accountability concurrent with the expansion of PMCs into more domestic and international security realms will certainly hinder and eventually degrade US national security objectives.

In chapter 3, Lt Col Kelly L. Varitz asks how changes in Western Europe's population and energy security will affect US-European foreign relations. This is her starting point as she scrutinizes the impact of increasing energy insecurity on an aging European society. Specifically, Varitz explores the dynamics of the "graying" of Western Europe's population and how this change in demographics affects jobs, migration, security, and energy demands. Using scenario-planning analysis, she identifies key critical trends that currently and/or potentially influence domestic and foreign relations with our Western European allies. These evolving trends are the demand for inexpensive sources of energy and the integration of migrant populations from outside Western Europe into the societies of their new homelands in Europe. Varitz's innovative application of the scenario process enables her to envision four plausible futures: (1) the future's so bright we gotta wear shades, (2) we didn't start the fire, (3) just can't get enough, and (4) it's the end of the world as we know it.

In each scenario she provides an imaginative and engrossing story of what that particular impending Western European future could look like. For example, a hypothetical speech by a European prime minister, a fictional letter from a German pensioners' lobby group to the president of Germany, an imagined *Wikipedia* entry about French economic challenges in 2020, and a superbly crafted fictitious blog by a Muslim extremist group are all used to generate plausible images of the social, economic, and political environment of a demographically and energy-challenged Western Europe. All of the captivating scenarios should drive debate and foster new ideas over how the future of Western Europe could alter international relations and US national security.

In chapter 4, Lt Col Lourdes M. Duvall explores a future trend closer to home for US military professionals—the cognitive evolution of situational awareness. Her research is an outgrowth of the rapid change in military information technology. Particularly, the US Air Force is expanding key information technology networks, harnessing more sensors, and employing greater computing processing power to link, evaluate, and display exponentially more data. Simultaneously, the challenges of human-system assimilation become more demanding and complex, such as when decision makers are separated by time and/or space from the initial sources of information via automated fusion processes.

As Duvall explains, "Removing decision makers from the sources of information . . . , if not approached with an understanding of how humans form mental representation, could be a limiting factor to achieving SA [situational awareness]." This awareness is ultimately critical to success on future battlefields. The abundance of available data points and shrinking time lines for making critical decisions may force decision makers to use more personal mental shortcuts. Thus, they may potentially inject predictable biases into the process that could degrade the overall quality of decision making. Human cognition lies at the heart of these critical decision-making activities that contribute to situational awareness.

In her detailed research, Duvall offers an intriguing hypothesis that emphasizing these human dimensions of information processing and decision making would greatly enhance prospective USAF command and control (C2) efforts. She asserts that impending C2 operations will be dominated by a demand for more computer support for ever-increasing, rapid decision making. Duvall's research draws from illustrative empirical examples of the activities of today's Joint Forces air component commander (JFACC) and the hundreds to thousands of personnel engaged in air operations centers (AOC) around the globe. Specifically, she sketches the strengths and weaknesses of human cognitive knowledge and underscores how improved understanding of the principles of human-system interaction affects USAF C2 operations both positively and negatively. Duvall aptly concludes that if the United States is to "maintain and expand our advantage in C2, the human aspects of information processing, decision making, and human-system interaction must be understood and integrated in the USAF C2 vision."

Chapter 5 moves the focus to the heatedly contested Arctic region. The last frontier for exploration on the surface of the planet has been the polar regions. These forbidding and unknown areas have only recently been reconnoitered by scientists and civilian tourists. Many of the polar ecosystems are still underexamined and pristine, but that could soon change. Global warming is quickly expanding both the temporal and spatial domains that can be safely traversed within both poles. In particular, the rapidly changing Arctic ecosystem has obvious international repercussions.

Lt Col Christopher S. Kean and CDR David C. Kneale investigate the changes occurring in the Arctic region and identify future geopolitical and national security implications of the warming polar environment. Specifically, they note that actions by the Arctic nations to claim newly developable natural resources and take advantage of freshly exposed sea lanes are having international security consequences and are worthy of extensive study. They further seek to ascertain the effect these changes can have on US national security and extrapolate potential courses of action that would enhance US national security as the transformation of the Arctic evolves. Their objective is to identify "solutions to mitigate threats to US national security while balancing economic rights and environmental responsibilities."

Their research process revolves around investigating the environmental, economic, political, and scientific aspects of the changes occurring in the Arctic. Kean and Kneale establish a solid analytical foundation of contextual factors and conduct an options analysis process, comparing current and potential Arctic policies. They next measure the efficacy of the options against certain key criteria. The evaluation criteria also incorporate many of the most important contextual factors identified during the research process. Their investigation concludes that successful future strategic Arctic policies must (1) peacefully resolve territorial sovereignty issues and promote free trade economics, (2) mitigate risks to human and environmental security in the region and around the globe, (3) provide a long-term solution to the sustainable development of the Arctic, and (4) include a mechanism for enforcing and monitoring compliance.

The authors evaluate three potential national Arctic strategies against the criteria above and find all to be incomplete to address future changes. As a result, Kean and Kneale formulate their own creative recommendations for a new Arctic national strategy that can bolster US national security and meet the strategic policy evaluation end state.

In chapter 6, Lt Col Jack Donahue expands the discussion above and beyond terra firma into the spatial milieu surrounding our planet as he explores the recent, rapid development of the near-Earth space environment. Daily, thousands of satellites used for a variety of commercial and military purposes circle our planet. Satellites now provide essential services in such diverse domains as national/international communications; Internet access; global navigation; military intelligence, surveillance, and reconnaissance; transnational commerce/ banking/finance; and worldwide environmental monitoring. Many of these services are taken for granted, but today these conveniences face a significant threat that is growing exponentially every year.

Keenly aware of the resulting vulnerability to our society's infrastructure, Donahue thoroughly investigates one aspect of the issue. He is legitimately concerned that the accumulation of over 300,000 small objects (chips of paint or specks of metal), 10,000 objects longer than five inches, and over 900 active satellites in orbit around the earth creates the potential for a major disaster in the near future. A collision between an active satellite, an orbiting spacecraft, or the International Space Station and one of these objects traveling at approximately 11,000 miles per hour could have catastrophic consequences.

Donahue's research into this potential threat to life, global commerce, and US national security exposes some interesting trends that could determine how the United States effectively deals with the challenge of orbiting space debris. He examines several factors that influence future space development, including space technology innovations, cyberspace vulnerabilities augmented by space vulnerabilities, global economic forces, and potential natural disasters. Donahue synthesizes these various critical trends, concluding that evolutionary or revolutionary advances in space technologies and the probability of future space/cyberspace conflict can be the most influential forces on how/if the United States overcomes the challenges created by the growing amount of space debris. Using these driving forces as a starting point for consideration, Donahue crafts four plausible scenarios that could impact US national security in the very near future, identifies the strategic implications of each scenario, and postulates conceivable comprehensive responses to address security repercussions.

In chapter 7, Lt Col Amanda S. Birch skillfully analyzes trends involving two ubiquitous and irreplaceable natural resources and succinctly addresses the security implications of the trends. She points out that fuel and clean water are the lifeblood of modern society and particularly of modern armed forces. No military of today can ignore or fail to plan for sufficient logistical supplies of fuel or fresh water and expect tactical, operational, or strategic success. Undoubtedly, the most advanced militaries are extraordinarily dependent on low energy efficiency, fossil-fuel-powered ships, tracked and wheeled vehicles, and jet-powered aircraft. All of these vehicles require enormous amounts of nonrenewable fuel to effectively and efficiently accomplish their missions.

Birch understands the enormous logistical requirements of an agile combat force in the twenty-first century and researches one of the most difficult challenges facing all combat support planners. How can future combat and support forces untether themselves from vulnerable supply lines and infrastructure networks? To this crucial question, she precisely applies relevance-tree research methodology, investigating the developmental status and utility of microbial fuel cell (MFC) technology for Department of Defense (DOD) use in modern austere operational environments. Birch scrutinizes key technological, social, industrial, and political nodal links to ascertain current and future capabilities and challenges to MFC deployment. She also surveys critical nodal links, such as the standing of basic MFC research, military utility of MFCs, organizational resistance to change, MFC industry standards, and MFC industry tax constraints, among others. Birch also examines the development stage of other technologies relevant to MFC production, determining the overall maturity level of this emerging new technology. She evaluates these factors to determine how they would impact research, development, and deployment of MFCs across a broad spectrum of uses and users. For instance, she inspects the efficacy of MFCs for homeland security missions and for use in domestic and international disaster response. Paradoxically, Birch's findings not only span current and future US military logistical requirements but also expand into international relations and foreign assistance domains. Overall, she finds broad applicability of capabilities that could make MFCs a force multiplier in both military and diplomatic applications.

While Birch's intriguing chapter investigates an alternative energy technology that has tactical, operational, and strategic security implications, chapter 8 provides an equally stimulating investigation into alternative energy sources that has national and specifically Air Force–wide tactical, operational, and strategic security ramifications. Maj Yvonne Gurnick documents that the future reliability of fossil-fuel sources and their global supply are diminishing rapidly and that, as a result, the dependability of these energy sources is fraught with uncertainties. The ensuing economic, technological, and military security concerns have raised the issue of energy sustainment to the highest levels of national security deliberations. Of note, the United States is the largest consumer of fossil fuels in the world; the DOD is the largest fossil-fuel consumer in the US government, and the USAF is the largest consumer in the DOD. Additionally, recent price volatility for oil and natural gas supplies creates huge repercussions for DOD and USAF operational budgets. Clearly, future energy insecurity is an impending national security challenge.

In partial response to this challenge, Gurnick thoroughly investigates three alternative fuels that may meet the USAF's aviation fuel requirements. She examines natural-gas-to-liquid (GTL), coal-to-liquid (CTL), and biofuel-from-algae technologies with an eye to their ability to replace current aviation fuels. She evaluates the alternative fuels across six critical aviation fuel characteristics to determine their suitability: performance capabilities, energy content, compatibility (with all USAF aircraft), low cost/low carbon manufacturing, source (renewable and sustainable), and storage/transport requirements. While all three of the alternative fuels meet the necessary performance, energy content, compatibility, storage, and transport requirements, not all measure up in other essential evaluation categories. Gurnick's conclusions and recommendations offer a clear path to greater energy security, especially in relation to the roles and functions the USAF provides in support of US national security.

Topics in this text are as varied as the methodologies and range from how we will fight in the near future, to where there will be conflict, to how we will process information about the conflict. The methodologies employed vary from impact analysis to scenarios of plausible futures. The conclusions are also unique, provocative, and insightful. As will become evident, the intent of this edited collection on future trends is to stimulate more discussion, dialogue, and research. Many Air Force officers are in the enviable position of possessing the technical expertise and intellectual skills to advance this research, especially when having the advantage of pursuing professional military education. We hope that this outstanding selection of research projects will stimulate enhanced situational awareness—especially the type of substantive thinking necessary to succeed in an uncertain future.

Notes

1. Glenn, "Introduction to the Futures Research Methods Series," 3.
2. Ibid., 4.
3. Ibid.
4. Ibid., 6.
5. Shaud, *Air Force Strategic Study 2020–2030*, 2.
6. Gordon and Glenn, "Environmental Scanning," 1.

Chapter 2

"Mercenarizing" the US Government

Maj Kelvin S. Fan

The use of mercenaries to fight wars is an age-old tradition. Military outsourcing of research and development (R&D), hardware production, and support services to private companies such as Boeing and Halliburton is also not a new concept. What is a fundamentally new trend, however, is the evolution of the mercenary into the modern-day private military company (PMC), which now provides not only peacetime-focused hardware and support services but also wartime-focused combat training and lethal combat services. Currently, the biggest employer of PMCs is the US government (USG); the resultant phenomenon in which PMCs are increasingly relied on in scale (i.e., value/number of resources), in scope (i.e., range/type of services), and for their lethal combat services is termed the "mercenarizing" of the USG.

Mercenaries have always engendered a certain fascination that has continued into their modern-day evolution into PMCs. Over the years, this fascination has spawned several Hollywood movies, a deluge of literature by academic scholars and fictional writers, as well as numerous online discussion forums. More recently, the phenomenal growth of the PMC industry into a $100 billion annual behemoth, the increasing use of PMCs in the ongoing global war on terrorism, and the congressional hearings into Blackwater (the controversial PMC) have pushed PMCs into the forefront of political debate.[1] In turn, the subject has evolved into a more probing questioning of the true effectiveness and impacts of PMCs.

A significant amount of literature on PMC effectiveness already exists, primarily focused on the cost-efficiency, legal, ethical, regulatory, and governance aspects.[2] The traditional story of the post–Cold War peace dividend, the privatization revolution, and the changing nature of war has led to smaller standing militaries and a greater reliance on outsourcing military capabilities to PMCs.[3] Therefore, military privatization or outsourcing has been argued for primarily as a cost-efficient strategy, allowing the US military to concentrate on being the spearhead while PMCs focused on the supporting back-end shaft of the spear.

However, this traditional argument does not fully account for the dual trends of increased reliance on and the privatizing of lethal combat services to PMCs. This study adopts a nontraditional approach and attempts a qualitative evaluation of the effect of MCs on US national security in terms of achieving defense strategy objectives; promoting freedom, justice, and human dignity; as well as advancing and leading democracy. At the core of this study is the underlying idea that, if left unregulated, the trend of USG reliance on PMCs will enrich the private sector but weaken US national security by degrading US long-term and strategic war-fighting capability, discrediting the US stand on justice and human rights, and undermining US international credibility for democracy promotion.

Three key arguments support this thesis. First, while military privatization is not a new phenomenon, recent trends point toward a fundamental shift similar to mercenarizing where PMCs are increasingly relied on in scale, in scope, and for their lethal combat capabilities. Second, while privatization of military functions to PMCs can enhance the capabilities of the USG across the range of military operations (ROMO), second-order repercussions could blunt US long-term and strategic military effectiveness. Third, without an appropriate regulatory framework for greater transparency and clearer accountability for PMCs, as well as a comprehensive information campaign, the continued mercenarizing of the USG risks enriching the private sector at the expense of the United States' national security interests.

This study provides the background on the definition, evolution, scale, and scope of PMCs, as well as on the issues that have been raised with regard to their use. It uses an evaluation methodology based on available US national security documents to assess the impact of the PMC industry. For greater granularity, this study uses case studies from the past two decades, including Blackwater's Nisour Square incident and Paravant's irresponsible actions. The study then makes policy recommendations and draws conclusions. By contributing to the growing body of research on PMCs, this study aims to provide insights for policy makers in determining how to best regulate PMCs.

Defining Private Military Companies

Dr. Christopher Kinsey, a noted security specialist, observes that categorizing the private military industry is difficult because the companies often provide a diverse range of services, catering to a range of customers.[4] Indeed, this has resulted in PMCs being called defense contractors, private military firms, private security companies, private military contractors, security contractors, military consultants, and so on. However, regardless of terminology, these entities are essentially private, profit-driven companies that provide military and security services to clients, often regardless of nationality. As such, the term *PMC* is used here to encompass any private company that provides military-related hardware and/or services that could range from support functions such as logistics to frontline operations to lethal combat services.

Peter Singer, a Brookings Institution senior fellow, helps provide greater understanding of and granularity to the functions of PMCs through his "tip of the spear" representation (fig. 2.1).[5] He states that PMCs can be seen as military providers, military consultant firms, and military support firms, depending largely on the level of lethality provided and the proximity to the combat front lines.[6] Comprising about 5 percent of all PMCs, military providers such as Blackwater (rebranded as Academi), Executive Outcomes, and Sandline International typically engage in frontline tactical operations and actual fighting.[7] Military consulting firms like MPRI (now Engility), Vinnell, and Armorgroup usually do not operate in the front lines but "provide advisory and training services integral to the operations," while military support firms like Kellogg Brown and Root (KBR) provide nonlethal services that include technical support, logistics, and transportation.[8]

PMCs—The Corporate Evolution of Mercenaries

The evolution of the legitimacy of mercenaries has behaved like a pendulum, swinging from general acceptance before the nineteenth century to one of abhorrence during the mid-twentieth century before swinging back to one of political acceptance of PMCs from the late twentieth century onwards. This evolution of mercenaries into the modern-day PMC can be illustrated in three broad stages.

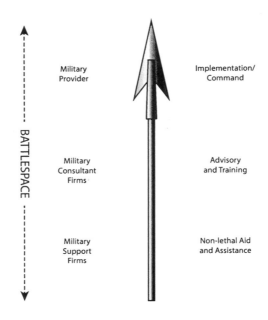

BATTLESPACE

Military Provider — Implementation/Command

Military Consultant Firms — Advisory and Training

Military Support Firms — Non-lethal Aid and Assistance

Figure 2.1. Singer's "tip of the spear." (*Reprinted from* Peter Singer, *Corporate Warriors: The Rise of the Privatized Military Industry* [Ithaca, NY: Cornell University Press, 2003], 93.)

The first stage, spanning from ancient times until the nineteenth century, was characterized by the accepted norm of paying private foreign soldiers to fight a nation's war. These private soldiers were generically called mercenaries and usually held no loyalty to any nation but rather sold their services to the highest bidder. The second stage, from the nineteenth century until the mid-twentieth century, saw the confluence of "bureaucratization, politicization and industrialization." This convergence transformed war so that only a nation-state could mobilize the entire population and take complete advantage of the destructive power of modern weapons, thus leaving little opportunity for mercenary forces to participate.[9] Nationalism was dominant in this stage and culminated in the development of the Geneva Conventions classifying mercenaries as unlawful combatants.[10]

From the late twentieth century onwards, the pendulum has swung back to the point where hiring private soldiers is again politically and socially acceptable. This third stage is notable for the corporatization of the mercenary trade. Indeed, many, including Singer, see the emergence of PMCs as the corporate evolution of mercenaries. This stage is also defined by the increased scale and scope of PMCs' involvement in both conventional and irregular conflicts across the globe, notably Sierra Leone, Angola, the Balkans, Iraq, and Afghanistan.

The Growing Scale and Scope of PMCs

The growth in scale and scope of PMCs in the past two decades has been nothing short of phenomenal. No longer perceived in the same unsavory mold as mercenaries, PMCs are now legally constituted private companies generally accepted as important components of a nation's fighting force. From constituting only about 1 to 2 percent of US forces in Operation Desert Storm, PMCs contributed 10 percent of the fighting force in Yugoslavia in 1999. They were estimated to comprise more than 50 percent of all US forces in Operation Iraqi Freedom.[11] From being involved in only 15 conflicts from 1950 to 1989, PMCs now operate globally in almost every form of conflict and have increased their involvement to about 80 conflicts from 1990 to 2000.[12] From being the individual mercenary soldier of the past who was motivated by cash, PMCs are now business-minded entities being awarded multimillion-dollar contracts (for example, Blackwater's $320 million deal from the State Department in 2004).[13]

Perhaps the most remarkable is the increasing trend for PMCs to move beyond providing peacetime-focused functions of logistics, consultancy services, and hardware production to providing wartime-focused functions of combat training assistance and lethal combat services—responsibilities that the nation's military services have traditionally monopolized. The classic example is Executive Outcomes, which in the 1990s garnered much publicity for its use of lethal combat capabilities to quell the civil unrest in Sierra Leone.[14] In Iraq, more than 13,000 PMC personnel, or 11 percent of the total PMC strength, were involved in "direct tactical assistance," manifested in numerous shooting incidents involving PMC personnel.[15] PMCs are now fundamentally different from the mercenaries in the past in terms of legitimacy, scale, and scope. What remains consistent, however, is the underlying motivation of selling military services for profit.

The USG has embraced the growth of PMCs more than any other country's government, as evidenced by Dr. Nicholas Dew and Lt Col Bryan Hudgen's findings that the PMC industry is a "50 percent US" phenomenon.[16] Security scholar David Isenberg further highlights that while the Department of Defense (DOD) and Department of State are the primary users of PMCs, the entire USG, including the intelligence agencies and homeland security and energy departments, relies heavily on them.[17] From 1994 to 2002, the DOD awarded $300 billion in contracts to US-based PMCs.[18] The scale of this privatization has increased, with Stockholm International Peace Research Institute (SIPRI) scholars Dr. Sam Perlo-Freeman and Elisabeth Skons indicating that the DOD awarded contracts for about $113.4 billion in 2006 to "companies whose services to the DOD appear to be wholly or mostly military."[19] It is no surprise that the key beneficiary is the PMC industry, with Kinsey noting that several leading PMCs saw their stock prices outperform the benchmark indices after the September 11 attacks.[20] As such, what seems to be happening is the mercenarizing of the USG in that it increasingly relies on PMCs in scale and scope and for their direct and lethal combat services. This trend has definitely enriched the private sector, and the question now is whether it has also benefited the United States.

Understanding the Rise of the PMC Industry

Attributing the phenomenal rise of the PMC industry to any single factor is futile. Instead, the confluence of several factors led to its growth. First, the post–Cold War peace dividend, coupled with increasing economic opportunities, led to a winding down of large standing militaries and the mismatch of resources to the US grand strategy.[21] Second, the rise of market-based approaches with promises of cost efficiencies led to a privatization revolution that favored the outsourcing of governmental functions. Third, the changing nature of war—as the revolution in military affairs (RMA) and rise of insurgencies illustrate—led to an expansion of the military's roles and thus greater demand for specialized support from PMCs.

The huge drawdown of standing militaries across the world is one of the most obvious trends that resulted from the end of the Cold War. As British journalist Tony Geraghty notes, the major powers downsized their military strength from 6,873,000 in 1990 to 3,283,000 in 1997, flooding the private sector with a huge supply of ex-military personnel.[22] However, the significant downsizing in the US military was not accompanied by a concomitant reduction in US military demands. Instead, the United States continued its "Cold War missions in Europe and Asia" and, ironically, seemed to intensify its operations tempo with involvement in Iraq, Kosovo, and the Balkans in the 1990s.[23] This huge mismatch between the demands of US grand strategy and the lack of supporting public resources fostered an environment for PMCs to "fill the gap between geopolitical goals and public means."[24]

The end of the Cold War also coincided with the privatization movement, which "provided the logic, legitimacy and models for the entrance of markets" into the traditional state domain of military services.[25] The privatization of military logistics is not a new phenomenon (e.g., George Washington's Continental Army relied on support from various private firms and individuals), but the privatization in the late twentieth century was marked by the emergence of large modern corporations that increasingly undertook a wider range of military functions.[26] In the 1980s and '90s, the United Kingdom privatized the national armaments industry and outsourced military pilot training.[27] In 1991 former US defense secretary Dick Cheney commissioned Brown and Root (later renamed KBR) to produce a report examining the benefits of increased privatization of military support services such as housing, food, and laundry.[28] Those findings set the foundation for privatizing regular military functions to PMCs and dovetailed into a 1995 Defense Science Board report suggesting that the Pentagon could save the United States $12 billion annually if it privatized all support functions except actual combat.[29]

As the privatization of military services gained traction, the Pentagon's contracted workforce exceeded its own civilian employees for the first time in 2001.[30] Further testimony to the heavy reliance on privatization came when Cheney, then chairman of Halliburton, mentioned that "the first person to greet our soldiers as they arrive in the Balkans, and the last one to wave goodbye is one of our [Halliburton] employees."[31] The privatization revolution has therefore created "a greater acceptance of outsourcing of government activities to the private sector," thus legitimizing the PMC industry.[32]

The changing nature of warfare in the past few decades has also played an increasingly important role in sustaining the rise of PMCs. First, former defense secretary Donald Rumsfeld, a strong RMA advocate, instituted a strategy to transform the US military into a lean outfit that relied heavily on technology and information superiority for its asymmetric advantages. However, as Kinsey mentions, "maintaining this sophisticated technology requires a level of expertise beyond that which is taught in the military."[33] Essentially, the move toward high technology and information dominance indirectly created a demand for complex technical expertise and logistical support that have been best filled by PMCs.[34]

Second, the changing nature of warfare, as evidenced by the insurgencies in Iraq and Afghanistan, has shown that irregular warfare will likely be the focus in the future. The nature of irregular warfare is such that specialized skills like country experts, linguists, bodyguards, and desert guides are required to support US personnel. Counterinsurgency operations also require huge security forces to protect against guerrilla and terrorist attacks, as well as trainers to enhance the capabilities of the host nation. More nimble than bureaucratic militaries, PMCs have been faster in adapting to provide such specialized services in counterinsurgencies, as evidenced by the 180,000 PMC personnel in Iraq in 2007 compared to just 160,000 US troops.[35] As such, it can be argued that the changing focus toward irregular warfare indirectly increased the demands for specialized skills from PMCs.

Looking ahead, the trends of the US strategy-resource mismatch, privatization, and the changing nature of warfare show no significant signs of abating. First, the United States continues to be involved heavily in Iraq and Afghanistan, but Iran and North Korea are already emerging to be the next hot spots. The demands on the United States and its military are therefore unlikely to ease. Second, while the idea of privatization might have lost some luster given the partial nationalization of banks in 2008–9, the fundamental idea of a lean government and a strong private economy still holds firm among the general public. Third, while al-Qaeda has been largely disrupted, trannational terrorism and insurgencies are likely to be threats for a long time given the protean nature of terrorists and the numerous weak and failing states. Fourth, PMCs are "the new reality, not only in foreign policy in the twenty-first century, but also of war fighting."[36] Indeed, the public has become so accustomed to minimal troop loss that some security commentators argue that PMCs will increasingly be used in the future to mitigate the public's concern about national military troop losses.[37] However, while the trends point toward the continued reliance on and growth of PMCs, Pres. Barack Obama decided to make the PMC industry more transparent and accountable, as evidenced by the congressional hearings on Blackwater and the PMC industry as a whole. How his actions might impact the PMC industry in the future remains to be seen.

Concerns Surrounding PMCs

The phenomenal growth of PMCs and burgeoning reliance on them to provide military services to governments have spawned several studies. Issues often discussed include the cost effectiveness, legal ambiguity, and ethical debates surrounding PMCs. Military privatization advocates "contend that the private sector is more cost-effective than the public sector."[38] While several reports, such as the 1995 Defense Science Board report, claim that privatization will yield tremendous savings, a survey of literature reveals that a preponderance of commentators such as Isenberg, Perlo-Freeman, and Skons are unwilling to accept wholeheartedly the claim that "outsourcing brings greater efficiency and lower cost."[39] Specifically, Perlo-Freeman and Skons use the economics theory to argue that privatization benefits accrue with "meaningful competition, a clear perception of requirements by the contracting authority, and effective monitoring and oversight by the client."[40] They contend that outsourcing to PMCs might not yield the expected gains because the PMC industry is dominated by a few major players with a general lack of contract oversight staff.[41] In a similar vein, Kinsey highlights that the privatization argument only works when there is transparent, competitive bidding of contracts; however, studies show that only 40 percent of outsourcing contracts are subject to open, competitive bidding.[42] The cost-effectiveness benefits of PMCs are therefore contentious at best.

Another controversial issue is the legal ambiguity of PMCs. As Kinsey notes, "The very narrow definition of mercenary found in the *1977 Additional Protocols I and II to Article 47 of the Geneva Convention (1949)* and the *International Convention against the Recruitment, Use, Financing and Training of Mercenaries (1989)* have made it easy for mercenaries, let alone PMCs, to avoid meeting the full criteria of the definition and thus prosecution."[43] PMC personnel are not treated as unlawful combatants, but are they afforded the same legal protection and subjected to prosecution as regular soldiers in a nation's military? Illustrating this ambiguity, Perlo-Freeman and Skons reveal that "the US Congressional Research Service found in 2007 that some contractors operating for the US Departments of Defense or State in Iraq—which had been granted immunity from prosecution in Iraqi courts—might not come under the jurisdiction of US civil or military courts."[44] The growth of PMCs has clearly outpaced the accompanying legal interpretation, and this legal ambiguity has plagued the treatment of several PMC infractions.

A third set of concerns questions the ethical aspects of using PMCs. The traditional notion has been that only nation-states "have the exclusive legitimacy to exercise violence."[45] Therefore, security commentator Herbert Wulf argues that rampant outsourcing to PMCs threatens the state's monopoly on sanctioned violence and could lead to ethical and accountability issues.[46] It can also be argued that using PMCs to meet the United States' grand strategy is essentially circumventing the citizenry's desires as manifested in the publicly approved size and resources of the military. The fundamental question here is, how ethical is it for governments to privatize the use of violence to profit-driven PMCs that are not as accountable to the public?

The Evaluation Methodology

The earlier literature review has shown that several academics have raised controversial issues regarding the use of PMCs: Are they cost effective? Are they accountable? What are their legal statuses? What are the ethical impacts of using PMCs? Despite the many years of using PMCs, the House Committee on Oversight and Government Reform delineated in a February 2007 congressional hearing that "there has been no comprehensive assessment of the quality of the work done by private security contractors."[47] In this regard, the study lays no claim to be comprehensive but seeks to develop a macro-evaluation framework that assesses the PMC industry's repercussions for US national security. After all, national security is what Clausewitz would argue that all military action should contribute toward. To this end, this section develops a set of national security criteria based on the objectives stated in the 2006 *National Security Strategy (NSS)* and the DOD's 2010 *Quadrennial Defense Review (QDR)* and evaluates the PMC industry against it.

The *NSS* emphasizes the twin pillars of promoting "freedom, justice, and human dignity" and promoting and leading a "community of democracies."[48] To support this, the 2010 *QDR* highlights the four priority defense strategy objectives: to "prevail in today's wars, prevent and deter conflict, prepare to defeat adversaries and succeed in a wide range of contingencies, and preserve and enhance the All-Volunteer Force."[49] These two documents provide an excellent reference point for developing a set of criteria against which the performance of the military and, by extension, the PMC industry can be evaluated. Synthesizing these two strategic documents, this paper proposes three broad criteria for measuring the performance of PMCs: the ability to achieve defense strategy objectives; promote freedom, justice, and human dignity; and promote and lead democracy.

Evaluation Criterion 1: Ability to Achieve Defense Strategy Objectives

The ability to achieve or support the *QDR*'s objectives is a critical measure of performance as they contribute directly to military victory and help "defend and advance [US] national interests."[50] Therefore, the PMC industry will be evaluated against the four stated defense strategy objectives.

First, the PMC industry will be evaluated against its ability to prevail in the wars in Iraq and Afghanistan, especially in counterinsurgency, stability, and counterterrorism operations. Well-documented case studies, such as Paravant's 2009 civilian shootings and Blackwater's 2004 Fallujah incident, are used to provide granularity for this evaluation. The key question here is, have PMCs contributed toward mission success in Iraq and Afghanistan at both the tactical and strategic levels?

Second, the PMC industry will be measured against its ability to prevent and deter conflict. As part of a multipronged approach, the 2010 *QDR* highlights that US deterrence "remains grounded in land, air, and naval forces capable of fighting limited and large-scale conflicts" and that there is a need to enhance partners' security capacity through foreign internal defense (FID).[51] To this end the key question is, have PMCs enhanced the deterrence capabilities of the United States and her allies?

Third, the PMC industry will be evaluated against its ability to "defeat adversaries and succeed in a wide range of contingencies."[52] The 2010 *QDR* suggests that when deterrence fails, the DOD might need to deal with challenges ranging from conventional wars to counterterrorism, counterinsurgency and stability, reconstruction, and disaster relief operations. This chapter reviews the PMC industry's contributions in current conflicts as well as its past performance in Sierra Leone and Angola to answer the question, how effective are PMCs across the ROMO?

Fourth, the PMC industry will be evaluated against its ability to "preserve and enhance the all-volunteer force."[53] The 2010 *QDR* seeks to preserve "the long-term viability of the all-volunteer force" and will "require policies that sustain the rotation base" and "provide care for our people."[54] This document assesses the role PMCs play in bridging the resource-demand gap that has emerged in the post–Cold War era and answers the question, how do PMCs preserve and enhance the all-volunteer force in both the short and long term?

Evaluation Criterion 2: Ability to Promote Freedom, Justice, and Human Dignity

A key objective of the *NSS* is to end tyranny by promoting freedom, justice, and human dignity. As noted by Richard Fontaine and Dr. John Nagl, scholars from the Center for a New American Society, the Iraqis and Afghans do not differentiate between actions conducted by US military personnel or by PMC personnel.[55] For all intents and purposes, these actions are perceived to have originated from the USG. The insight is that PMC personnel can behave like "strategic corporals" where their actions can affect US national security directly and indirectly. Indeed, civilian casualties caused by PMCs could "anger the very people the coalition is to protect, fuel the insurgent's propaganda machine," and portray the coalition as ignoring human dignity and freedom.[56] Blackwater's Nisour Square incident illustrates the impact of civilian casualties and the legal ambiguity of PMCs as well as helping answer the question, do PMCs behave as "benevolently" as the USG with regard to freedom, justice, and human dignity?

Evaluation Criterion 3: Ability to Promote and Lead Democracy

The second pillar of the *NSS* is to promote and lead a growing community of democracies. To do so, the United States needs to maintain and enhance its international credibility and reputation as a desirable democracy. As Isenberg states, "Constitutionalism, transparency and public consent are features common to democracy."[57] US international credibility and reputation can therefore be affected by the perceived accountability of the actions of PMCs and of the USG, as well as by the transparency and regulatory framework of the PMC industry. In this regard, DynCorp's involvement in Plan Colombia is used to answer the question, does the PMC industry enhance US international credibility and reputation for democracy promotion?

Evaluating the PMC Industry

Tactical and Short-Term Successes but Strategic and Long-Term Concerns

A key question when determining the ability to achieve defense strategy objectives is whether PMCs have helped the United States prevail in the current conflicts. According to Kinsey and Fontaine and Nagl, the ratio of US military troops to PMC personnel has fallen steadily from about 50:1 during the first Gulf war to 10:1 during the Balkans conflict and about 1:1 in the current conflicts.[58] The third quarter 2009 US Central Command (USCENTCOM) contractor census report shows that 199,706 and 73,968 PMC personnel in Iraq and Afghanistan, respectively, were performing a wide range of functions (fig. 2.2).[59] Therefore, at the macro level, PMCs appear to be heavily relied upon as a critical component of the total fighting force.

	Total Contractors	US Citizens	Third Country Nationals	Local/Host Country Nationals
Iraq only	119,706	31,541	56,125	32,040
Afghanistan only	73,968	10,036	11,806	51,126
Other USCENTCOM locations	50,061	9,381	35,053	5,627
USCENTCOM area of operations	243,735	50,958	102,984	89,793

Figure 2.2. PMC personnel in USCENTCOM. (*Reprinted from* DOD, *US-CENTCOM 3rd Quarter Contractor Census Report* [Washington, DC: DOD, June 2009]).

At the micro level, PMCs have registered a track record of mission successes and accomplishments. Blackwater, despite being one of the most controversial PMCs, has conducted over 16,000 private security detail operations without losing a protected principal in either theater, successfully worked with US Marines to defend the Coalition Provisional Authority infrastructure in Najaf against a Shia uprising, and saved several Marines using its private medical evacuation helicopters.[60]

PMCs such as DynCorp and Vinnell have demonstrated their value in the important mission of FID, training the 62,000-strong Afghan police (at a cost of $1.1 billion) and the Iraqi army, respectively.[61] The largest PMC in theater, KBR, has also successfully established and supplied the in-theater bases that US and allied troops depend greatly on.

There is no doubt about the contributions of PMCs to the current conflicts at the tactical level. However, an increasing number of PMC missteps threaten to hinder the ability to prevail at the strategic level. Senate Armed Services Committee chairman Carl Levin and Gen Stanley McChrystal correctly emphasize that the key to prevailing in both wars is to win the support, hearts, and minds of the people, and one way of doing so is to involve the locals in the rebuilding of their nation. However, as foreign policy expert Allison Stanger notes, "Democratization required Iraqization, yet contractors steered clear of hiring Iraqi nationals." This strategic mistake will likely inhibit a self-sustaining prosperous nation.[62]

In addition, irresponsible PMC conduct can also adversely affect US foreign policy. "In the fight against the Taliban, the perception of Afghans is crucial," and any civilian casualty caused by irresponsible PMC personnel is likely to erode public support and hinder victory.[63] The following case study of Paravant clearly illustrates how irresponsible actions by PMC personnel could harm US national security interests and foreign policy by exacerbating the insurgency and fostering anti-American sentiment.

Case Study 1: Paravant in Afghanistan

On 5 May 2009, Justin Cannon and Christopher Drotleff, two men working for Paravant in Afghanistan, fired their weapons, killing two Afghan civilians and injuring a third. Then-CSTC-A commanding general Richard Formic said that it appeared that the contractor personnel involved had violated alcohol consumption policies, were not authorized to possess weapons, violated use of force rules, and violated movement control policies. According to the Department of Justice prosecutors, the 5 May 2009 shooting caused diplomatic difficulties for United States Department representatives in Afghanistan and impacted the national security interests of the United States. According to one media report, the shooting turned an entire neighborhood against the US presence and quoted a local elder as saying, "If they keep killing civilians, I'm sure some Afghans will decide to become insurgents."[64]

While irresponsible PMC actions can undermine US strategic objectives and foreign policy, PMCs can also alter the strategic course of the war, endanger US troops, and undermine coalition cohesion, as illustrated by the 2004 Fallujah incident. As the House Committee on Oversight and Government Reform highlighted, "The Fallujah incident was highly publicized and had a significant impact on the course of the war in Iraq."[65] Many academics see the insurgent's attack on the Blackwater personnel as a trap where the United States took the bait and then retaliated strongly with a widespread military assault, resulting in the "bloodiest month for US troops and civilians."[66] The USG's strong response in Fallujah incurred "much casualties and political cost," created more anti-American sentiment, and caused the British government to have "deep misgivings" over the US strategy.[67]

Case Study 2: Blackwater in Fallujah

On 31 March 2004, four Americans working as private security personnel for Blackwater, all of whom were military veterans, were ambushed and killed in Fallujah while on a protection mission. Their tragic deaths became a turning point in public opinion about the war and directly resulted in a major US military offensive, which is known as the First Battle of Fallujah. Twenty-seven American soldiers and over 800 insurgents and Iraqi citizens died in that battle, and military observers believe it helped fuel an escalation of the insurgency.[68]

PMC missteps undoubtedly get more media attention than their successes. However, the Paravant and Blackwater case studies clearly demonstrate that any misstep can undermine the achievement of US strategic objectives. Therefore, in prevailing in the current conflicts, PMCs have been tactically successful but strategically inhibitive.

The second question that must be answered is whether PMCs help in deterring conflicts. Deterrence is almost impossible to prove, but "deterrence is a product of effective capability." Evidence shows that PMCs have substantially increased the capabilities of both the United States and its allies.[69] First, the PMC industry has always been heavily involved and relied upon to enhance the logistics, R&D, and hardware production of US air, land, sea, nuclear, space, and cyber capabilities. Second, the PMC industry increasingly serves as a reserve force that can be flexibly called upon to boost the numbers and capabilities of the standing US military. Indeed, the USCENTCOM report highlights that PMCs have boosted the USG's strength by over 243,000 in just the USCENTCOM area.[70] Third, the PMC industry has greatly improved the security capacity and deterrence capabilities of US allies through numerous FID operations. For example, it was MPRI's training and modernization of the US-backed Croatian military in the 1990s that enabled the Croats to force the Serbs to the negotiating table.[71] Therefore, the PMC industry does seem to contribute positively to effective capability and deterrence.

The third question is whether PMCs assist the USG in defeating adversaries across the ROMO. The scope and scale of PMCs are "unprecedented in US history" and demonstrate that the PMC industry is a critical component of the USG's total force.[72] Indeed, PMCs are involved in the full spectrum of operations and have assisted the USG in a wide range of missions including major combat, counterinsurgencies, counterterrorism, support, disaster relief, and counterdrug operations.[73] Fontaine and Nagl also state that without PMCs, the "US cannot engage in hostilities or in reconstruction and stabilization operations."[74]

With regard to reconstruction and stabilization operations, PMCs have demonstrated immense value by involvement in everything—training of security forces, rebuilding roads, managing internally displaced personnel, and rescuing people from disaster regions. For example, while better known for its combat capabilities, Blackwater performed admirably in disaster relief operations in the aftermath of Hurricane Katrina. Further, while humanitarian and disaster relief demands have increased, the personnel strength of the US Agency for International Development (USAID) has paradoxically fallen from 17,500 at its peak to slightly above 1,000, according to recent statistics, with PMCs undertaking much of the slack.[75]

In the area of counterinsurgencies, PMCs have not only demonstrated implicit value in the Iraq and Afghanistan wars but have also solved several previous counterinsurgency conflicts in timely fashion, such as the restoration of state power in Sierra Leone and Angola.[76]

Case Study 3: Executive Outcomes in Angola and Sandline in Sierra Leone

Executive Outcomes (EO) was founded in 1989 by Eben Barlow, a former assistant commander of the 32nd Battalion of the South African Defense Force (SADF). EO provided five services: strategic and tactical military advisory services; an array of sophisticated military training packages in land, sea, and air warfare; peacekeeping or "persuasion" services; advice to armed forces on weapon selection and acquisition; and paramilitary services. Training packages covered the realm from basic infantry training to armored warfare specialties to parachute ops. In Angola, EO's combat capabilities were demonstrated in March 1993 when they launched a commando assault that successfully seized the Soyo oil installation from the National Union for the Total Independence of Angola (UNITA) rebels. However, when EO withdrew, the Angolan army lost the oil installation back to the UNITA rebels. Singer therefore concluded that EO provided the Angolan army with crucial military expertise and played a "determinate role" in ending the war.

In 1995, EO was engaged to fight the Revolutionary United Front (RUF) rebels and reestablish the government's control over the economically productive parts in Sierra Leone. Within eight months, EO achieved its military objectives, successfully forced the rebel RUF leader to negotiate for peace, and restored peace to the region. Sierra Leone, however, did not retain EO to train up its paramilitary forces, and when EO left, the RUF rebels launched another coup. This led to the hiring of Sandline International, which performed the same missions as EO and successfully ended the coup.[77]

No one can predict how and when the Iraq and Afghanistan counterinsurgencies will end and therefore the determinate effectiveness of PMCs for those conflicts. However, from Blackwater in New Orleans to EO in Angola to Sandline in Sierra Leone, history does seem to show that PMCs can be a significant force multiplier for the USG across the ROMO.

A fourth question is whether PMCs preserve and enhance the all-volunteer force. In the short term, PMC advocates emphasize that PMCs enhance the all-volunteer force by boosting the total fighting strength of the USG, thereby allowing a more sustainable deployment and rotation cycle for national troops. Indeed, the absence of the 243,000 PMC personnel in the CENTCOM area is not only likely to impair the USG's operational capability but also to undermine its sustainable deployment cycle and require more than the announced surge of 50,000 US troops into Afghanistan.

However, PMC critics stress that PMCs could erode the war-fighting capability of the USG in the long term by undermining recruitment, retention, and the national prestige of serving in the USG. First, Kinsey and CNN executive producer Suzanne Simons have pointed out an emerging trend of PMCs poaching personnel from the US military and intelligence communities.[78] This is hardly surprising given that PMC personnel could be paid about four times that of an equivalent soldier in the US military.[79] The poaching situation in the United Kingdom got so bad that the elite Special Air Service (SAS) had to allow its soldiers to exit temporarily to earn money at PMCs before returning to the SAS.[80] The US Special Operations Command has identified "loss of qualified personnel to security companies as a problem in maintaining its strength."[81] Indeed, most of Blackwater's personnel—including Cofer Black, the ex-director of the Central Intelligence Agency (CIA) Counterterrorist Center—were poached from both the military and the CIA.[82] Poaching from the intelligence community in the 1990s also caused the intelligence agencies to lose "core capability in some cases by as much as 40 percent."[83]

As academic Deborah Kidwell indicates, the unequal economic advantages between national militaries and PMCs "can be extremely detrimental to soldier morale and decrease the prestige of national military service."[84] Therefore, while the PMC industry can enhance the all-volunteer force by allowing a more sustainable deployment cycle in the short term, the longer-term risks are the hollowing out of the USG and the undermining of the prestige of the all-volunteer force.

Isolated PMC Missteps Undermine Freedom, Justice, and Human Dignity

Fontaine and Nagl emphasize that "most private contractors appear to make a positive contribution, and to be honest, patriotic, and dedicated to the mission at hand."[85] However, it takes just one PMC transgression, accentuated by the CNN effect and the insurgents' propaganda machine, to undermine all the positive contributions. Indeed, several media reports have often painted a poor performance of PMCs regarding civilian casualties and human rights. As the *Times* highlighted, PMC personnel "are supposed to obey the same rules as the military in warning civilian motorists not to approach convoys. . . . Protecting convoys requires split-second decision-making. Scores of Iraqi civilians have been killed and injured by mistake."[86]

Several other documented case studies involving civilian casualties also seem to point to improper PMC conduct. The 2007 congressional hearings on Blackwater concluded that its personnel "shoot first and sometimes kill and then ask the questions," firing first in 84 percent of its incidents.[87] Investigations into the Paravant shootings of May 2009 reveal that the Paravant personnel had criminal records and "abysmal military records," which included "assault, insubordinate conduct, absence without leave, [and] failure to obey order or regulation."[88] Stanger reports that PMC personnel performing the sensitive job of interrogation are being implicated in the human rights violations in Abu Ghraib.[89] In the eyes of the local people, the collective impact of such damaging publicity is that the United States has lost much credibility in intervening to end tyranny.

Of greater concern is the local population's perception that despite these civilian casualties and infractions, justice does not get served. The treatment of Blackwater personnel involved in the 2007 Nisour Square incident best illustrates this controversy.

Case Study 4: Blackwater in Nisour Square

On 16 September 2007, Blackwater guards shot and killed 17 Iraqi civilians in Nisour Square, Baghdad. This occurred while Blackwater personnel were escorting a US State Department convoy en route to a meeting in western Baghdad. Blackwater personnel claimed that they were ambushed and thus responded lawfully with gunfire. However, the Iraqi authorities concluded that the Blackwater personnel fired on the civilians without provocation. While the Iraqi authorities wanted to try the case in Iraq, the US House, on 4 October 2007, passed a bill making all PMC personnel in combat zones subject to the Military Extraterritorial Jurisdiction Act and thus prosecution by US courts. In December 2008, five Blackwater personnel were therefore indicted in the United States on manslaughter and weapons charges accusing them of killing and injuring unarmed civilians. Charges were initially dropped in January 2010 due to a technicality but a US appeals court reinstated the criminal charges and the case is still under adjudication.[90]

Not surprisingly, the Nisour Square incident created much anti-American sentiment and greatly discredited the US justice system. The apparent nonchalant attitude toward human rights and civilian casualties, as well as the seemingly above-the-law treatment received by PMCs, has not only outraged the people whom the coalition is trying to win over but has also undermined the credibility of the US justice system that the USG wants to promote in Iraq. Therefore, while the majority of PMC actions have contributed positively to the mission and are largely well intentioned, just one PMC misstep undermines the promotion of freedom, justice, and human dignity.

Accountability and Transparency Issues Undermine US International Credibility

The accountability of PMCs and the USG is often called into question because PMCs are inherently profit motivated and act as an additional layer between the government and the public. While the USG is account-able to the public and national interests via Congress and the Consti-tution, PMCs are private entities that must account for shareholders' interests. PMC personnel are also not in the chain of command and hence not subject to the same discipline that governs national troops.[91] As Singer reveals, while national soldiers are prevented from desertion, treason, and revolt by a combination of patriotism and a fear of prosecution, PMC infractions constitute only a breakage of a commercial contract.[92] The alignment of privately accountable PMCs to national interests is therefore not straightforward.

More concerning is that by privatizing military functions to publicly unaccountable PMCs, the USG is essentially circumventing "time-tested congressional and public reviews that are integral to the demo-cratic system" of accountability in government.[93] The use of DynCorp in Plan Colombia illustrates such questionable government actions.

Case Study 5: DynCorp in Plan Colombia

In the late 1990s, the United States initiated Plan Colombia, a war on drugs in Colombia. Given the controversy, Congress placed restrictions on the type of operations the US forces could be involved in and restricted the United States to help only Colombian units that were free of human rights violations. A manifestation of the restrictions was that US forces could only conduct counter-narcotics operations and could not be involved in counterinsurgency opera-tions. While DynCorp was engaged officially to provide pilot training and technical support to the Columbian National Police, Singer highlights that DynCorp was reportedly engaged in aerial reconnaissance, combat advisory roles for the Colombian military, and counterinsurgency operations against rebels. He therefore asserted that DynCorp was "utilized as an alternative way to circumvent" policy restrictions and has no oversight from Congress.[94]

Apart from accountability issues, the PMC industry also does not measure well against the transparency criteria. Isenberg reports that only 40 percent of PMC contracts were open to competitive bidding, attributing this to warfare's characteristics of "secrecy, heavy time constraints and the imperative of victory."[95] Perlo-Freeman and Skons support this and state that the resultant anticompetitive nature of the PMC industry can lead to "corruption capture" whereby the USG overpays for PMC services.[96] For example, the US Army privatized certain military base services in Bosnia and was billed by a PMC for 116 personnel despite the Army's own calculations showing that 66 personnel would have sufficed.[97] It is not surprising that several PMCs are currently under investigation for fraud (e.g., the Custer

Battles PMC "for cheating the US government out of tens of millions of dollars").[98]

The shortage and quality of contract oversight personnel in the military appear to have fostered and exacerbated this lack of transparency. As Fontaine and Nagl note, the number and prestige of contract supervisory jobs in the DOD have fallen over the years.[99] The downsizing of the USAID's staff strength, despite rising demands, has also led to a shortage of regulatory and contract oversight personnel.[100] The irony is that a PMC, Aegis, had to be awarded a $293 million contract to oversee and coordinate the other 60 PMCs in Iraq.[101] As a result, for the first three years of the Iraq War, the USG had no accurate count of the number of PMC personnel involved.[102] Fortunately, deliberate steps such as the appointments of special inspector generals in Iraq and Afghanistan were taken to enhance the audit process and address the lack of transparency in the PMC industry.[103]

The US key national strategic goal is to promote and lead the growing number of democracies. However, the apparent absence of the two key democracy tenets of accountability and transparency, coupled with the perceived lack of justice, is likely to undermine the international credibility and reputation of the United States to lead and promote democracy.

Policy Recommendations

The evaluation reveals that PMCs have a strong record of mission success and can be a significant force multiplier for the USG. However, the analysis also shows that the trend of mercenarizing the USG, if left unchecked, could adversely undermine US national security objectives, long-term war-fighting capability, and international credibility. An appropriate regulatory framework to retain the benefits of PMCs while mitigating the potential downsides is recommended.

Enhance Accountability and Transparency through Greater Regulation

The exercise of sanctioned violence on the battlefield is inherently a governmental responsibility that impacts national security and public interests. Privatizing military functions to PMCs should be regulated in a similar manner to the regulation of essential services like electricity production and water supply. Regulation should be done to enhance accountability and transparency as well as to help quell concerns that PMC infractions could undermine US national security objectives and international credibility.

First, the USG could address the accountability issues by clarifying the legal status of PMCs. The military tried to clarify the legal status of PMCs through the Military Extraterritorial Jurisdiction Act, but Fontaine and Nagl argue that the act is hardly used because the scope of its jurisdiction is ambiguous and the practical application difficult.[104] Given that the actions of PMC personnel are indistinguishable from those of a uniformed soldier, this study regards PMC personnel as agents of the US military and thus recommends a review of the applicability of the *Uniform Code of Military Justice* to PMC personnel.

Second, the USG could instill greater transparency within the PMC industry by reviewing its contract oversight capabilities. Competitive bidding ensures that privatization yields cost efficiencies and prevents complacency and corruption capture. The USG could review its open, competitive bidding process and award no-bid contracts only under extenuating circumstances. In addition, transparency requires a proper vetting process regarding the quality of PMCs engaged by the USG. The numerous congressional hearings reveal that some PMCs foster a trigger-happy culture and fall "well short of any reasonable standard for vetting personnel."[105] In this regard, the recommendation is to enhance the USG's contract oversight, supervisory, and audit capabilities by creating a "white and black" list of reputable and discredited PMCs.

Foster PMCs as a Supplement and not a Competitor to the USG

The PMC industry is a significant force multiplier in the short term, but it is now important to clarify the PMC industry's long-term role in the total force. First, the USG could review the contracting relationship with the PMC industry. Specifically, the USG could insert a noncompete clause within the contract awarded to prevent PMCs from poaching USG personnel. This is similar to what the UK's Ministry of Defence did when it told the PMCs in Iraq not to recruit serving soldiers.[106] The USG could also encourage PMCs to hire Iraqi and Afghan locals instead to boost the local economy, reduce the recruitment pool for insurgents, and portray the USG as genuinely wanting to help the local people.

Second, to ensure the sustainability of its war-fighting capability, the USG must ensure that PMCs only supplement and do not take over capabilities critical to US national security. Specifically, the PMC's expanding share of the force mix is of concern, especially given that Singer's studies show Brown and Root provided US forces in the Balkans with a full "100 percent of food, hazard material handling, and maintenance for tactical and nontactical vehicles."[107] Fortunately, the 2010 *QDR* realizes the government's overreliance on PMCs and will now "work to reduce the number of support service contractors, thereby helping to establish a balanced workforce that appropriately aligns functions to the public and private sector."[108] The recommendation is to review the role of PMCs with an aim of fostering PMCs as a sustainable supplement and not a competitor to the USG.

Implement a Comprehensive Information Campaign

Just as the CNN effect can exacerbate the missteps of PMCs, a well-crafted information campaign can also enhance the PMC industry's positive contributions and reputation. Coupled with greater regulation of the PMC industry, an information campaign should aim to prevent the pendulum from swinging back to where PMCs are seen as money-grubbing, trigger-happy mercenaries. Thus, the recommendation is to implement an information campaign highlighting the positive value of PMCs in improving the welfare of the local population, rectifying the half myths of PMCs' nondemocratic behaviors, and rebranding the PMC industry as a responsible and integral part of the total USG force.

Conclusion

Kinsey correctly observes that there "is nothing unique about the privatization of violence."[109] Therefore, this study's focus has been the emerging trend of mercenarizing the USG, where the USG increasingly relies on PMCs in terms of scale and scope and for their lethal combat services. This trend has manifested in PMC personnel outnumbering US troops in Iraq, as well as PMCs providing virtually 100 percent of all US base services (e.g., water, food, waste management), being awarded multimillion-dollar global contracts, supplying the USG with a wide range of military services across the ROMO, and increasingly being placed in positions where the actual firing of weapons occurs. By itself, this trend is not concerning except that now it appears to be enriching the PMC industry at the expense of US national security.

There is no doubt that PMCs can contribute positively to the USG, but the long-term and strategic effects of the unregulated PMC industry now appear questionable. Senator Levin noted that "even one irresponsible act by contractor personnel can hurt the mission and put our troops in harm's way"; and the House Committee said that "Blackwater's missteps in Iraq are going to hurt us badly" by "creating resentment among Iraqis."[110] Such observations motivated this study, coupled with the fact that "Iraq was a dream contract for . . . mak[ing] millions" (e.g., Halliburton was awarded contracts totaling $13.5 billion for the Iraq war).[111] This study developed three broad evaluation criteria to measure the PMC industry's impact on US national security, namely the ability to achieve defense strategy objectives; promote freedom, justice, and human dignity; and promote and lead democracy. Based on these criteria, this study has the following findings:

- *Tactical and short-term successes but strategic and long-term concerns.* While PMCs are generally effective at tactical-level missions and enable a sustainable deployment cycle by boosting the USG's total strength, their infractions, especially with civilian casualties, have undermined support at the strategic level. PMC poaching practices can potentially hollow out the USG in the long term.

- *Isolated PMC missteps undermine freedom, justice, and human dignity.* While the majority of PMCs are well intentioned and contribute positively, it takes just one highly publicized PMC misstep to damage the advancement of freedom, justice, and human dignity. In reality, several highly publicized PMC missteps—exacerbated by the perceived nonprosecution of PMCs—greatly discredit the US notion and promotion of justice.

- *Accountability and transparency issues undermine US international credibility.* While PMCs are legitimate private corporations providing goods and services in a marketplace, the lack of regulation creates accountability and transparency issues. In particular, the legal ambiguity of PMCs, the accountability of the USG, and the noncompetitive nature of PMC contracts undermine the United States' international reputation and credibility to promote and lead democracy.

Singer advocates that "as long as war exists, so will a demand for military expertise."[112] Indeed, the PMC industry appears to be here to stay as an integral nonstate actor for the USG. Thus, rather than turning back the clock, this study proposes three broad policies to retain the benefits of PMCs while mitigating their downsides. Specifically, the USG should regulate the PMC industry for greater transparency and accountability, foster it as a supplement and not a competitor to the USG, and implement a comprehensive information campaign. In this regard, recent moves by Congress to investigate the impact of PMCs, by the DOD to reestablish a right balance with PMCs, and by the Obama administration to improve the quality of supervisory staff are a step in the right direction.[113]

This study has found that the USG's increasing reliance on PMCs is concerning. If left unregulated, this trend of mercenarizing the USG is likely to be a boon for private military companies but a bane for national security, especially in the long term. Moving forward, it is imperative to comprehensively review the USG-PMC relationship and to incorporate an appropriate regulatory framework that better aligns the PMC industry with US national security interests.

Notes

1. Scahill, *Blackwater*, 41.
2. Isenberg, *Private Military Contractors*, 3.
3. Ibid., 5.
4. Kinsey, *Corporate Soldiers and International Security*, 9.
5. Singer, *Corporate Warriors*, 93.
6. Ibid.
7. Fontaine and Nagl, "Contractors in American Conflicts," 5.
8. Singer, *Corporate Warriors*, 95–97.
9. Kinsey, *Corporate Soldiers and International Security*, 42.
10. UN General Assembly, Resolution 44/34, "International Convention against the Recruitment, Use, Financing and Training of Mercenaries."
11. Singer, *Corporate Warriors*, 94.
12. Isenberg, *Private Military Contractors*, 12–13.
13. Scahill, *Blackwater*, 165–66.
14. Singer, *Corporate Warriors*, 114–15.
15. Fontaine and Nagl, "Contractors in American Conflicts," 8.
16. Dew and Hudgens, "Evolving Private Military Sector," 9.
17. Isenberg, *Private Military Contractors*, 7.
18. Singer, *Corporate Warriors*, 15.
19. Perlo-Freeman and Skons, *Private Military Services Industry*, 8.
20. Kinsey, *Corporate Soldiers and International Security*, 108.

21. Perlo-Freeman and Skons, *Private Military Services Industry*, 22.

22. Geraghty, *Soldiers of Fortune*, 5.

23. Isenberg, *Private Military Contractors*, 22.

24. Ibid., 5.

25. Singer, *Corporate Warriors*, 49.

26. Fontaine and Nagl, "Contractors in American Conflicts," 6.

27. Krahmann, "Controlling Private Military Companies," 5–6.

28. Scahill, *Blackwater*, 28.

29. Isenberg, *Private Military Contractors*, 19.

30. Ibid.

31. Kidwell, *Public War, Private Fight?*, 30.

32. Perlo-Freeman and Skons, *Private Military Services Industry*, 3.

33. Kinsey, *Corporate Soldiers and International Security*, 95–96.

34. Perlo-Freeman and Skons, *Private Military Services Industry*, 3.

35. Stanger, *One Nation under Contract*, 84.

36. Fontaine and Nagl, "Contractors in American Conflicts," 11.

37. Kinsey, *Corporate Soldiers and International Security*, 96.

38. Isenberg, *Private Military Contractors*, 23.

39. Perlo-Freeman and Skons, *Private Military Services Industry*, 14.

40. Ibid., 15.

41. Ibid.

42. Kinsey, *Corporate Soldiers and International Security*, 23.

43. Ibid., 134.

44. Perlo-Freeman and Skons, *Private Military Services Industry*, 14.

45. Ibid., 13.

46. Wulf, *Internationalizing and Privatizing*, 169–70.

47. *Iraqi Reconstruction: Reliance on Private Military Contractors and Status Report*, 33.

48. Bush, *National Security Strategy*, ii.

49. US DOD, *Quadrennial Defense Review Report*, v.

50. Ibid.

51. Ibid., 14.

52. Ibid., 15–16.

53. Ibid.

54. Ibid.

55. Fontaine and Nagl, "Contractors in American Conflicts," 17.

56. McFeely, *Balancing Kinetic Effects*, 17.

57. Isenberg, *Private Military Contractors*, 44.

58. Kinsey, *Corporate Soldiers and International Security*, 94; and Fontaine and Nagl, "Contractors in American Conflicts," 7.

59. Fontaine and Nagl, "Contractors in American Conflicts," 8–9.

60. O'Brien, "Private Military Companies," 43.

61. Geraghty, *Soldiers of Fortune*, 245; and Perlo-Freeman and Skons, *Private Military Services Industry*, 11.

62. Stanger, *One Nation under Contract*, 104.

63. Levin, "Opening Statement."

64. Ibid.

65. *Iraqi Reconstruction: Reliance on Private Military Contractors and Status Report*, 33.

66. Geraghty, *Soldiers of Fortune*, 189–90.

67. Ibid.

68. *Iraqi Reconstruction: Reliance on Private Military Contractors and Status Report*, 5.

69. US DOD, *21st Century Air Force*, 9.

70. US DOD, *USCENTCOM 3rd Quarter Contractor Census Report*.

71. Stanger, *One Nation under Contract*, 93.

72. Fontaine and Nagl, "Contractors in American Conflicts," 7.

73. Kinsey, *Corporate Soldiers and International Security*, 109.

74. Fontaine and Nagl, "Contractors in American Conflicts," 5.

75. Ibid., 10.

76. Burge, "Effectiveness and Efficiencies," 8.

77. Singer, *Corporate Warriors*, 102, 104, 108, 110, and 114–15.

78. Kinsey, *Corporate Soldiers and International Security*, 107.

79. Kidwell, *Public War, Private Fight?*, 54–55.

80. Singer, *Corporate Warriors*, 324.

81. Elsea and Serafino, *Private Security Contractors in Iraq*, 26.

82. Simons, *Master of War*, 57–61 and 152–54.

83. Ibid., 157.

84. Kidwell, *Public War, Private Fight?*, 54–55.

85. Fontaine and Nagl, "Contractors in American Conflicts," 17.

86. Richard Beeston and Catherine Philip, "Security Guards Investigated over 'Iraq Shootings' Videos," *Times* (London), 1 December 2005.

87. *Blackwater USA: Hearing before the Committee on Oversight and Government Reform*, 20–21.

88. Levin, "Opening Statement."

89. Stanger, *One Nation under Contract*, 100.

90. Ryan Devereaux, "Blackwater Guards Lose Bid to Appeal Charges in Iraqi Civilian Shooting Case," *Guardian*, 5 June 2012, http://www.guardian.co.uk/world/2012/jun/05 /blackwater-guards-lose-appeal-iraq-shooting.

91. Fontaine and Nagl, "Contractors in American Conflicts," 14.

92. Singer, *Corporate Warriors*, 159–65.

93. Ibid., 212.

94. Ibid., 208.

95. Isenberg, *Private Military Contractors*, 24.

96. Perlo-Freeman and Skons, *Private Military Services Industry*, 15.

97. Singer, *Corporate Warriors*, 156.

98. Stanger, *One Nation under Contract*, 3.

99. Fontaine and Nagl, "Contractors in American Conflicts," 10.

100. Ibid.

101. Geraghty, *Soldiers of Fortune*, 237.

102. Isenberg, *Private Military Contractors*, 29.

103. Ibid., 12.

104. Fontaine and Nagl, "Contractors in American Conflicts," 15.

105. Levin, "Opening Statement."

106. Kinsey, *Corporate Soldiers and International Security*, 107.

107. Singer, *Corporate Warriors*, 145.

108. DOD, *Quadrennial Defense Review Report*, xiii.

109. Kinsey, *Corporate Soldiers and International Security*, 157.

110. Levin, "Opening Statement"; and *Blackwater USA: Hearing before the Committee on Oversight and Government Reform*, 3.

111. Geraghty, *Soldiers of Fortune*, 210, 334.

112. Singer, *Corporate Warriors*, 230.

113. Isenberg, *Private Military Contractors*, 15–16.

Chapter 3

Western Europe's Future Role in US International Relations

Lt Col Kelly L. Varitz

Major changes in demographics have identifiable and predictable consequences for countries around the globe. Demographers have distinguished key trends that, if they continue according to projection, could cause shifts in the geopolitical climate. Trends of potential concern are population declines, aging populations, and ethnic diasporas due to migration. These shifts will contribute to a reshaping of the global landscape over the next several decades.[1] They also have intrinsic links to national security as they are tied to a country's resources and therefore affect its ability to create economic wealth and political and military strength.[2]

The United States and its allies face challenges associated with these demographic factors because of the consequences for key elements of national power—economic, political, and military.[3] Consequently, these issues merit further study as they are poised to impact relationships between the United States and its allies—specifically, US partnerships with its longtime allies in Western Europe.

Issues and Background

During the global exploration and colonization era, the growth in a country's population directly influenced its political strength. Large boons in a country's population correlated to past periods of global expansionism and economic growth—population had a major role in the geopolitics of power. This factor favored Western Europe for about 500 years, ending around 1940.[4] However, much of Western Europe is no longer experiencing high levels of population growth; many projections expect this trend to continue. Population growth requires a replacement rate of more than two children born to every woman.[5] Recent research indicates that fertility rates for Western Europe are between 1.5 and 2.1—depending on the country—with most of Western Europe experiencing numbers closer to 1.5 (fig. 3.1).[6]

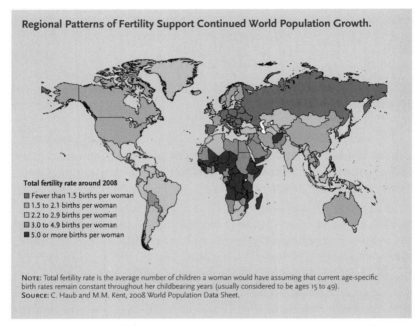

Figure 3.1. Regional fertility rates. (*Reprinted from* Population Reference Bureau, "World Population Highlights: Key Findings from PRB's 2008 World Population Data Sheet," *Population Bulletin* 63, no. 3 [September 2008], 1, http://www.prb.org/pdf08/63.3highlights.pdf.)

The failure of Western Europe to reach replacement rate indicates the potential for a future decline in overall population. This alone isn't Western Europe's only distressing demographic trend. As Peter Peterson states in his 1999 *Foreign Affairs* article on the global aging crisis, "Global life expectancy has grown more in the last fifty years than over the previous five thousand."[7] Many consider this as a positive trend, and from a personal perspective, this may indeed be true.

However, when examined from a regional or governmental point of view, that is not necessarily the case. Globally, life expectancy since World War II has increased from age 45 to 65.[8] In the most developed nations of the world, life expectancy is projected to increase from age 77 today to around age 85 at midcentury.[9] Western Europe is, of course, included in the figures for the developed world. The life expectancy numbers in some Western European countries are already higher than the overall developed world average: Italy–79 years, France–78, and Germany–77.4.[10] The increase in the number of the elderly that naturally comes about with greater life expectancy can bring with it social and economic strain. Those specifics are discussed later, but it is important to introduce life expectancy as a demographic trend because of its links to what many demographers see as Western Europe's most challenging demographic trend—population aging.

Population decline and increased life expectancy taken individually may not be cause for much concern, but most of Western Europe is facing both of these issues. They create one looming problem when brought together.[11] Increased life expectancy automatically causes an aging population, but falling population levels coupled with this rise in longevity bring about a much more rapid transformation in population age structures and growth rates.[12] This "hyperaging" is occurring in much of Western Europe, where by 2050 the proportion of the population that is age 65 and above will increase from the current 19 percent to 28 percent. Of the Western European countries, Germany, France, Great Britain, and Italy are projected to experience the most rapid growth rates in this demographic group.[13]

When examining aging population numbers, it is crucial to understand not only the percentage of the elderly but also the ratio of the working-age population (those persons aged 15–64) as compared to the elderly population (65 and older, who can draw on pension plans). This ratio is the nexus of the social and economic stress that aging populations create. Currently, the ratio of the working population to the elderly in the developed world is 4:1. Over the next 50 years, this is expected to drop to 2:1 or even lower for some countries in Western Europe.[14] Figure 3.2 represents this trend graphically by showing the 2050 projection of the working-age population for various countries as compared to the 2000 ratio.

Migration is another trend to watch when analyzing the demographic climate of Western Europe. Western Europe attracts over one million immigrants annually, contributing to its overall foreign-born population of 65 million.[15] Many of Western Europe's immigrants come from Muslim countries in sub-Saharan Africa.[16] Migrants are leaving sub-Saharan Africa due to the effects of a population explosion in the region that is expected to continue into the next decade. Because of a drastic reduction in infant and child mortality rates, sub-Saharan Africa's population is projected to increase by half by 2025, creating a large youth bulge.[17] The region does not have the economic vitality to support such a boom, so its youth are looking to Europe for better opportunities.

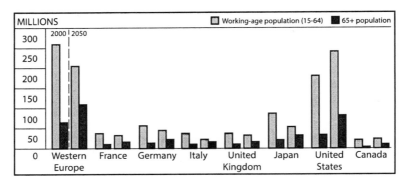

Figure 3.2. Changes in working-age populations. (*Reprinted from* Central Intelligence Agency [CIA], *Long-Term Global Demographic Trends: Reshaping the Geopolitical Landscape* [Washington, DC: CIA, July 2001], https://www.cia.gov/library/reports/general-reports-1/Demo_Trends _For_Web.pdf.)

Migration of large ethnic groups from their traditional homeland to a region with a much different ethnic or religious makeup can create diasporas. This is characteristic of what is occurring and expected to continue to occur between sub-Saharan Africa and Western Europe. The phenomenon can bring social unrest as two or more cultures work to cohabit the region. However, if managed correctly, it has the potential to mitigate Western Europe's aging population challenges.

Figure 3.3 is a geographical representation of the prominent demographic trends around the globe and provides a good summation of the previously discussed trends affecting Western Europe. Its depiction of the global nature of demographic trends illustrates their interconnectedness and, therefore, why they are geopolitical forces of change.

Although significant in analyzing the future of Western Europe, demographic trends aren't the only challenges that will affect the geopolitical map of the region. Despite its declining population, the region will need more energy resources as its indigenous energy supplies dwindle (fig. 3.4).[18] Energy dependency is defined as a situation where net imports as a percentage of gross consumption are robustly positive. All Western European countries are energy dependent with the exception of Denmark, and all dependent countries except the Netherlands and Italy showed an increased level of dependency from 2007 to 2008.[19]

Russia is Western Europe's biggest source of natural gas, oil, and coal, supplying about 44 percent of its total energy consumption.[20]

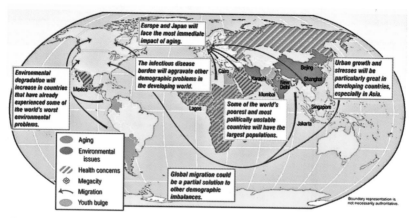

Figure 3.3. Demographic trends affecting Western Europe. (*Reprinted from CIA, Long-Term Global Demographic Trends: Reshaping the Geo-political Landscape* [Washington, DC: CIA, July 2001], https://www.cia.gov/library /reports /general-reports-1/Demo_Trends_For_Web.pdf.)

Natural gas comprises around 25 percent of the energy consumed, making its secure supply a prime concern for Western European nations.[21] Western Europe is one of the dominant markets for Russian natural gas exports.[22] Due to the interdependent nature of Western Europe's and Russia's energy relationship, it has typically been marked by stability and cooperation. However, recent events have brought this relationship into question.

Russia stopped natural gas supplies to the Ukraine and Georgia in an attempt to exert political influence in 2006. Some Western European countries saw this as a warning of Russia's willingness to use its energy resources as a political weapon to gain power in the region.[23] To compound this issue, the Russian natural gas pipeline system runs through many European and central Asian states, creating an interconnection among all of the countries in the region. Therefore, an energy dispute in one region could disrupt energy supplies in another. The geopolitical climate is altered when the potential of partnerships develops between nations that would not normally align. This was demonstrated in 2007 when natural gas supplies from Russia to Western Europe were disrupted when Russia terminated natural gas supplies to Belarus because of a dispute over prices and pipeline access.[24] Unless mitigated by factors such as reductions in natural gas dependency or increases in domestic production, the codependent relationship between Russia and Western Europe is expected to continue and could even grow more crucial as Western Europe's reliance on natural gas increases.

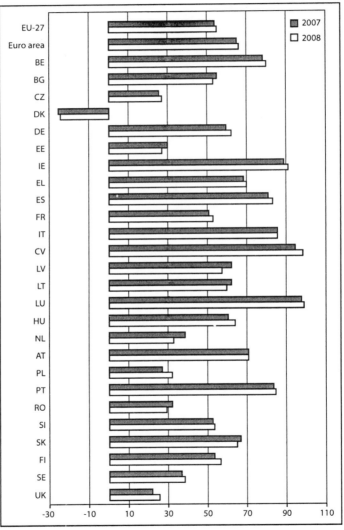

Figure 3.4. EU [European Union] energy dependency. (*Reprinted from* Rita Keenan and Antigone Gikas, *Statistical Aspects of the Energy Economy in 2008* [Luxembourg: Eurostat: Statistics in Focus, 55/2009].)

Research Question

The principal question this research serves to answer is how Western Europe's future demographic and energy trends will affect its national security and, thereby, its relationship and global partnership with the United States. Western Europe faces coming challenges with the potential to negatively affect the region's security. Many of the states in the region display demographic and energy dependency trends that could strain economies and challenge social climates.

Research Method

What is the best way to answer the research question presented? How do researchers even begin to answer questions about the future? The complex, unstable nature of prospective events makes answering questions about the future difficult. Without a structured methodology for examining the future, answers to questions can be ambiguous and present themselves as a researcher's best guess. A proper approach requires more than analyzing data and making predictions about what the future might look like. That is where scenario planning (also called scenario thinking) comes into play. Scenario planning assists researchers in ordering and framing complex future problems and allows them to develop plausible accounts of how relevant external forces might interact to create challenges and opportunities for businesses or, in the case of this study, nation-states.[25]

Global Business Network (GBN) is a pioneer in the evolution of scenario planning. Although its scenario planning is geared for nonprofit organizations, GBN states throughout its literature the utility of this tool for other public- and private-sector institutions. GBN's publication *What If? The Art of Scenario Thinking for Nonprofits* presents scenario planning as a disciplined way to ask "what if?" by creating "stories about how the future might unfold" and "provocative and plausible stories about diverse ways in which relevant issues outside our organizations might evolve."[26] These "stories" form the basis for the scenario-planning process.

The scenario-planning process has five core steps: orient, explore, synthesize, act, and monitor (fig. 3.5). These phases are described below.

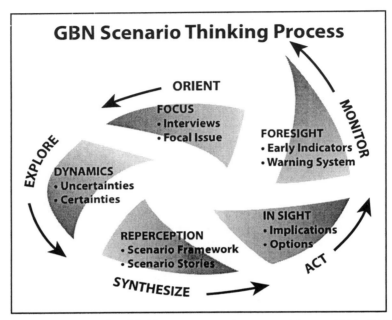

Figure 3.5. Scenario thinking process. (*Reprinted from* GBN, "Why Scenarios?," http://www.gbn.com/about/scenario_planning.php.)

Phase 1: Orient

Clarify the issues by learning more about the challenges facing an organization. Next, take what is learned about the challenges and frame the focal question to be answered. The focal question should have a time frame associated with it to focus the process. GBN recommends slow-changing trends such as societal issues (e.g., aging and migration) that have longer time frames.[27] This paper applies this process by first providing the background on the challenges facing Western Europe. This background led to the research question, how will Western Europe's future demographic and energy trends affect its national security and, thereby, its relationship and global partnership with the United States? The time frame for this question is 2030 as most of the research material forecasts trends leading up to 2030 or after.

Phase 2: Explore

Examine the information from the orient phase to explore the "driving forces" that form the focal question. Driving forces are "forces of change outside the organization that will shape future dynamics in predictable and unpredictable ways."[28] Driving forces are either "predetermined"—highly likely to develop in a known direction, or "uncertainties"—important but unpredictable in how they will develop.[29]

Phase 3: Synthesize

Start with prioritizing the driving forces according to the degree of importance to the focal question and the degree of uncertainty of the driving forces. The goal is to identify the driving forces that are most important to the focal question and the most uncertain. These driving forces are "critical uncertainties" and will be the foundation of the scenarios.[30] The next step is to use the critical uncertainties to develop a scenario framework by thinking of each critical uncertainty along an axis with the range of extremes of each uncertainty at each end of the axis. Next, by crossing the two axes, form a framework. The intersection of each axis creates a possible scenario. This is a scenario matrix and is used to further develop and explore the scenarios (fig. 3.6).[31] After the matrix is developed, transform each identified scenario into a short narrative, beginning in the present and ending in the future.[32]

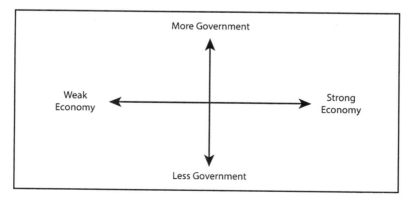

Figure 3.6. Example scenario matrix. (*Reprinted from* Diana Scearce and Katherine Fulton, *What If? The Art of Scenario Thinking for Nonprofits,* Emeryville, CA: Global Business Network [GBN], 2004.)

Phase 4: Act

Use the scenarios developed in phase 3 to inform action. Assuming this scenario is the future, what actions can be taken to prepare? The answers to this question are the scenario implications. Use the implications to highlight strategic choices that an organization may need to make. These are the building blocks of a strategic agenda—a set of strategic priorities that help organizations meet long-term goals.[33] This paper does not fully address this phase as it is meant to identify possible problems that could affect US national security and not to suggest solutions to these problems.

Phase 5: Monitor

Identify mechanisms that will track changes in the environment so organizations can identify changes and adapt strategy accordingly. Devise a monitoring system to track "leading indicators"—signs of potentially significant change—to specify if a particular scenario is beginning to unfold.[34] This study uses the possible Western European strategies discussed earlier as key indicators the United States should consider as they may demonstrate signs of changes in Western Europe that could initiate a shift in the relationship between the two regions.

Analysis

This study introduces the demographic and energy issues facing Western Europe and provides a context in which to consider the significance of these issues. The major demographics trends of focus are population aging—as a factor of population decline and increased life expectancy—and migration. The major energy trend to consider is Western Europe's dependence on Russia for a significant portion of its oil and natural gas needs. Key driving forces are uncovered that form the basis of the scenarios.

Population Aging

The current global aging phenomenon is a fundamental demographic shift with no parallel in human history.[35] According to aging experts Alan Pifer and Lydia Bronte, the impact of global aging will be at least as powerful as any of the "great economic and social movements of the past."[36] In 1950 no nation in the world had a median age higher than 36. Now, 16 countries in Western Europe have a median age of 40, and by 2050 six are projected to have a median age over 50.

This trend is not limited to Western Europe; it will also be prevalent in the developed countries of East Asia and in Eastern Europe and Russia.[37] On a global scale, aging populations may cause a slowdown in economic growth in the developed world and a rearranging of the geopolitical order as the economic output of the developed world shrinks as a percentage of the world total. In 1950 six of the 12 most populous countries were developed; by 2050 the United States will be the only developed country in the 12 most populous.[38] For individual countries, the most serious impact of aging will be its fiscal cost. According to projections by the Center for Strategic and International Studies, public spending on pensions and health benefits in developed countries could grow from an average of 11 percent of gross domestic product (GDP) to upwards of 23 percent—five times greater than the typical developed country currently spends on national defense.[39]

Along with these fiscal costs come greater expenses to individuals and societies overall. As the developed world is aging, its populations are also shrinking, meaning that by the time the aging projections begin to unfold, the number of workers in the population will have declined. Fewer workers will mean fewer resources available to contribute to pension and health care programs, leading to an unprecedented economic burden on working-age populations.[40] This burden could bring serious dangers that manifest in various ways throughout societies, including destabilizing swings in interest rates, steep tax hikes, and deep benefit cuts.[41]

In the years following World War II, many developed countries began to expand their public pension programs and evolve them to "pay-as-you-go systems."[42] This worked well when the number of retirees was small and the number of workers was growing, but as the numbers of elderly dramatically increase and the numbers of workers decline, these systems will be put to the ultimate test. Pension plans and other retirement benefit systems not designed to provide the additional payout that global aging will require will be strained and may even break under the added pressure. The pressure to keep up with the added expenditure of growing pension and health care programs will create mounting debt in countries with aging populations.[43] This added debt could be mitigated by raising interest rates and taxes on the working population.

Less manpower in the labor force also means slower improvement in living standards. The Organization for Economic Cooperation and Development (OECD) estimates that the cumulative effect of a decrease in labor will reduce the living standard of Japan by 25 percent and that of EU countries by 18 percent by 2050.[44] With this added pressure, the young, working-age population may see the responsibility to "pay for" the elderly as an unwanted millstone, especially when it hits home in the form of higher taxes, larger interest rates, and a lower standard of living. The working-age population's perceived encumbrance of paying for the elderly at the expense of its own quality of life could strain the relationship between the two groups. This stress may be exacerbated as elderly groups gain a larger voice in national politics due to the increase in their numbers. The political power of the elderly is already rising in Europe with the influence of senior-sponsored labor unions and political parties that adopt pro-retiree platforms.[45] The question future-trends researchers are asking is, with ever more electoral power in the hands of the elderly, what will motivate political leaders to act on behalf of the future of the young?[46] There likely isn't a stronger indicator of a potential rift between the young and old than the truth behind that question.

In addition to these economic and social impacts, aging countries will find it increasingly difficult to maintain strong militaries. Not only will aging countries have less of their GDP to devote to national defense, they will also have a smaller manpower pool from which to draw their military strength. With the number of military service-age youth expected to decline in most developed countries, militaries will be hard-pressed to maintain force levels—even more so if small families are not willing to send their children to war.[47]

Most countries in Western Europe will have fertility rates between 1.5 to 2.1 children for every woman. Since that is below replacement level, populations are expected to decline. The percentage of the population over age 65 is expected to increase from around 19 percent to 28 percent across Europe with the Western European countries of Germany, Italy, and the United Kingdom increasing the most. Western Europe's population decline coupled with its aging population will result in a worker-to-elderly ratio of 2:1, down from its current 4:1 ratio. As demonstrated by the general global aging impacts, these demographic trends are poised to cause serious issues inside Western Europe.

The overwhelming set of issues Western Europe faces as its population ages creates at least two main problems it must tackle: how to support the elderly population and where to find the labor force to continue contributing to the economy.[48] These issues point to the primary driving force related to the focal question of how demographic trends will affect Western Europe's national security. That main driving force is the proportion of elderly to the working population. According to demographers, this trend is nearly a foregone conclusion. Barring any unforeseen catastrophes such as natural disasters or pandemics, the number of the elderly certainly will not change between now and 2030 since that segment of the population has already been born. Most demographers do not believe Western Europe can reduce its population decline, and any successful initiatives to do so would take much longer than the 2030 time frame covered by this research.[49] These factors are ranked high in importance and low in uncertainty. Therefore, they qualify as a driving force.

Migration

Currently, an estimated 40 million people live outside their native countries.[50] This migration trend is expected to increase over the next 10 to 20 years, especially from developing states to the developed world. Migration already accounts for over 70 percent of the total share of population growth in developed countries, an increase of 45 percent since 1990.[51] The migration of people from underdeveloped to developed countries is often spurred by the lure of higher living standards, generous welfare systems, and good educational opportunities. This is illustrated in the current and projected future migration patterns from sub-Saharan Africa to Western Europe, where large numbers of migrants are fleeing countries with no infrastructure to support their booming populations and heading to countries where they believe opportunities are better.

According to the US Joint Forces Command's (USJFCOM) *Joint Operating Environment 2008*, "Such migrations disrupt patterns of culture, politics and economics and in most cases carry with them the potential of further dislocations and troubles."[52] Large influxes of immigrants to regions ethnically and religiously different from their parent countries have the potential to strain economies, generate violence, and cause political upheaval in host nations.[53] Given that a large number of immigrants are coming from countries ethnically and religiously different from the majority of Western Europeans, the substantial increase in immigrants could rapidly change the cultural balance. For example, foreigners are projected to make up 30 percent of Germany's total population by 2030. This kind of change in the cultural makeup of a country has the potential to cause instability for several reasons.

Most countries in Europe (including Western Europe) have historically been ethnically and religiously homogeneous. Their populations traditionally desire to maintain their cultural identity and are less likely to intermingle and intermarry with immigrants. Thus, migrant populations are separated, creating a "second class" of people without access to the economic advantages of the "first class." This formula fuels xenophobic backlash from native populations and creates anger among the immigrant populations.[54]

Also, a flood of immigrants from developed countries will initially overload the host nation's infrastructure and resources.[55] As native populations begin to feel this strain in their homes, they will become increasingly resistant to immigration and immigrants, further polarizing the native population and immigrant groups. This phenomenon could especially impact Western Europe as it will already be facing economic issues from funding the government programs required to support its aging populations. The additional drain on resources caused by migration could further damage already stretched economies.

Migration, however, can have positive effects, especially by helping solve the problems of aging populations in the developed world. The OECD predicts that the labor force in the developing world will double by 2025, while developed countries like those in Western Europe will require more workers to add to their dwindling working-age population.[56] Migration could provide a substantial working class, forming a tax and consumer base for Western Europe's aging societies. This tax base could help pay for the pension and health care programs for the elderly.[57] However, if Western Europe chooses to use migration to alleviate problems brought about by aging populations, it must consider that the number of immigrants required by many countries to support retirees would far exceed immigration levels of the past decade.[58] For example, to support its retirees, Germany would have to boost immigration to record levels through 2050, above the 1 million caused by German reunification in 1990.[59]

Given the considerable potential to mitigate Western Europe's most looming problem, the issue Western European governments should examine is how they can properly manage immigration so their migrant populations will help offset the effects of their aging populations. Managing immigration involves many different governmental actions, including developing immigration policies, work permit procedures, citizenship laws, and integration strategies. The issue of immigration integration is the focus of this study because of its potential to cause most of the negative economic and societal factors if improperly managed. This is especially true given the large number of immigrants it will take to support the growing number of Western European retirees.

The proper integration of immigrants is the driving force behind the focal question of how demographic trends will affect Western Europe's national security. It is high in importance and in uncertainty as it is not apparent how well Western European governments will manage the integration of their immigrants into Western European societies.

Western European countries are currently taking different approaches to immigrant integration with varied levels of success. France has adopted an assimilation approach whereby immigrants are integrated as individuals as opposed to members of an ethnic minority community. This has led to isolated ethnic populations that are frequently relegated to ghetto-type environments that have become breeding grounds for antisocial behavior.[60] The Dutch have experienced similar results from their multicultural approach to immigrant integration. In their approach, immigrants belonging to minority groups are integrated with full respect to their cultural and religious differences. Critics blame the Dutch version for the creation of parallel societies that fail to recognize and capitalize upon commonalities between ethnic and religious groups but instead magnify differences and polarize population groups.[61] The British have also used a multicultural approach for minority group integration but have taken steps to ensure that minority groups have the opportunity for economic advancement, particularly into the middle class. They have seen some success in this approach, but recent evidence shows that extremist groups, which seek to play on the differences among minority populations and create division between these populations and society at large, are beginning to find recruits from universities attended by the offspring of integrated middle-class immigrants.[62]

The question of how to best integrate immigrants into host-nation societies has no easy answers. Integration efforts are most likely to succeed when immigrants feel they have a stake in the success or failure of their host society. How to most effectively achieve this in historically homogeneous societies like Western Europe remains a challenge. It is clear from the terrorist attacks in London and Madrid—where evidence indicates the terrorists involved were homegrown—that the proper integration of immigrants is not only an economic issue but also a national security concern.

Continued terrorist attacks in Western Europe could bring an outcry for increased investment in military forces. Also, if the frequency and intensity of terrorist attacks increase, Western European governments may respond to them not as localized, internal security issues but on an international scale.[63] The challenge will then be fielding the forces necessary to conduct international military operations. On the one hand, migration could bring a larger pool from which to draw a military force. On the other hand, this new pool of recruits could resist fighting for a country it isn't culturally connected with. In addition, as minority groups grow in number, they will garner a larger voice in the political systems of host countries. Minority groups may use this increased political influence to affect the foreign policy decisions of the host nation. They likely will not support host-nation foreign policy actions seen as attacking their own ethnic or religious groups, even if those groups reside outside the host or parent country.

Given the positive and negative effects of migration, Western Europe will face tough challenges as its governments decide how to handle the flow of immigrants the region will face in the future. Handled properly, migrants can be an answer to some of the problems of aging populations. Handled improperly, migrants can add additional burdens to already strained societies.

Energy Dependence

Global energy demands are on the rise. By 2030 energy demands are expected to be 50 percent greater than today. Meeting this demand would require the addition of about 1.4 million barrels per day of energy resources every year.[64] Fossil fuels such as oil, coal, and natural gas will remain the dominant source of energy in the coming decades. Projections indicate that the discovery of new petroleum and gas fields sufficient to meet this demand is unlikely.[65] This indicates major energy challenges in the future as the world faces energy shortfalls. The effects of these challenges are hard to predict but will likely shape the prospects for growth in both developing and developed countries and intensify unresolved political and social tensions among opponents and allies.[66]

As the availability of energy resources begins to shrink, countries will experience greater stress due to scarcity of resources. Countries will be forced to preserve their access to energy supplies as they may be deemed necessary for domestic stability and nation-state survival. This could lead to conflict over resources—war or a buildup in armed forces that could increase regional tensions. Diplomatically, it could mean a reshuffling of alliances and partnerships that may alter relationships among longtime friendly countries.[67] It is this latter phenomenon that is poised to affect future US and Western European relations.

Europe is projected to remain dependent on Russia for its energy (primarily natural gas) into and likely past 2025.[68] Recent events have raised doubts as to the security of Russia's energy supply into Western Europe. At a minimum, this concern will cause Western Europe to watch the actions of Russia more closely. Since Russia's natural gas companies are nationalized, they are directly tied to the national security decision making of the country, increasing the likelihood that Russia will use its energy resources for political purposes. This creates a dangerous situation for Western Europe. The potential exists for Russia to leverage Western Europe's energy dependency to exert pressure on Western European governments to set foreign policy favorable to Russia.[69] In addition, since Russia has a veritable monopoly on gas supplies from central Asia into Western Europe, it can dictate the cost of natural gas, meaning Western Europe will likely continue to pay a high price for its natural gas needs.[70] This could further degrade Western European economies already under stress due to an aging population and a potentially large influx of immigrants.

If the Russian energy supply is perceived to be too unstable, Western Europe may be forced to look elsewhere for its natural gas needs. One potential source is Iran, whose natural gas reserves are second only to Russia.[71] Such a partnership would give Iran tremendous diplomatic leverage as one ominous example illustrates. Western Europe has partnered with the United States in an attempt to thwart Iran's efforts to develop nuclear weapons. An energy partnership between Western Europe and Iran could significantly hamper that effort, especially if it involved Britain and France; both countries have veto rights in the United Nations Security Council.[72]

Given the possible effects discussed, Western Europe's dependency on Russia for its energy needs is the driving factor linked to the focal question of how demographic trends will affect Western Europe's national security. It is high in importance because of the potential effects on Western Europe's national security and economy. Thus far, Western Europe's efforts to decrease Russian energy dependency have fallen short of success.[73] That it will maintain some level of dependency on Russia for energy needs is certain—how much is uncertain. It is this level of dependence that will drive the effects discussed earlier. Therefore, the driving force is ranked high in uncertainty.

Previously, this chapter presented the ways in which future demographic and ene gy trends could affect the geopolitical environment of Western Europe and introduced the driving factors that will be the basis of the scenarios used to describe the possible futures for Western Europe as it deals with the challenges of these trends. Next, this chapter covers four future scenarios for Western Europe regarding aging populations, migration, and energy dependency.

Four Futures for Western Europe

Three driving forces related to the focal question of this study were previously identified: (1) the proportion of the elderly to the working class population, (2) the integration of migrants into Western European societies, and (3) the level of dependency of Western Europe on Russia for energy needs. Two of the three driving forces—proper integration of migrants into societies and the level of dependency on Russia for energy needs—were ranked as high in importance and in uncertainty. According to scenario planning guidance, these driving forces should be labeled as critical uncertainties and used to develop effective scenarios for future planning.[74] These two critical uncertainties will be combined to form the axes of a scenario matrix; each of the scenarios presented later will represent one of the quadrants of the scenario matrix (fig. 3.7).

The driving force of the proportion of elderly to the working class population was ranked high in importance but low in uncertainty because most researchers are convinced Western Europe's population will continue to age at the rates predicted. Researchers are certain Western Europe's native population will continue to decline. Migration has the potential to improve the elderly-to-worker ratio, but that will be addressed through the immigration integration driving factor.

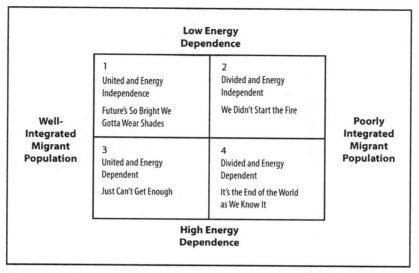

Figure 3.7. Scenario matrix for possible futures for Western Europe.

Scenario 1: United and Energy Independent—Future's So Bright We Gotta Wear Shades

Good immigrant integration, low energy dependence. More than 20 years ago, futurists were making dire predictions concerning the health and welfare of Western Europe. They predicted major economic and social turmoil due to hyperaging, energy challenges, and large immigrant populations. Today, in the year 2030, those futurists are eating crow, as their dire predictions have not materialized. In fact, most countries in Western Europe have turned their demographic and energy challenges into opportunities: their economies have flourished, and their societies are strong. As Western Europe's population expectedly aged, the governments of Western Europe worked diligently to mitigate the economic problems brought about by the graying of societies. They capitalized on the growing immigrant population, providing viable opportunities to contribute to society and improve their quality of life. Recognizing the dangers of remaining overly dependent on Russia for oil and natural gas, Western European governments promoted initiatives to wean their countries off their reliance on fossil fuels and worked to diversify supply sources for remaining fossil-fuel needs. Great Britain, in particular, achieved remarkable success, as portrayed in excerpts from its prime minister's address to the British Parliament. Gavin Nasser, the son of immigrant parents, is Britain's current prime minister.

> My fellow parliamentarians, it is with great honour that I address you today on the state of this grand nation of ours. As you know all too well, the past decades were challenging ones for Great Britain. We faced an economy burdened by the costs of an aging population and a diminishing workforce and further weakened by the need for massive government subsidies to ease the effects of increases in natural gas and oil prices. Our citizens suffered greatly because of this downturn in our economy. Our elderly saw cuts in their pensions and health care. Unemployment was at an all time high. Natural gas and oil shortages and price hikes put additional strain on nearly every member of our society.
>
> Great Britain was headed for its darkest days. However, as they always do, the people of Britain faced these challenges with the fighting spirit ever present in this great country of ours. We were determined to conquer the challenges before us and emerge a stronger, more vibrant nation. And conquer those challenges we did!
>
> Thanks to Britain's determined citizens and the great leadership of those who came before me, Britain is on the road not only to recovery but to becoming an even stronger nation and a larger presence in the international community. Under the banner of liberty, civic duty, and fairness to all, the British people stood together to contribute to the rebuilding of society. No matter the class, colour, or creed, citizens threw aside their prejudices and xenophobia and worked hard to preserve the British way of life. Through sacrifice and hard work we were able to reduce our dependency on oil and natural gas by creating viable, renewable energy alternatives affordable to all. We made energy conservation more than a slogan; it is now a British way of life. The parliament achieved its goal of getting Britain out from under the shadow of Russian energy dependence by seeking strong energy partnerships with other countries. We have been especially successful in developing energy partnerships with governments in sub-Saharan Africa and now receive a substantial portion of our remaining energy needs from this region—a region particularly important to many of our citizens as they, their parents, or grandparents emigrated from many of the countries there.
>
> Speaking of our immigrants . . . I commend our immigrant population for their commitment to Great Britain. Despite their short history in this country, our immigrants have become integral members of society. Many continue to hold much necessary jobs in the service industry, while others have started businesses of their own. Still many more are filling shortages in the medical and teaching fields. In our public schools and universities, it's impossible to tell recent immigrant children from the children of those who have been in Britain for generations; all play and study together with no care of race, religion,

or country of origin. Thanks to the contributions of our immigrants, Britain's economy has continued to grow.

Our elderly citizens have also carried much of the burden for our society. Facing cuts in pensions and health care, many have remained in the workforce, adding much-needed revenue to our economy. We have recently been able to return pensions and health benefits to the levels before the cuts. Now, many of our elderly are enjoying their much-earned retirement. I have great admiration for all of our citizens and thank them immensely for their sacrifice and hard work.

I promise you that, as leader of this parliament, I will continue the efforts of those before me. I will work hard to further strengthen our economy. I will strive to preserve the national unity we have worked so hard to build. Together, we, the citizens of Great Britain, will carry this country into the bright future we have all worked so diligently to ensure. I very much look forward to continuing to serve as your prime minister.

Scenario 2: Divided and Energy Independent—We Didn't Start the Fire

Poor immigrant integration, low energy dependence. It is the year 2030, and Western European countries continue to face challenges. The population has aged. Almost 30 percent of the population is over the age of 65 and eligible to collect on pension plans and health care benefits promised to them by their governments. However, many aren't collecting at the rates expected due to the inability of their governments to fully fund the benefits programs. This is causing hardship for the elderly populations. Many are working past what was once considered retirement age, and many are forced to go without needed medical care and prescription drugs. Families are unable to care for their aging parents and grandparents because of the additional taxes the government has levied on individuals and private businesses to assist in stimulating economies. The economies of Western Europe are further burdened by the need to provide welfare support to large immigrant populations that cannot find employment beyond minimum wage and that live in government-provided housing in ghetto sections of the larger cities.

Western European governments have been successful in easing the dependence on Russia for natural gas and oil supplies by reducing their dependence on nonrenewable energy sources and partnering with additional countries to import the fossil fuels still needed. This has brought down energy costs to the consumer, but the people have not seen the benefits as governments have raised taxes on oil and natural gas to help fund programs for the elderly.

Immigrant groups increasingly lobby governments for more welfare assistance, mostly to no avail. This is creating a feeling of disenfranchisement among immigrants, leading to protests—some becoming violent—in major cities across Western Europe. The elderly are also becoming more and more dissatisfied with their living conditions. They have formed large lobby groups as vehicles to continue pressuring Western European governments to increase funding of pension and health care programs. Some governments are choosing to increase retirement benefit funding, but it comes at the expense of other government programs such as national defense. Below is an open letter to the president of Germany as published by the English-language *Deutsche Welle*, a German online news repository. It was written by the leader of a particularly large and influential pensioners' lobby group.

Dear President von Hindenburg,

I'm writing to you on behalf of the elderly citizens of Germany.

As you well know, we are in dire straits. We're suffering and dying at the hands of your government. During the past several years we've sat idly by while your government pours taxpayer money into the ghettos of Frankfurt, Berlin, and Hamburg to support the foreigners who are unwilling to work while we, who've given the best years of our lives working for our country, can't collect the benefits we've rightfully earned.

We watch our friends and relatives suffer every day, making inhumane decisions between paying for medical treatment or buying food. We watch as their medical care is rationed, leaving them in severe pain while they slowly die of curable diseases. We see their families emotionally wrecked as your government's overtaxation has rendered them financially incapable of helping their dying mothers and fathers.

We appreciate your government's recent efforts to ease the effects of Germany's overdependence on Russia for oil and gas. This showed promise in lowering our soaring natural gas costs and relieving our suffering. As I'm sure you remember, the winter of 2026 was especially bad for us. We lost many of our friends and neighbors who couldn't afford to heat their homes, as they succumbed to the extremely frigid temperatures during the coldest winter in Germany's recorded history. With these memories fresh in our minds, we saw your new energy plan as a shining light in a sea of darkness, only now to have that light extinguished by increased government taxes on natural gas and oil—taxes you use to fund more programs to help the foreigners who do nothing to help themselves or us.

As if all of that were not enough, we're forced to endure violence in our neighborhoods with little protection from the police. Foreigners riot in our streets, damaging our property and threatening us with brutality. We fear for our lives as they prey on our weakened state. Instead of our government helping us, they show pity on those who inflict fear and violence by calling them "disenfranchised youth." How about us, the "disenfranchised elderly"? Where is the government in our time of need?

Now your government is contemplating providing military assistance to the United States for its war in Yemen. We want as much as anyone to see Germany's relationship with the United States remain strong, but at what cost? More suffering and death for Germany's elderly? There are far too many problems inside Germany to commit ourselves to the dilemmas of others.

We understand you have tough decisions to make, but is it too much to ask for the loyal citizens of Germany to be taken care of in the manner in which their government promised? We're not asking for something for nothing or more than we deserve, as so many in this country are. We simply want the right to live in peace and with dignity.

We can no longer endure this terrible treatment. We represent the largest voting population in the country. We've been energized and mobilized by your government's unfair treatment. We will now take action.

I assure you that the pensioners of Germany are united in their resolve to make you and your government pay for the pain and suffering you've inflicted upon us.

Remember, President von Hindenburg, we didn't start this fire. It was started by the failed policies of you and your government and stoked by the laziness and disloyalty of the "disenfranchised youth."

Your day of judgment is here.

Sincerely,
Ada Vanderbon
President, Sozialverband VdK

Scenario 3: United and Energy Dependent—Just Can't Get Enough

Good immigrant integration, high energy dependence. It is a new decade in Western Europe—2030. In recent years the region has experienced a large influx of immigrants, many coming from countries in sub-Saharan Africa where populations continue to explode. Western European governments have had decades of experience with immigrant populations, learning many lessons from integration policies of the past. Most of the Western European countries have been successful in integrating their immigrant populations, making immigrants productive members of society. Immigrants contribute to the economic growth of the country by working in all sectors of society, operating private businesses, and holding government jobs. Their children attend the same public and private schools as those of nonimmigrants, and they actively participate in local civic and political organizations. Generally, immigrants feel they have a stake in society and believe they are well represented by the local and central governments of their host countries.

With a larger pool of workers, Western European countries are able to continue providing pensioners with the social benefits they expect. Although the increase in taxpayers brought about by the influx of immigrants has not eliminated the economic impact of population aging, it has mitigated it enough to stabilize Western European economies. The elderly pension plans and health benefits are not straining the region's economies to the extent some futurists had predicted.

However, one issue Western Europe still faces is dependence on Russia for energy needs. All Western European countries except Denmark remain energy dependent, and most still rely on Russia to fulfill a significant percentage of their oil and natural gas needs.[75] Due to the relatively stable nature of most of the economies of Western Europe, governments have been able to provide government subsidies to offset the high costs of natural gas resulting from Russian energy companies' recent price increases. Western European governments have engaged with Russia regarding the recent price hikes, but thus far the Russian government has been reluctant to do anything about the issue. Current Russian rhetoric indicates additional price hikes may be likely if Western Europe continues to oppose Russian initiatives in the United Nations. The following excerpt is from a 2030 *Wikipedia* entry, "French Economy in the 2020s and Beyond":

> Ahmed Buchez from the Union pour un Mouvement Populaire party was appointed prime minister of France in 2020 after the dismissal of his predecessor, Jacques Fabius, from the Front National Party due to a public uprising over their anti-immigrant policies. Buchez entered office in the midst of a period of widespread social and political unrest. The years 2019 and early 2020 were marked with several social movements by migrant groups fighting for improved working conditions, better compensation, and more leeway in extending working visas and applying for citizenship. Elderly interest groups were lobbying the French government to repeal the earlier cuts in the rates of payment for senior citizen pension and health care plans. The French economy was on a downturn; GDP had dropped to its lowest level since the global economic crisis of 2009, and budget deficits were at an all-time high.

Upon his appointment, Ahmed Buchez and his Union pour un Mouvement Populaire party undertook several governmental reforms to address the issues of the nation. Most notable were his efforts to speak to the situation faced by the large number of immigrants present in France. Buchez worked to undo many of the divisive immigrant policies of the Front National Party, engaging in negotiations with leaders representing the major ethnic and religious immigrant groups in France. He reinvigorated the Law of Equal Opportunities implemented in 2006 to prevent discrimination in the workplace. He also worked with many French corporations and businesses on instituting hiring practices that would bring more immigrant workers into their workforces. Initiatives such as this significantly lowered unemployment in immigrant communities and drastically reduced the number of immigrants receiving state welfare payments.

With a stable job base in place, Buchez reinstituted worker visa programs in an endeavor to recruit additional immigrant workers to fill shortages in the French labour market. He also relaxed the restrictions on family reunification, allowing the families of many migrant workers to join them in France. By the latter part of the 2020s, many of Buchez's immigrant initiatives began to show an effect on France's economy. With migrant workers easing the shortages in the French labour markets, more revenue was available to the government to curb the deficit and fund elderly pension and health care programs. The French GDP was again on the rise.

Where does this leave France now as it enters the new decade? With the economy on an upswing, the French parliament has now turned its attention to tackling the problem of energy dependence. Many of the energy policies of the 2020s have fallen short of reducing France's dependency on Russia for oil and natural gas. Now, with a healthier economy, the French government has instituted an initiative program promoting the development of renewable energy and energy conservation solutions to decrease French citizens' reliance on fossil fuels. It has also begun negotiation with governments in sub-Saharan Africa to develop energy trading partnerships in hopes of diversifying France's nonrenewable energy supply network. How much these efforts will succeed is yet to be seen, but what is certain is France's overdependence on Russia for energy can't be ignored.

As it stands now, in 2030, it seems as if France just can't get enough of Russia's oil and natural gas. Russia understands this all too well. The Russian nationalized oil company, Gazprom, raised French natural gas prices in February 2030. Although the Russian government has denied the accusation, it is widely believed that the increase in natural gas prices was an attempt to pressure the French government to vote with Russia in favor of the UN resolution against US military action in Yemen. The French government was able to provide subsidies to the French natural gas distributors to deflect the effects of the increase in prices to the consumer, but further moves such as this by Russia are poised to impact the recent growth in the French economy. It is also unclear how this move will affect Russian/French diplomatic relations. French president Jean-Pierre Masur is expected to visit Russia in the summer of 2030 to discuss this and other political concerns.

Although the future looks promising for further growth in the French economy, more work is to be done to bring it back to its pre-2020 levels, and additional disruptions like the recent energy disputes with Russia will only prolong this effort.

Scenario 4: Divided and Energy Dependent—It's the End of the World as We Know It

Poor immigrant integration, high energy dependence. The decade has not been a good one for Western Europe. The once powerful region is now in desperate decline—economies are in ruins, and societies are in disorder. With over 30 percent of the population of most countries over the age of 65 and a worker-to-elderly ratio of 2:1, Western European governments are straining to fund pension programs for the elderly. Some countries have decided to cut funding; others have not. Those governments that have not are struggling to keep their economies afloat. Those who have cut funding are seeing their elderly populations suffer from inadequate health care, hunger, and poverty. Immigrants have flocked to Western Europe from Africa. Most Western European governments initially welcomed the immigrants because they saw them as a pool of workers whose taxes could mitigate the economic effects of their hyperaging populations. However, with little immigration control and large numbers of immigrants entering the region, countries are finding it difficult to integrate immigrants into mainstream society.

Despite government programs to assist with integration, most immigrants remain separated from the native populations. They live in separate neighborhoods, and their children attend mostly separate schools. Many immigrants hold jobs in the service sector where they earn less than the average native citizen. There is little immigrant representation in local and state governments, leaving immigrants feeling increasingly disenfranchised and hopeless. There is a tremendous rift between the native population and recent immigrants, especially between the elderly and the immigrant population as the elderly become increasingly agitated by the perceived lack of contribution of the immigrants. It is not uncommon to witness violent protests in many major Western European cities. Some cities have also experienced terrorist attacks. Added to the social and economic troubles facing Western Europe are the challenges surrounding its continued dependence on Russia for oil and natural gas. The Russian energy company Gazprom has acquired majority stakes in energy companies throughout Europe and owns the preponderance of natural gas pipelines supplying Western Europe. The company is now in the position to almost fully control the volume and price of natural gas entering Western European countries. As Gazprom is owned and controlled by the Russian government, it can and has been used as an instrument of Russian national power. Below is an entry found on the blog site of a Muslim extremist group recently uncovered by Centro Nacional de Inteligencia, Spain's central intelligence service. Muslim extremists are actively recruiting members from Spain's growing disenfranchised immigrant population.

First, I commend my Muslim brothers for their bravery in undertaking the recent Islamic liberation attacks in Madrid and Barcelona. These attacks were tremendous, far dwarfing the Madrid bombings of 2004. The death and destruction caused by these attacks brought fear to the hearts of Spaniards and dread to infidels around the globe. My Muslim brothers' continued commitment to the cause of jihad is to be admired by Muslims the world over.

For years now, we have been subjugated by the secular government of Spain, forced to live among infidels who call themselves Christians but behave like beasts. These materialistic, sexually immoral animals treat us as dogs. We're forced to take jobs serving these infidels just to earn enough money to feed ourselves and our families while they live in their palaces filled to the top with excess.

I'm happy to report, my friends, that this situation will not last for long. The end is near for Spain. Not only are our Muslim brothers' brave actions causing the collapse of this illegitimate state, it is also eroding on its very own. The infidels are tearing down their own nation from the inside. Their love of money and riches is proving to be their doom. Their government has long focused on providing more than necessary for its people. Now their government can no longer provide, and their old are starving, their young are fighting, and their society is in disarray.

God has also handed us another victory. He has caused Spain great pain and suffering at the hand of its former enemy, Russia. Spain is being squashed under Russia's mighty hammer as Russia deprives it of the natural gas and oil that is its lifeblood. Now the infidel citizens are suffering, and their government is spending its treasures to keep them alive. Spain has gone to Russia on its knees begging for mercy, but Russia has not backed down. Isn't it a great day when one infidel nation wreaks havoc on another, and we, devoted Muslims, can stand by and watch?

With the permission of Allah, Spain will continue to bleed itself into bankruptcy, and its citizens will get a taste of the poverty and despair we've tasted in this country for decades.

My Muslim brothers, the winds of change have come to free us from oppression. We can capitalize on the failings of the Spanish government. It is weak, and its people are vulnerable; now is the time for us to rally. I urge you to join with me and the rest of your Muslim brothers in the fight against the Spanish infidels. In accordance with the teachings of the great Sayyid Qutb, violence will be our means to transform this infidel society. When we are finished, it will be the end of the world as the infidels know it, and we will once again live as respectful Muslims.

May peace and God's mercy be upon you.

Conclusions and Recommendations

Summary of Findings

This paper describes future demographic and energy trends facing Western Europe and presents scenarios depicting how the convergence of these issues might affect the region. Of these trends, energy dependency is likely to have the least impact. However, even if Western Europe "fixes" its energy dependency issues with Russia, it will still have large challenges to deal with as its population ages.

There is almost no chance that the global age shift will not happen or will be reversed. Anyone who will be over the age of 45 in the year 2050 has already been born.[76] The factor that could change is the number of young people that will be present in aging societies—the number of people that have yet to be born. However, most demographers are confident of the population projections for the developed world. If the actual numbers were to be higher than currently projected, demographers don't believe they'll increase enough between now and 2030 to make a marked impact on the age structures. Therefore, without another source of workers, the worker-to-elderly ratios predicted for the countries of Western Europe are still destined to be as small as demographers' projections.

As the scenarios depict, one of the biggest issues with hyperaging societies is the economic impact of "paying for" the elderly population. In immigration, Western Europe has potential help with this problem. Immigrants could represent the pool of workers Western European countries need to positively change their worker-to-elderly ratio and thereby provide an additional source of government revenue. That leaves migration as a credible mitigating factor to the problem of the worker-to-elderly ratio. How successfully that potential pool of workers can be utilized will partially depend on how well Western European governments are able to properly integrate immigrant populations.

Obviously, the most desirable of the scenarios presented is scenario 1—the "perfect world." Scenario 3 is the next most desirable as Western European countries have addressed their most serious problem: mitigating the economic effect of their aging populations.

US Implications

Why should the United States care about the demographic and energy issues facing Western Europe? The results of the demographic and energy trends will have varying effects on Western Europe's relationship with the United States. On one hand, if these future demographic and energy trends drain Western European economies and, consequentially, their GDPs fall, countries will find it increasingly difficult to fund the militaries necessary to assist with US military actions around the globe. A small military force would mean Western Europe would focus inward on territorial integrity or on small expeditionary operations on the Western European periphery.[77] On the other hand, even if GDPs are not significantly reduced, a shift in the ethnic and religious makeup of Western European countries could produce a change in political focus and greater resistances to engage in military actions—especially those that are not popular with growing immigrant groups with increasing domestic political influence.

Willingness to engage in global operations could also be diminished by a continuing overdependence on Russian energy supplies, diverting the attention of Western European countries to Russian political interests versus those of the United States. In both of these cases, national will more than military force size will determine the Western European decision to engage in political or military actions outside their immediate borders.[78] Whether a small military force or lack of national will is the cause for Western Europe's absence, the United States will pay a hefty price. Either situation would be disastrous to historically strong US/Western European alliances, leaving the United States to find other allies or go it alone in combating conditions detrimental to its national security.

This study does not present solutions to Western Europe's demographic and energy problems. In that respect, it stops at the "act" phase of the scenario planning model; it offers no suggestions for action or scenario implications. This study instead presents the problems facing Western Europe and their possible impacts on US national security to generate thought and discussion on the matter. It is a starting point for strategic thinkers as they look at possible challenges the United States will face in the future. It is a vehicle for spurring creative thought about how to tackle issues surrounding future trends that may seem distant but that, if not discussed and analyzed now, will sneak up on leaders before they have a chance to even plan to act.

Notes

1. Central Intelligence Agency (CIA), *Long-Term Global Demographic Trends*, 6.
2. Sciubba, "Defense Implication of Demographic Trends," 121.
3. CIA, *Long-Term Global Demographic Trends*, 4.
4. Murawiec and Adamson, *Demography and Security*, 14.
5. CIA, "Country Comparison."
6. Population Reference Bureau, "World Population Highlights," 1.
7. Peterson, "Gray Dawn," 2.
8. CIA, *Long-Term Global Demographic Trends*, 22.
9. United Nations, *World Population Prospects*, xi.
10. CIA, *Long-Term Global Demographic Trends*, 22.
11. Jackson and Howe, *Graying of Great Powers*, 1.
12. Ibid.
13. Jackson and Strauss, *Geopolitics of World Population Change*.
14. CIA, *Long-Term Global Demographic Trends*, 8.
15. National Intelligence Council (NIC), *Global Trends 2025*, 24.
16. Ibid.
17. Ibid.
18. Cohen, "Russia and the European Union," 380.
19. Keenan and Gikas, *Statistical Aspects of the Energy Economy*, 4.
20. Ibid., 2.
21. Ibid.
22. European Commission, "EU-Russia Energy Relations."
23. Smith, *Russian Energy Pressure*, 1.
24. Ibid.
25. Global Business Network (GBN), "Why Scenarios?"
26. Scearce, Fulton, and GBN, *What If?*, 7.
27. Ibid., 24–26.
28. GBN, "Why Scenarios?"
29. Ibid.
30. Scearce, Fulton, and GBN, *What If?*, 27–28.
31. Ibid., 28–29.
32. Ibid., 29–30.
33. Ibid., 30–31.
34. GBN, "Why Scenarios?"
35. Jackson and Howe, *Graying of the Great Powers*, 2.

36. Ibid.
37. Ibid.
38. Jackson, *Global Retirement Crisis*, 3.
39. Ibid.
40. Peterson, "Gray Dawn," 2.
41. Jackson, *Global Retirement Crisis*, 6.
42. Ibid., 10.
43. CIA, *Long-Term Global Demographic Trends*, 27.
44. Ibid., 25.
45. Peterson, "Gray Dawn," 7.
46. Ibid.
47. Jackson and Howe, *Graying of the Great Powers*, 12.
48. McCarthy, *World Population Shifts*, 18–19.
49. Jackson and Howe, *Graying of the Great Powers*, 3.
50. CIA, *Long-Term Global Demographic Trends*, 43.
51. Ibid., 42.
52. USJFCOM, *Joint Operating Environment 2008*, 13.
53. Geokas, "European Union," 358.
54. Galvin, "Changing Face of Europe," 53.
55. CIA, *Long-Term Global Demographic Trends*, 52.
56. Ibid., 43.
57. Ibid., 42.
58. Ibid., 51.
59. Ibid.
60. Sendagorta, "Jihad in Europe," 65.
61. Ibid.
62. Ibid., 63.
63. USJFCOM, *Joint Operating Environment 2008*, 46–47.
64. USJFCOM, *Joint Operating Environment 2010*, 24.
65. Ibid., 29.
66. Ibid.
67. NIC, *Global Trends 2025*, x.
68. Ibid., 33.
69. Smith, *Russian Energy Pressure*.
70. Ibid.
71. Andrés Cala, "Isolated, Iran Offers to Supply Europe with Natural Gas," *New York Times*, 6 November 2009.
72. Ibid.
73. Ibid.
74. Scearce, Fulton, and GBN, *What If?*, 27.
75. Keenan and Gikas, *Statistical Aspects of the Energy Economy*, 4.
76. Jackson and Howe, *Graying of the Great Powers*, 3.
77. CIA, *Long-Term Global Demographic Trends*, 86.
78. USJFCOM, *Joint Operating Environment 2008*, 24–25.

Chapter 4

Accounting for Human Information Processing

Lt Col Lourdes M. Duvall

The Air Force is the gold standard of command and control of air and space forces. We do that better than anyone in the world, but we're not satisfied. We're always trying to make it faster, better, more accurate and more flexible.

—Lt Gen Ronald E. Keys
Former Commander
Air Combat Command

Effective command and control (C2) of air and space forces is essential for maintaining a decisive advantage over any adversary.[1] Remarkable improvements in C2, "the processes and systems the commander uses to develop the strategy, to plan operations, to control execution, and to assess the effects in crisis or combat," have occurred in the last 15 years.[2] Nevertheless, Air Force leadership continues to emphasize a need for drastic improvements in the coming years.[3] Key characteristics of future US Air Force C2 include integration of unprecedented amounts of information to produce tailored visual depictions of the battlespace, drastic reductions in decision time lines, and a focus on creating and assessing operational effects.[4]

This research proposes that USAF C2 operations would benefit from greater emphasis on the human aspects of information processing and decision making. This emphasis will be particularly critical in a future where C2 operations are characterized by increasing computer support, with the objective of rapid decision making and a focus on operational effects.

Airmen, whether the joint force air component commander (JFACC) or one of the thousands working in air and space operations centers (AOC) today, remain at the core of operational C2 decision processes. Therefore, human cognitive strengths and limitations and the principles of human-system interaction affect C2 operations. To maintain and expand our advantage in C2, the human aspects of information processing, decision making, and human-system inter-action must be understood and integrated in the USAF C2 vision.

The recommendations made are not revolutionary. However, the improvements in operational decision making that would result are worth pursuing. As in other fields that emphasize extensive study of human-system interactions, such as aviation, medicine, and space operations, the stakes can be extremely high in C2. Operational mistakes can be a matter of life or death. They also quickly can have strategic ramifications that might preclude the United States from achieving its national objectives.

Future USAF C2 Capabilities

Understanding the desired capabilities for USAF C2 at the macro level is an important first step in assessing different approaches to achieving them. USAF vision documents and Air Force leaders consistently mention a number of desired capabilities for future C2 operations. They include providing tailored visual access to unprecedented amounts of battlespace information to provide predictive and common situational awareness (SA), enabling drastic reductions in decision time lines, and focusing on achievement and assessment of desired effects. Department of Defense, joint, and other service documents, such as *Joint Vision 2020*, the Office of the Secretary of Defense's *The Implementation of Network-Centric Warfare*, and the Navy's *FORCEnet* concept of operations (CONOPS), repeat similar themes.[5]

The *US Air Force Space and C4ISR [Command, Control, Communication, Computer, Intelligence, Surveillance, and Reconnaissance] Capabilities CONOPS*—one of seven USAF-level capability CONOPS developed to define the conduct of current and future air and space operations—lists the following needed C2 capabilities among 16 high-level requirements:

- Locate, identify, track, and observe friendly, enemy, nonfriendly, and nonaligned forces/actors anywhere/anytime in near real time.
- Provide the right information to the right decision maker, at the right time, in actionable format.
- Assess global conditions and events.
- Establish and maintain battlespace situational awareness.

- Provide routine and dynamic battle management.[6]

The *Air Force Transformation Flight Plan 2004* similarly identifies a "real time picture of the battlespace" and "predictive battlespace awareness" as transformational capabilities required by the Air Force to execute its CONOPS.[7] The plan cites current deficiencies in battlespace awareness, integration of rapidly expanding data streams, and accuracy of the real-time picture of the battlespace.[8] As commander of Air Force Materiel Command, Gen Gregory S. Martin described a need for "unprecedented battlespace visualization" and the ability to "understand the battlespace at a touch of a screen" to create effects in near real time.[9]

This desire for future C2 to operate within tighter decision time lines is reflected in many sources.[10] Air Force Doctrine Document (AFDD) 2-5, *Information Operations*, provides a clear statement of this objective:

> The Air Force goal is to leverage this [information] technology to achieve air, space, and information superiority and to be able to operate in a faster decision cycle (decision superiority) than the adversary. Decision superiority is a competitive advantage, enabled by an ongoing situational awareness, that allows commanders and their forces to make better-informed decisions and implement them faster than their adversaries can react. Decision superiority is about improving our ability to observe, orient, decide, and act (OODA loop) faster and more effectively than the adversary.[11]

Gen John Jumper, former Air Force chief of staff, provides a succinct version of the time compression objective, stating, "The day is coming . . . when the kill chain will be reliably and consistently compressed to minutes instead of hours or days, and when the sum of all our sensor, command and control, and information capabilities will be a cursor on the target and steel on the enemy."[12]

Finally, the concept of effects-based operations (EBO) is central to the USAF discussion of future C2. The focus of EBO is "to design campaign actions based on desired national security outcomes rather than merely attacking targets to destroy adversary forces. The goal is to understand the effect that is desired in the battlespace and then create that effect more efficiently and effectively."[13] To this end, EBO focuses more on an adversary's behavior than physical attributes. This requires extensive knowledge of an adversary's will, the enemy's values, and the dynamic perception of the conflict.[14]

In summary, key components of the Air Force vision for enhancing C2 are creating improved, shared, and tailored battlespace awareness using unprecedented amounts of information, significantly reducing the decision cycle time relative to the adversary, and focusing efforts to achieve desired operational and strategic effects.

Analogs in a Digital World

Machines don't fight wars. Terrain doesn't fight wars. Humans fight wars. You must get into the mind of humans. That is where the battles are won.

—Col John Boyd
Military Strategist

Underlying the vision for future Air Force C2 is the reality that information technology will play an ever-increasing role, as it will in almost every conceivable area of military operations. To accomplish the mission and win wars, Airmen will engage in two-way interactions with systems. Understanding the complementary nature of people and computer systems and accounting for human information-processing capabilities are prerequisites for designing useful systems that help people make better decisions. Key aspects of the design include determining the right coordination space between humans and technology as well as designing intuitive user interfaces to the system, including system layout, display, and controls. The fields of human factors and human-computer interaction have a critical role to play in future C2 systems.[15] Consider a list of positive attributes of humans and machines developed by Donald A. Norman (table 4.1).

Table 4.1. Attributes of humans and machines

People	Machines
Creative	Precise
Compliant	Orderly
Attentive to change	Undistractible
Resourceful	Unemotional
	Logical

Adapted from Donald A. Norman, *The Invisible Computer* (Cambridge, MA: MIT Press, 1998), 160.

The characteristics of machines—information technology—allow for the collection, processing, storage, dissemination, and quick and accurate analysis of immense amounts of data, enhanced by the ability to network systems across the globe for even greater combined power. Machines have enabled the mapping of the human genome, provided near-instantaneous access to the contents of the Library of Congress, and transformed modern warfare as demonstrated in Operations Enduring Freedom and Iraqi Freedom.

Yet for all of the wonders of technology, machines have not been able to replicate the incredible capability of the human brain. Our combined sensory abilities—how we think about objects and people and how we plan actions—are uniquely human.[16] Wickens and Hollands said that the basic model of human information processing serves as a road map to highlight the amazing abilities and predictable limitations relevant to C2.[17]

The model depicts five major stages of human information processing: sensory processing, perception, cognition and memory, response selection, and execution. These roughly equate to John Boyd's theories of the OODA loop, with perception, cognition, and memory being components of orientation.[18]

The first stage, sensory processing, involves how information and events get to our brain through our senses. The second, perception, is where meaning is given to the raw sensory data. It involves a combination of what is often called "bottom-up processing" driven by the sensory input and "top-down processing" based on inputs from long-term memory on what events are expected. The third stage, cognition and memory, involves the complex realms of reasoning and understanding. The fourth, response selection, is decision making. The final stage is execution of the selected action. Feedback, attention, and metacognition play important roles throughout the process. Feedback represents the idea that the results of the executed actions will, at some point, be sensed and perceived. Attention is the supply of mental resources available. Finally, metacognition is the overall "awareness of one's own knowledge, effort, and thought processes."[19]

The mind shows remarkable abilities for information processing, adapted over generations, to function in our environment. For example, we are able to sense small changes in our surroundings. We can also focus on what our mind perceives as the most important sensory inputs and block out an amazing amount of "noise" that can be selectively sampled if needed. We have the ability to pull, consciously and unconsciously, from complex mental models in our memory to form quick, creative conclusions about new inputs. Furthermore, we have the aptitude to select responses and execute them based on a few critical pieces of information without the need to process all cues from our environment.

For most of daily life, the power behind our incredible human information processing goes unnoticed. Our day is a series of innumerable OODA loops. We seem to unconsciously navigate through traffic, make judgments about people's intentions, avoid dangerous situations, participate in complex social relations, and add countless mental representations to our memory.

Yet times when our information processes fail us often make headlines: aviation accidents, medical misdiagnoses, and industrial accidents. The human information-processing system, for all of its power, consistently demonstrates certain limitations. While usually of no concern, they have the potential for catastrophic consequences. These limitations need to be understood to enable effective C2, as they must for other high-risk activities, such as aviation, medicine, and industry. The following is a small sample of limitations found in the first four stages of information processing and their potential impact on C2.

From the start, sensory processing has distinctive limits. The visual system has sensitivity limits for contrasts and color.[20] For example, these limitations determine whether icons on a map display show up as a blob or as distinct objects. The auditory system has limits in processing speech and noise, influencing how we perceive sounds and whether a sound effectively transmits information.[21] How far can someone talk across an AOC floor and expect that the message will be heard? When should a system use an alarm to signal receipt of important data? These questions require designers to account for auditory limitations. As Wickens explains, each sensory modality appears to have particular strengths and weaknesses, and collectively the ensemble nicely compensates for the collective weakness of each sensory channel alone. Clever designers can capitalize on strengths and avoid weaknesses in rendering the sensory information available to the higher brain center for perception, interpretation, decision making, and further processing.[22]

Stepping through the information-processing model to perception, we find that the limitations to human attention directly influence perception. People have an imperfect ability to share attention between multiple cues. We are susceptible to distractions; our attention preference is toward an abrupt, distinct stimulus (an alarm or a flash) over less prominent cues.

In commercial aviation, selective attention is recognized as playing a considerable role in the greatest cause of fatal accidents—controlled flight into terrain. This has led to a number of compensating system design initiatives.[23] In C2, another information-rich environment, the impact of attention limitations might not be as evident but can be as great. C2 systems design, to the same extent as cockpit design, requires deliberate accommodations for selective attention.

Experience also plays a role in perception. Individual experiences can lead operators to "see" different things from the same display/environment. Humans sample the environment based on where they expect to find information. People show a preference for sources personally attributed as having the greatest value.[24] Given the same cues, the perception and therefore the decisions and actions of experts and novices may significantly differ.

How information is presented or displayed is also extremely important for perception. People give some cues, such as information at the top of a display, stark contrasts, or an alarm, more perceptual weight even if that cue is not the most important. Edward Tufte provides compelling research and examples of how the data presentation method can influence how data is perceived and interpreted.[25] His analysis of the ill-fated space shuttle *Challenger* launch shows that the correlation between cold weather and O-ring failure could be depicted in a variety of ways. Tragically, the methods NASA scientists used were poorly designed, and decision makers did not accurately perceive the danger.[26]

Practically speaking, the immense effort to collect, process, fuse, and display information may be of little benefit if the decision maker does not notice or pay attention to the information as it is presented or misses key data relationships. Of equal concern, the C2 environment of the future might provide such rich data presentation that operators might not accurately perceive that their display environment is showing only a subset of the information desired for a decision. For example, a textual human intelligence report or situation report from a ground unit may be more difficult to display than an electronic collection or video feed, yet it might have greater value for a decision. Critical information such as enemy morale, intentions, and fatigue are difficult to display yet are extremely important for

EBO. Without purposeful study and accommodation of C2 perception, we might fly right into the mountain.

Cognition and memory also present limitations. Working memory is used to take in new information and update hypotheses.[27] How much information can be maintained in working memory, its capacity limit, is well documented at seven plus or minus two pieces of information.[28] For example, when an operator must manually transfer geocoordinates from one system to another, limitations of working memory are at play. Verbal and spatial items are only held in working memory for a limited time and can be easily lost if attention is diverted to another task. Unaccounted for, these constraints can cause data interpretation or input error or extend task time lines if an operator must reacquire the information.

Long-term memory is the storage center that provides the background knowledge to sort and evaluate new information and form hypotheses for decisions. Different experts describe the organization as associative networks, conceptual models, cognitive maps, schema, and mental representations.[29] At a basic level, humans store items with related items and generate mental models about how they expect things to relate to one another.

There are a number of implications for C2 design related to long-term memory. Understanding the role of long-term memory is essential in the design of decision and memory aids. It is also important for SA since much understanding of current and future events is based on prior experiences stored in long-term memory. Norman also discusses the value of creating conceptual models for systems consistent with existing mental representations.[30] Ideally, the conceptual model is understandable enough that the user should be able to discover how to use a system with little need for training or manuals and feel suitably in control of the operation.[31]

Response selection is central to any discussion about C2. While some C2 decisions are a result of a slow and deliberate process, a great many need to be made quickly. Many of the characteristics of future C2 closely resemble features of naturalistic decision making: an uncertain, dynamic environment; a lot of information with rapidly changing situational cues; time constraints or time stress; a high degree of risk; and multiple persons involved in the decision.[32] For this kind of response selection in particular, people often rely on powerful and efficient mental shortcuts—heuristics—to make decisions. In general, these shortcuts provide huge advantages for quick decision making, particularly for experts drawing from broad experiences. They are able to quickly relate the current situation to past experiences to make a decision. However, as with other adaptive strengths in our information processing, heuristics have downfalls, or biases. These biases can lead to poor decisions, particularly when the uniqueness of the current situation is underestimated. The dynamic nature of warfare is ripe for the use of heuristics; therefore, an understanding of biases is essential.

People often create a hypothesis based on the first cues received and tend to stick to or "anchor" on the hypothesis supported by initial evidence. People then pay less attention to later cues, despite possibly being more relevant.[33] In general, people more easily retrieve hypotheses that they considered recently or have considered frequently. If something easily comes to mind, it is common and therefore thought to be a good hypothesis.[34] People often relate a current situation to past situations because a pattern of cues is similar and thus overlook differences in the situations.[35] Additionally, they tend to be overconfident in their selected hypothesis and less likely to seek out evidence for alternative hypotheses or prepare for the chance that they are wrong.[36] Finally, people tend to seek out confirming evidence for their working hypothesis, discount contradictory evidence, and fail to evaluate the absence of cues.[37] Studies show this bias is more severe in high-stress situations where the mental workload is demanding.[38]

C2 systems must account for common biases through data presentation, decision aids, and training. Many demonstrated "debiasing" techniques could have great utility, including prompts to generate counterreasons to a working hypothesis, aids that highlight new information that conflicts or disconfirms earlier information/hypotheses, and tools that help identify and maintain awareness of unknowns and assumptions.[39] For example, the concept of a common operational picture depicting all relevant information known about enemy, friendly, and neutral parties should be augmented by a complementary display that depicts the most critical unknowns to keep this information prominent during decision making.

In the past, a discussion of the stages of human information processing was mainly theory. Now science is quickly adding quantitative evidence to these theories. Cognitive research using advanced technologies, such as functional magnetic resonance imaging (MRI), is providing hard evidence on how the mind works. For example, an

MRI can depict differences in the brain activity of a novice versus an expert performing the same task.[40]

Research is providing greater insight into the relation between visual and language processing, the interplay between components of working memory, and the characteristics of decision making under time constraints and different levels of uncertainty. As discussed earlier, each of these has relevance for C2.

To achieve its vision for C2, the USAF will need to harness both the power of machines and the human mind. The latter requires a commitment to account for the human component in system design and operations. Experts in the fields of human factors and human-computer interaction will be invaluable for future C2 systems. Humans have remarkable minds and bring unmatchable attributes to C2, particularly for effects-based analysis and assessment. "People excel at perception, at creativity, at the ability to go beyond the information given, making sense of otherwise chaotic events. . . . This ability to put together a sensible, coherent image of the world in the face of limited evidence allows us to anticipate and predict events."[41] The challenge is to take advantage of human cognitive strengths, mitigate the limitations, and mesh human information processing with technology to get the most out of both.

Status Check on USAF C2 Efforts

The USAF has achieved great advances in C2 in the past 15 years. One measure indicative of the increased ability to conduct flexible and adaptive C2 operations is the percentage of sorties that received their targets or had their targets changed after launch during contingency operations. This percentage has steadily grown from 20 percent during Operation Desert Storm, to 43 percent during Operation Allied Force, to 80 percent during Operation Enduring Freedom, and to an estimated 90 percent during Operation Iraqi Freedom.[42] Air Force leadership emphasis on the operational level of war in recent years has advanced C2, leading to the designation of the AOC as a weapon system in 2000 and the development of standard C2 tactics, techniques, and procedures and numerous new training standards for C2 operations.

Nevertheless, there is much work to be done, particularly with optimizing the human-system interaction component of C2 operations.

The 2000 USAF Scientific Advisory Board (SAB) study on C2 supports more attention to this area: "Arguably, there is no other warfighting function where human-system interface (HSI) is more important than in C2 because of the volume, complexity, importance, and time-critical nature of C2 decision making."[43] The report cites the overall lack of attention and resources devoted to this important area, provides a number of specific recommendations, and concludes, "Unless these human-related issues can be resolved satisfactorily, there is little hope that the other corrective measures cited in this report will have the desired impact."[44]

In 2004 the Air Force chief of staff, General Jumper, told a story suggesting that many of the SAB concerns about HSI deficiencies remain valid.

> If you walked into an Air Operation Center today . . . you'll see somebody sitting there with three work stations in front of them. You say "why do you have the three screens in front of you?" "Well I need to get this information off of this one, I enter it into this one over here, and that will give me information I have to enter into the third one."
>
> "Why don't you have them all together?" "Well of course this company makes this software, this company has this one, and this company has this one."
>
> "Why don't you make it so that it serves your needs?" "Well hell, I don't know. Can we do that?"[45]

Snapshots from other perspectives of today's C2, particularly the AOC system development, integration, and operational employment, point to systemic shortfalls in emphasizing the human cognitive component of C2 operations.

The system program office for the AOC used to reside in the Operational C2 Support Group at Electronic Security Command (now the Air Force Intelligence, Surveillance and Reconnaissance Agency). Its operations tempo matched that of most operational units. It fielded Falconer AOCs around the world and successfully worked critical wartime improvements. However, according to the AOC Pacific Air Force program manager, five years after the SAB report a procedure has yet to be set up for considering human factors or HSI issues throughout the AOC acquisition process. Program managers have no requirement for training on human factors or HSI. HSI expertise is sought out in special cases where there is an obvious problem but is not routinely consulted.[46]

At Langley AFB, another part of the Operational C2 Systems Group brings in the applications developed by other programs and integrates these independently developed systems into the AOC baseline. As of March 2005, the group focused on ensuring that the disparate systems work together within the AOC from a technical, engineering perspective. Little time or expertise is available to explore human factor considerations for specific applications, crew positions, or teams during systems integration.[47] This lack of HSI emphasis might improve when the Air Force hires a lead integration contractor for the AOC in the coming year. However, without Air Force leadership support of more HSI research, the daunting technical challenges of system integration will continue to overshadow the less tangible human-system integration challenges.

Human-systems interface and cognitive considerations are not stressed in Air Force guidance for the floor plan and layout of new AOCs. According to Air Force Operational Tactics, Techniques, and Procedures (AFOTTP) 2-3.2, *Air and Space Operations Center*, the C4I system manager is responsible to the joint air operations center (JAOC) director to "ensure the systems are set up and operating in a manner that meets operational needs."[48] A JAOC operator, as knowledgeable as a JAOC systems user, mans this position. Considerations listed in the AFOTTP for designing the floor plan include classification requirements, available workspace, and number of personnel in each team/division.[49] There is no mention of a need to consider human factors issues, nor is there any reference to experts in the Air Force available to provide guidance on human factors or HSI considerations.

The experiences of individuals who have served in AOCs highlight both the great advances in C2 within the past five years as well as persistent challenges of information overload, poor system design, and lack of attention to HSI considerations. Individuals working in AOCs today have near-real-time access to significantly more information sources than five years ago.[50] Among these are Blue Force Tracker, providing positional data on friendly ground forces, and a proliferation of feeds from unmanned reconnaissance systems such as the Predator system.[51] Additionally, advances in information technology, such as voice collaboration over the InfoWorkSpace collaborative tool, widely networked online chat tools, and controls that allow for single keyboard/mouse entry to multiple screens, have dramatically improved collaboration and information management capabilities.[52]

Nevertheless, evidence that the AOC would benefit from accentuating the human aspects of information processing and decision making abounds. A member of the special operations liaison element (SOLE) working in current operations during Operation Iraqi Freedom recalls that tasks included directly obtaining and inputting data related to emerging calls for fire and intelligence, surveillance, and reconnaissance taskings from seven different functional programs and two chat systems, each with a separate window display. These programs resided on two systems with two computer screens for display. On average, the member was responsible for monitoring 21 active chat sessions, both internal and external to the AOC, and two radio nets. Verbal communication "over the shoulder" with another operator who had a theater battle management core system, the primary AOC subsystem, provided other critical data. The task load also included many time-consuming processes prone to human error, such as the need to cut and paste chats from one chat program to the other for information dissemination, resulting in information overload.

Some remedies to basic HSI issues were available but largely unknown to operators. For example, there was no system or trained operator for programming key words—such as "troops in contact"—where the chat program would set the specific screen to "blink red" when the key words were used. This user fix, provided to the operator days into major operations, proved to be potentially lifesaving.[53] Other HSI remedies would require a system-level fix. Three-dimensional (3-D) audio could assist in discriminating between radio calls by making radio output "appear" to be coming from different directions. Using color and size variations to better highlight symbology on map displays could also be beneficial. For example, using slightly different colors and sizes for ground unit symbology could help to discriminate between units of different sizes or composition.

Promising efforts are under way. The Air Force Research Lab (AFRL) Human Effectiveness Directorate has programs examining cognitive architectures, visualization tools, and system interfaces for C2. A representative from AFRL with an HSI-related PhD is currently assigned to the C2 Battlelab. A smaller C2 program, the Battle Control System, which has replaced the control and reporting center, recently incorporated a number of HSI technologies, such as 3-D audio.[54] As part of the new system's development process, human factors experts made extensive operator observations during Joint Expeditionary

Force Experiment 2004 to assess the performance of individuals and teams using the new system and to isolate HSI issues.[55]

However, the findings of the 2000 SAB still resonate: "Performance of some C2 systems is limited by counter-intuitive computer programs, unnecessary complex or error-prone procedures, excessive operator workload, labor-intensive training, and proliferation of local fixes or workarounds."[56] There is substantial room for improving the way USAF C2 systems account for the cognitive domain. The volume of information, speed of decisions, and desire for greater fidelity in linking means to ends are increasing within C2. The entire human-machine system needs to be optimized to ensure we maintain our decision advantage. Improving C2 performance will require greater use of processes, tools, and technologies that deliberately account for human information processing and HSI.

Accounting for the Human Cognitive Domain

To expand our advantage in C2, the human aspects of information processing, decision making, and human-system interaction need to play a more central role in Air Force C2 from system design to operational use. While not a panacea, the processes, tools, and technologies currently available to assist in accounting for this human dimension offer insight into the potential of an approach that redefines how technology and people can best interact to make a more effective C2 system.

A necessary starting point is a human-centered development process for all USAF C2 systems. A number of models describe this type of process from requirements enhancement, design, development, and testing through fielding.[57] Each model includes a systemic and structured approach to address HSI and human factors considerations throughout the process. As advocated by the SAB, "a structured, systems engineering approach, comparable to that employed routinely in the development of HSI for combat aircraft, should be applied in the acquisition and modernization of future C2 systems."[58]

Human-centered system engineering approaches share many common characteristics. Each begins with an early and persistent focus on the user, his or her tasks, and output goals, all in the context of his or her work environment. Starting with user analysis, characteristics such as age, familiarity with similar systems, and experience are among the factors included in a typical operator profile.[59] For example, the user profile for the director of combat operations in an AOC will be substantially different from the profile for the senior intelligence duty officer or an airspace management technician.[60] This user analysis drives tailored interfaces for each group and influences the requirement for decision support systems.

Task analysis is another critical part of human-centered design. It includes the study of how users currently perform their tasks, workflow and information requirements, the decision-making process, and the underlying goals of the activity.[61] A variety of well-documented techniques for collecting and analyzing task data are available.[62] These range from observations and interviews to detailed analysis of how a user would perform a specific system design task.[63] Task data—particularly analysis of decision processes—is a critical input throughout the system engineering process.

Another important element to human-centered design is an iterative design process. This involves extensive up-front design work on developing and evaluating conceptual models before moving to the design of detailed user interfaces. By using paper mock-ups or other prototypes of high-level design concepts, users and designers can evaluate various alternatives and eliminate major usability problems early on. A good example is the design work done by the US Strategic Command (USSTRATCOM) C2 modernization team in 2001–2 while developing a state-of-the-art video display system in the USSTRATCOM commander's situation room. The team and user groups evaluated—with mock-ups and limited prototypes—over 30 design concepts before they arrived at the selected design.[64]

In a human-centered approach, the focus is not on automating tasks. Rather, it is on determining the best cooperation between humans and technology for given tasks, acknowledging the importance of creating a consistent conceptual model for users, and explicitly addressing usability and human-computer interaction factors to achieve the specific performance goals. User feedback and expert observation continue throughout the process and real-world operational use to inform system upgrades and modifications.

Fortunately, a growing toolbox is available to help address usability and HSI factors. For example, cognitive architectures are an increasingly promising tool for quantitative predictions of some aspects of HSI. Michael Byrne defines *cognitive architecture* as "a broad theory of human cognition based on a wide selection of human experimental data and implemented as a running computer simulation."[65] Susan

Chipman and David Kieras describe the term as referring to "the (relatively) fixed features of the human information processing system, the basic characteristics of the typical human operator."[66]

According to Chipman, manager of the Cognitive Science Program at the Office of Naval Research, recent advances in cognitive science research have led to the development of computational cognitive architecture theories that are "making it possible to make precise quantitative predictions about human performance in quite complex situations."[67] Cognitive architectures can be compared to an aerospace engineer's use of computer simulations to represent the quantitative theory of aerodynamics. Engineers can run a design through computational fluid dynamic models instead of only wind tunnels.[68] Similarly, cognitive architectures provide repeatable, quantitative predictions about human performance and information processing that in the past was applied to the design of systems by observations, intuition, and experience.

Current cognitive architectures can model some aspects of human information processing such as sensory interaction with computer displays, capacity limits of working memory, memory retrieval, and motor control.[69] "It is possible to use model predictions instead of user testing for a large fraction of the system design effort," Dr. Chipman said.[70] Based on predictions of cognitive workload, designers can revise interfaces or select different interface alternatives, enhancing usability before building prototypes for a system. For time-sensitive decision tasks, cognitive models help identify both human and design limitations that can effect achieving desired time goals.

Cognitive architectures have a number of specific limitations. Currently, they are best at modeling "the relatively simple forms of perception and motor action that are typically involved in interacting with computer displays and computer input devices, as opposed to the full complexity of perception and action in the natural world."[71] The architectures, consisting of hard-to-use, complex software, require development efforts to connect models with each new interface and good knowledge of the tasks to be performed.[72] Fortunately, researchers are making progress and are using the latest cognitive research to build more comprehensive models.[73]

Another set of tools with great application for USAF C2 systems includes measures and methodologies to assess SA and decision processes. SA is our perception of elements in the environment, comprehension of their meaning, and projection of their status in the future.[74] The vision for USAF C2 cites requirements for battlespace SA and predictive battlespace awareness. Research suggests that "situational awareness is one of the most important components of effective decision making."[75] However, one of the ironies of automation is that it can lead to reduced SA—exactly the opposite of the desires for USAF C2. Wickens et al. state that "people are better aware of the dynamic state of processes in which they are active participants."[76] A person who is out of the loop while technology collects, processes, and analyzes information without human intervention and is then provided a recommendation for action might not have the requisite SA to make an appropriate and timely decision. There is a tradeoff between the benefits of automation in terms of speed and reduced workload and the potential degradation in SA required for decision making. Similarly, there are tradeoffs between reducing information overload through data presentation of fused information and providing requisite access to raw data that can influence SA. As described in the Navy FORCEnet concept, "while an information-processing capability is necessary so that commanders do not need to wade through seas of mostly unimportant data, commanders must not be isolated from the data level. They must have direct access to the raw data as needed because they often base their understanding on a few key pieces of information."[77]

Also related to SA is metacognition—a person's understanding of what he or she does not know and the limitations of his or her thought processes. Studies have shown that when the sum of the knowable information is not apparent, people often overestimate the amount of relevant information they have obtained. This situation can lead to an inflated assessment of confidence level in their analysis or SA.[78] Providing a realistic sense of uncertainty is essential for decision making.

Determining how C2 systems can enhance SA and allow operators to accurately assess their level of uncertainty requires a study of operators in their environment. It involves gauging how much SA they have at a given point in time, how SA evolves over time, and how SA deviates from the known ground truth or that of an expert.[79] Dr. Valerie Gawron, an expert in SA assessment, provides a description of a number of measurement tools in the *Human Performance Measures Handbook*. Many were developed to measure pilot or aircrew SA in flight; however, they can be generalized to other systems.[80]

Basic SA tools combined with advanced data capture and retrieval instruments and with analysis methodologies, such as process tracing, can help account for how SA evolves over time and how automated processes affect it.[81] Process tracing uses multiple data collection methods at various stages of the decision process in either a realistic exercise or operational setting.[82] Observations of decision makers' or analysts' actions, communications, and decisions, along with data captures of what information is potentially available to them for decisions, are used to characterize their SA and decision processes. One of the great benefits of this approach is that it helps assess the contributions of both technological and human aspects to SA and decision making. In an AFRL-sponsored study, a process-tracing methodology provided significant insight into how intelligence analysts dealt with data overload in a time-constrained environment.[83] Potential sources for poor SA, such as information overload, or inadequate display design can be isolated using process tracing.

As in aviation, tools that evaluate operator SA and decision processes under realistic conditions can help with C2 system design. These tools aid critical trade-off decisions among automation, SA, and focus training.

Finally, USAF C2 can exploit new areas of technological development to improve HSI and decision making. These range from controls and displays to visualization tools to decision support systems. The 2000 USAF SAB assessed 34 HSI technologies for potential USAF C2 applications and concluded that the Air Force "has not fully exploited HSI technologies, automation, and decision support tools that are available or under development for other applications."[84] Four of the most promising areas SAB and HSI experts identify include information visualization, untethered computing, decision support systems, and system recording capability.

Advances in computing have opened up new opportunities to augment our cognitive ability through information visualization, exploiting our visual strengths to understand increasing amounts of information. Successful information visualization can present large amounts of data tailored to a real task or problem and also allows users to get to desired specifics without being overwhelmed.[85] Examples of powerful information visualization tools, such as SmartMoney's "Map of the Market," demonstrate the power of creative information visualization in a task that requires interpretation of large amounts of data.[86] Numerous AOC tasks—such as target development, airspace deconfliction, and assessment—would benefit from imaginative approaches to information visualization to augment the spreadsheets and maps used today. Since the format of the presentation of information has such an influence on understanding, technologies that provide the ability to display data/information in various formats, such as net diagrams, trees, 3-D, tables, or maps, can provide opportunities to better understand the information and critical relationships.

As the amount of available information grows, C2 tasks will increasingly benefit from tailored information visualization tools that provide an overview of data, enable dynamic queries, allow easy zoom on specific areas and filter data, and provide details on demand.[87] Visualization works because it increases human memory and processing resources, reduces search requirements by presenting large amounts of data in a small space, enhances detection of patterns, and offers greater exploration of data relationships.[88]

C2 organizations could also significantly benefit from the use of untethered computers and/or transportable credentials for certain duty positions. The convergence of a number of technological advances—such as those in semiconductor power, mobile communications, and miniature displays—has led to the development of powerful untethered or wearable computers.[89] For example, these systems would allow individuals to move to different areas of the AOC to collaborate with other teams while maintaining access to their system displays, databases, and other information sources and staying in communication with other groups. The systems could allow decision makers dynamic interaction with information displays or provide for speech or other input to systems.[90] Evaluations of various wearable computers show significant time savings for a variety of tasks where immediate access to data on the move is required.[91] Security considerations may hamper widespread use of this technology, but a risk/benefit analysis is needed. Additionally, technologies such as multilevel security thin clients that accept a common access card for user authentication, tailoring the system to the specific user's profile, may provide a similar effect in terms of mobility and access to data without the security concerns.[92] Both technologies provide advantages for collaboration and continual access to data sources.

Decision support systems enable cooperative problem solving and decision making by taking advantage of the strengths of each. Simple decision support systems can provide a "flag" to focus attention or alert decision makers to critical events, such as the "flash red" chat window.[93] More advanced systems, such as the Pilot's Associate project, a joint effort of the Defense Advanced Research Project Agency

(DARPA) and the US Air Force, have demonstrated an ability to significantly augment and enhance human judgment in a time-urgent, high-stakes environment of combat aviation.[94] The US Navy Space and Naval Warfare Systems Center–San Diego has extensive experience designing decision support systems for a variety of C2 tasks, most recently under the Tactical Decision Making under Stress (TADMUS), Command 21, and USSTRATCOM Knowledge Wall programs.[95] Decision support tools developed for TADMUS have resulted in better SA and reductions in decision errors in antiair warfare missions.[96]

Decision support systems designed with an understanding of human performance and the decision-making process greatly enhance C2 in terms of efficiency (time) and decision quality. The systems can alert decision makers to possible biases in decision processes, conduct information management to support decision needs, and act on behalf of the user when authorized. They will provide much of the foundation needed to achieve the USAF C2 vision.

Another useful technology is a system recording capability to "provide the AOC with the 'performance instrumentation' that is similar to that used to characterize and improve the performance of test aircraft."[97] Technologies exist to record screen captures of AOC displays and index them with time-matched database captures and other related decision information. These technologies are essential for the process-tracing methodology and SA assessment. The USAF SAB envisioned numerous other excellent uses for these technologies, in that "such a system could be used for briefings, debriefings, crew changeover, post-mission effectiveness assessment, requirements definition, training, experimentation, and development of decision-support tools."[98]

If the USAF chooses to pursue a more human-centered approach for C2, it will not be in uncharted territory. At its disposal are well-established processes, exciting tools based on the latest psychological research, and commercially available technologies. Within the Air Force, many of the processes and tools discussed are used in the development of combat aircraft. Within the larger C2 community are exciting efforts sponsored by DARPA, the US Navy, and AFRL relevant to future USAF C2 challenges.

Clearly, the limits to our understanding of human information processing as well as of information technology will remain barriers to achieving optimum HSI. However, enough is known and available to be of value to other high-stake endeavors. These processes, tools, and technologies should be applied more systematically to USAF C2.

Conclusion

While changes in the information environment have led some to focus solely on the contribution of information superiority to command and control, it is equally necessary to understand the complete realm of command and control decision making, the nature of organizational collaboration, and especially, the "human in the loop."

—Chairman of the Joint
Chiefs of Staff
Joint Vision 2020

The science behind our understanding of how the human mind works is growing rapidly. In *How the Mind Works*, Steven Pinker describes how dozens of mysteries of the mind "have recently been upgraded to problems" because, while we may not know the solution, we now have greater insight and know what we are looking for.[99] Numerous areas, such as aviation and medicine, have a history of practical application of cognitive research to system design and engineering with an emphasis on human-system interaction.

There is a growing need for USAF C2 to join other high-risk endeavors and apply cognitive research more consistently, from system design to actual operations. Achieving predictive and tailored SA, drastic reductions in decision time lines, and decisive EBO will clearly require incredible contributions from advanced technologies. However, in the end, decision superiority occurs in the minds of people. A great challenge is to create a C2 system that deliberately teams humans with technology to play on the strengths and to cover the weaknesses of each. It is not clear that the Air Force is currently positioned to meet this challenge.

Many of the 2000 SAB recommendations related to HSI remain open. The Air Force has not adopted a structured engineering approach that accounts for HSI at all stages of C2 acquisition processes. The ties between laboratory-based theoretical research and operationally relevant problems, particularly in the AOC, appear weak. The use of HSI-related technologies, such as advanced visualization tools and decision support systems, is limited. Data overload is a real and growing issue.

As the Air Force expands its networks, obtains more sensors, and harnesses greater computing processing power to fuse, analyze, and display data, the issues of HSI become more complex. Removing decision makers from the sources of information through automated fusion—if not approached with an understanding of how humans form mental representations—could be a limiting factor to achieving SA. Faster decision time lines may drive people to rely more on mental shortcuts, introducing predictable biases that influence the quality of decision making. Rich data presentation environments could mask a lack of information on critical cues for effects-based operations, such as our adversary's behavior, intent, and motivations.

Accounting for the human aspects of information processing and decision making in C2 presents unique challenges. The AOC is a conglomeration of hundreds of positions, a myriad of tasks, dozens of systems, and a wide range of experience levels. It is not a cradle-to-grave program with extensive influence over initial system design where HSI considerations can have the greatest benefit. The AOC integrates systems developed by other programs and does not have in-house expertise to adequately address human factors or HSI considerations. It also does not have the long-standing institutional infrastructure to supports HSI, unlike aviation systems engineering. While not nearly as bounded a challenge as examining aircrew and aircraft interactions, the AOC is arguably equally important.

This paper concludes that even small improvements in the application of human factors and HSI principles can matter. An HSI expert observing the decision needs of the SOLE liaison may have identified the simple decision support system fix during a workup exercise, helping to create more specific chat procedures. Greater awareness within the AOC program office and among C2 operators of the research efforts of DARPA, the Office of Naval Research, AFRL, and commercially available technologies could generate imaginative ideas for near-term practical applications in USAF C2. Any efforts that deliberately tie human factors expertise and laboratory-based research to current C2 operations and system development are likely to have payoffs. Human factors and HSI should not be an afterthought.

Notes

1. Joint Publication (JP) 3-30, *Command and Control*, I-1; and Air Force Doctrine Document (AFDD) 2, *Organization and Employment of Aerospace Power*, 5.
2. USAF Scientific Advisory Board (SAB), *Report on Air Force Command and Control*, vol 2, 1-2.
3. Jumper, "Future Force"; Martin, address to the Air Force Association (AFA); and Martin, address to the AFA Policy Forum.
4. *US Air Force Space and C4ISR Capabilities CONOPS*, 10–11; and Department of the Air Force, *US Air Force Transformation Flight Plan*, 45.
5. Chairman of the Joint Chiefs of Staff, *Joint Vision 2020*, 10–13, 28–29; DOD, *Implementation of Network-Centric Warfare*, 8–10; and Department of the Navy, *FORCEnet*, 2, 7, 11–19.
6. *US Air Force Space and C4ISR Capabilities CONOPS*, 10–11.
7. Department of the Air Force, *US Air Force Transformation Flight Plan*, 45.
8. Ibid., 54.
9. Martin, address to the AFA; and Martin, command briefing, slides.
10. DOD, *Implementation of Network-Centric Warfare*, 9; and *US Air Force Space and C4ISR Capabilities CONOPS*, II, 1, 4.
11. AFDD 2-5, *Information Operations*, 1.
12. Jumper, "Chief's Sight Picture."
13. Department of the Air Force, *US Air Force Transformation Flight Plan*, 6–7.
14. AFDD 2, "Operations and Organization," 16.
15. The field of human factors is generally defined in broad terms as a subset of engineering with a focus on "system design, accounting for those factors, psychological and physical, that are properties of the human component" (Wickens, Lee, and Becker, *Introduction to Human Factors Engineering*, 6). Human-computer interaction is a multidisciplinary field incorporating research and theories from computer science, psychology, anthropology, education, design, engineering, math, and physics concerned with the design, operation, and evaluation of user interfaces to ensure technology is usable, universal, and useful for human needs (Jacko and Sears, *Human-Computer Interaction Handbook*, xvi, 19).
16. Pinker, *How the Mind Works*, 5.
17. Wickens and Hollands, *Engineering Psychology and Human Performance*, 11, 295.
18. Fadok, "John Boyd and John Warden," 16.
19. Wickens and Hollands, *Engineering Psychology and Human Performance*, 297.
20. Wickens et al., *Introduction to Human Factors Engineering*, 69–73.
21. Ibid., 91.
22. Ibid., 119.
23. Ibid., 123.
24. Wickens and Hollands, *Engineering Psychology and Human Performance*, 69–70.
25. Tufte, *Visual Explanations*.
26. Ibid., 38–53.
27. Wickens et al., *Introduction to Human Factors Engineering*, 128–29.
28. Ibid., 129.
29. Ibid., 136; Norman, *Invisible Computer*, 173; and Pinker, *How the Mind Works*, 85–88.

30. Norman, *Invisible Computer*, 154.

31. Ibid., 180.

32. Wickens et al., *Introduction to Human Factors Engineering*, 162.

33. Ibid., 165. These biases are referred to as the *anchoring heuristic* and *cognitive tunneling*, respectively.

34. Ibid., 166. This bias is called the *availability heuristic*.

35. Ibid. This bias is called *representativeness/analogies*.

36. Ibid. This bias is referred to as *overconfidence*.

37. Ibid., 167; and Schrag, "First Impressions Matter," 37–83.

38. Wickens et al., *Introduction to Human Factors Engineering*. Greater detail on all of the biases discussed can be found in Gilovich, Griffin, and Kahneman, *Heuristics and Biases*.

39. Neustadt and May, *Thinking in Time*, 273–75.

40. Chipman and Kieras, "Operator Centered Design," 20; and St. John et al., "Overview of the DARPA [Defense Advanced Research Projects Agency]."

41. Norman, *Invisible Computer*, 136.

42. Department of the Air Force, *US Air Force Transformation Flight Plan*, 54.

43. USAF SAB, *Report on Air Force Command and Control*, vol. 1, 51.

44. Ibid., 54.

45. Jumper, "Future Force."

46. Maj Dwayne Gardner, AOC Weapon System Program Office, interview by the author, 8 April 2005.

47. Maj Thomas Gill, ESC/RC, interview by the author, 7 February 2005.

48. Air Force Operational Tactics, Techniques, and Procedures (AFOTTP) 2-3.2, *Air and Space Operations Center*, 2.7–2.8.

49. Ibid.

50. Maj Daniel Simpson, interview by the author, 20 March 2005; Maj Jill Bergovoy, interview by the author, 15 April 2005; and personal experience of the author.

51. Tiboni and French, "Blue Force Tracking."

52. Simpson, interview.

53. Ibid.

54. Bergovoy, interview.

55. Garrambone, Goodman, and Hughes, "Battle Control Center," 2–5.

56. USAF SAB, *Report on Air Force Command and Control*, vol. 1, 51.

57. Norman, *Invisible Computer*, 184; Mayhew, "Requirements Specification," 915; and USAF SAB, *Report on Air Force Command and Control*, vol. 1, 52.

58. USAF SAB, *Report on Air Force Command and Control*, vol. 1, 52.

59. Mayhew, "Requirements Specification," 914.

60. AFOTTP 2-3.2, *Air and Space Operations Center*, 4-95, 5-6, 6-5.

61. Redish and Wixon, "Task Analysis," 935.

62. Wickens et al., *Introduction to Human Factors Engineering*, 41; and Redish and Wixon, "Task Analysis," 928–34.

63. Chipman and Kieras, "Operator Centered Design," 9–10; and Redish and Wixon, "Task Analysis," 923.

64. Hinckley, interview.

65. Byrne, "Cognitive Architecture," 98.

66. Chipman and Kieras, "Operator Centered Design," 3.

67. Ibid., 5.

68. Byrne, "Cognitive Architecture," 99.

69. Ibid., 104–15; and Chipman and Kieras, "Operator Centered Design," 2–7. Byrne and Chipman and Kieras provide details on the most prominent cognitive architectures in use today: SOAR [State, Operator and Result], EPIC [Executive-Process/Interactive Control], and ACT-R [Adaptive Control of Thought—Rational].

70. Chipman and Kieras, "Operator Centered Design," 9.

71. Ibid., 18.

72. Byrne, "Cognitive Architecture," 115.

73. Ibid.

74. Wickens et al., *Introduction to Human Factors Engineering*, 143; and Gawron, *Human Performance Measures Handbook*, 155.

75. Wickens and Hollands, *Engineering Psychology*, 298.

76. Wickens et al., *Introduction to Human Factors Engineering*, 427.

77. Department of the Navy, *FORCEnet*, 25.

78. Patterson, Roth, and Woods, "Aiding the Intelligence Analyst," 27.

79. Miller and Shattuck, "Process Model of Situated Cognition," 3.

80. Gawron, *Human Performance Measures Handbook*, 155–67.

81. Miller and Shattuck, "Process Model of Situated Cognition," 7.

82. Ibid.

83. Patterson, Roth, and Woods, "Aiding the Intelligence Analyst."

84. USAF SAB, *Report on Air Force Command and Control*, vol. 1, 52.

85. Merholz, "Information Visualization," 43.

86. Card, "Information Visualization," 547–49; and Merholz, "Information Visualization," 42.

87. Card, "Information Visualization," 547.

88. Ibid., 552.

89. Siewiorek and Smailagic, "User-Centered Interdisciplinary Design," 636.

90. USAF SAB, *Report on Air Force Command and Control*, vol. 2, 5-23.

91. Siewiorek and Smailagic, "User-Centered Interdisciplinary Design," 652–54.

92. Gardner, interview.

93. USAF SAB, *Report on Air Force Command and Control*, vol. 2, 5-23.

94. Smith and Geddes, "Cognitive Systems Engineering," 666–70.

95. San Diego Knowledge Management and Decision Support.

96. Moore et al., "Understanding and Improving Knowledge," 8.

97. USAF SAB, *Report on Air Force Command and Control*, vol. 2, 5-24.

98. Ibid.

99. Pinker, *How the Mind Works*, ix.

Chapter 5

Arctic Security: An Adaptive Approach for a Changing Climate

Lt Col Christopher S. Kean and Cdr David C. Kneale

It is not the strongest of the species that survives, nor the most intelligent; it is the one that is most adaptable to change.

—Charles Darwin

Overview

Climate change in the Arctic potentially can create severe, long-lasting impacts on global security. As a result, warming Arctic waters present new challenges to US national security interests that can be categorized into three main areas: (1) heightened sovereignty disputes over access to natural resources, commercial shipping routes, and increased military presence; (2) environmental security resulting from changing ecosystems; and (3) human security of indigenous Arctic cultures and members of the global community due to changing migration patterns. Faced with new resource challenges from climate change, human and animal populations will be forced to adapt, migrate, or face extinction. These three main concerns are inherently interdependent and tied to the interplay of national interests in energy, economy, and environment.

What exactly has changed in the Arctic? A steadily changing natural climate has brought a daunting duality of resource competition and environmental concern. A report from a conference on the Arctic at the National Defense University (NDU) states, "Climate change is gradually uncovering an Arctic which stands at the crossroads of development and risk."[1] The challenge facing the United States as a world leader is how to harness the uncertain future of the Arctic as a possible turning point. Therefore, the strategic outlook for US national security needs to consider both the current political and natural environment with caution for the sustainable future. Past paradigms of political realism and classical economics may not best fit the sustainable development of the Arctic, making traditional sovereignty and resource interests secondary to more important security concerns. Instead, the shared natural environment and its understanding through the scientific community may be the new drivers to shape the political response to climate change. The United States must reprioritize its long-term security interests to achieve a sustainable Arctic strategy.

Current US Strategy

The 2006 *National Security Strategy* (*NSS*) outlines a basic backbone to a strategy for the Arctic: "We choose leadership over isolationism, and the pursuit of free and fair trade and open markets over protectionism. We choose to deal with challenges now rather than leaving them for future generations."[2] The *NSS* also specifically mentions the need to "engage the opportunities and confront the challenges of globalization."[3] Essentially this means that "many of the problems we face . . . reach across borders."[4] The Bush administration said, "Effective multinational efforts are essential to solve these problems. Yet history has shown that only when we do our part will others do theirs. America must continue to lead."[5] These statements imply that an effective Arctic strategy is one that the United States does not pursue alone. More importantly, the changing natural and political environment presents a timely stage for the United States to embrace a leadership role to ensure responsible actions by Arctic nations.

Regarding the Arctic, however, current US engagement policies do not follow the guidance articulated in the *NSS*. Two key examples of this are the failure of the United States to ratify the United Nations Convention on the Law of the Sea (UNCLOS) and the Kyoto Protocol for greenhouse gas emissions. On 12 January 2009, during his final days in office, Pres. George W. Bush released a new *Arctic Region Policy*, replacing the one from 1994. The new policy emphasizes the need to protect US resource interests in the Arctic and identify new areas for international cooperation. In the Obama administration, the United States can lead on issues involving the changing climate in the Arctic derived from a perception of newfound American "soft power" appeal.[6] In addition, a more liberal-minded Congress may be more apt to adopt the administration's spirit of change in general and, therefore, more actively pursue a sustainable multilateral Arctic strategy. A US decision to lead peaceful multinational efforts in the region could also bolster this soft power. If it is true, as stated in the NDU report, that "policy initiatives in the next 5–10 years will disproportionately influence US strategic posture in the Arctic over the next half century,"[7] the Arctic should be a high priority for the Obama administration. As suggested in the current *NSS*, the United States must face these challenges now.

Research Methodology

The NDU report highlighted that the biggest challenge in the region is that the United States has "so far excluded itself from an emerging international framework designed to manage the anticipated changes."[8] The report recommends three possible options for US policy makers with varying degrees of multilateral cooperation:

1. Retain current levels of low international involvement (status quo).
2. Pursue "limited enhancement" to US security strategy through more cooperation and specific articulation of US national interests.
3. Pursue "enhanced engagement," which outlines short- and long-term actions to engage in the region.[9]

This research is, in large part, a calculated response to the report, as it explores the impact of these three options on US security. The research method used is the problem/solution method. The problem examined is how US national strategy should address the uncertain future geopolitical environment in the warming waters of the Arctic. This study explores solutions to mitigate threats to US national security while balancing economic rights and environmental responsibilities, both of which are in the interests of US strategy for future involvement in the Arctic. More specifically, the research process revealed four criteria for comparing potential solutions. US Arctic strategy must

1. peacefully resolve territorial sovereignty issues and promote free trade economics,
2. mitigate risks to human and environmental security in the region and around the globe,
3. provide a long-term solution to the sustainable development of the Arctic, and
4. include a mechanism for enforcement and monitoring compliance.

This paper is organized into four main areas: natural environment, economics, politics, and science. The research explores these inter-related subjects as they are assessed in the context of US national security and relevance to Arctic strategy. Next, an options analysis compares the three basic options from the NDU report using the criteria for success. An additional analysis compares current US Arctic Region Policy and the 1994 policy using the same criteria. Lastly, the author makes overall conclusions and recommendations.

Natural Environment

Perhaps indicative of the challenge to fostering true international cooperation in the Arctic, the very definition of "Arctic" is still subject to debate. The region around the earth's North Pole bounded by the Arctic Circle is the most widely accepted definition. The Arctic Circle circumscribes the earth through the eight "Arctic nations" of Russia, Finland, Sweden, Norway, Iceland, Denmark (Greenland), Canada, and the United States. Defined as the southernmost latitude that experiences the phenomena of midnight sun and polar night, the Arctic Circle defines a definite geophysical boundary. However, other boundaries are recognized based on ecology and climate, for example the 10° Celsius (C) (50° Fahrenheit [F]) July isotherm (appendix A). This climatologic definition roughly corresponds to the ecological boundary formed by the Arctic tree line. Until recently, this defined where life transitioned from more temperate sub-Arctic plants and animals to the treeless frozen tundra and polar ice cap with their unique and delicate Arctic life forms.

As global warming pushes temperate species steadily northward, the size of the Arctic is decreasing.[10] Effectively, the Arctic climate and the Arctic species that thrive within it are being steadily pushed off the planet. It was precisely this realization that prompted former US interior secretary Dirk Kempthorne to announce in May 2008 that "the drastic loss of Arctic sea ice had forced him to list the polar bear as an endangered species because their populations could collapse within a few decades."[11]

The most dominating physical feature of the Arctic is the Arctic Ocean. Geologically unique, it is commonly recognized as the smallest and shallowest of the world's oceans. However, oceanographers define it as a "mediterranean" sea, defined in oceanographic terms as "a mostly enclosed sea that has limited exchange of deep water with outer oceans and where the water circulation is dominated by salinity and temperature differences rather than winds."[12] Other dissenters see it as the northernmost lobe of a single world ocean. While "Arctic Sea" may be a more geologically accurate term, to avoid confusion this research will use the term Arctic Ocean.

Sea Change

A sea change is taking place in the Arctic, both literally and figuratively, with profound geologic, climatic, economic, commercial, environmental, and political implications. The Arctic Ocean is largely covered by sea ice a majority of the year. Melting induced by global warming has increased the extent to which it is ice free, particularly in the summer months. Earth's climate varies gradually over long periods of time with cooling and warming periods evidenced by cyclical glacial formation and retreat. However, without including a component for human-induced variations, climate models cannot account for the rapid pace of Arctic sea ice melting.[13] This human warming component is due to increased atmospheric carbon dioxide levels from human activity such as fossil fuel (oil, coal, and natural gas) usage and deforestation.[14]

September 2007 witnessed a new record minimum Arctic summer ice cover of just 4.3 million square kilometers, which was 39 percent below the long-term average from 1979 to 2000.[15] This was nearly repeated again in September 2008 with just 4.7 million square kilometers of ice cover.[16] Professor Wieslaw Maslowski, a researcher from the Naval Postgraduate School in Monterrey, California, believes the pace of melting has quickened to the point where the Arctic could be ice free in the summer as soon as 2013.[17] Presciently, his prediction was made prior to the drastic new record minimum set in 2007 using data from 1979 to 2004.

The Arctic is warming at a significantly faster rate than the rest of the planet. According to the United Nations (UN) Intergovernmental Panel on Climate Change (IPCC), "The warming in the last 30 years is widespread over the globe, and is greatest at higher northern latitudes. . . . Average arctic temperatures have been increasing at almost twice the rate of the rest of the world in the past 100 years."[18] Scientists believe one reason for this uneven warming has to do with Arctic albedo, which refers to how well a surface reflects solar energy.

Snow-covered ice reflects roughly 90 percent of solar energy. As snow and sea ice melt, the darker ocean left behind reflects just 6 percent of this energy, absorbing 94 percent into the water.[19] This solar absorption causes ocean water to warm, melting more ice, exposing additional ocean surface to solar absorption, and thus creating a self-reinforcing melting cycle commonly known as an "albedo feedback loop."

A similar feedback loop is believed to occur on land as the Arctic tree line slowly advances northward and the darker trees absorb more solar energy than the snow-covered tundra they replace. Further still, as permafrost thaws, large amounts of carbon dioxide and methane trapped in the permafrost are released into the atmosphere, producing yet another feedback that increases warming and thaws more permafrost. In this way, it is believed that the Arctic has been acting as a "heat sink" for a warming world.

The melting of sea ice and warming of frigid Arctic waters absorb a tremendous amount of heat energy, which has had a mitigating effect on the rise of heat globally. Predictions of this sea-ice heat sink disappearing in the summer foretell a future where rates of global temperature rise may increase sharply. Dr. Mark Serreze, a geographer at the National Snow and Ice Data Center, has stated, "We could think of the Arctic as the refrigerator of the northern hemisphere climate system. What we are doing by getting rid of that sea ice is radically changing the nature of that refrigerator. We are making it much less efficient. But everything is connected together so what happens up there eventually influences what happens in other parts of the globe."[20]

The profound changes occurring in the Arctic Ocean could have catastrophic effects on global climate by affecting a mechanism known as thermohaline circulation. Thermohaline circulation refers to the ocean temperature and salinity variations that help drive the conveyor of ocean currents. Ocean currents play a critical role in determining regional and global weather patterns. A radically changed ice-free Arctic, coupled with runoff from a thawing Greenland ice sheet, could alter the current temperature and salinity balance of the North Atlantic Ocean enough to slow or even collapse the thermohaline circulation.[21] The effects would be rapid, global, and catastrophic. Estimates are that England and northwestern Europe would be most affected, becoming colder, drier, and windier, much like Siberia.[22] This scenario is not as unlikely as it sounds. Climatic records obtained through Greenland ice core samples indicate at least eight abrupt cooling episodes documented in the geological record going back

730,000 years. The most recent event occurred 8,200 years ago, lasted for roughly 100 years, and resulted in an average annual temperature decrease in Greenland of 5° F.[23] By historical standards, this was a relatively minor event and more likely involved just a slowing of ocean circulation. More dramatically, roughly 12,700 years ago, an event known as the Younger Dryas appears to have been precipitated by a total collapse of thermohaline circulation. The effects were much more severe, with a cooling of over 27° F in Greenland that lasted over 1,000 years.[24]

Geologically speaking these are recent events, yet modern human civilization has never been subjected to weather conditions so persistently disruptive. Dr. Robie Macdonald, a leading Canadian oceanographer who has worked with the IPCC, worries, "The Arctic really can feed back into the global climate system. You know what happens when you get feedbacks—you get surprises and we don't like surprises."[25] Clearly, mankind would be ill-advised to assume that global warming will progress gradually. Changes in the Arctic could have profound effects upon the earth's climates and the creatures depending on those climates for survival.

Climate Change Impacts in the Arctic

The effects of global warming are becoming increasingly difficult for scientists to disprove. To put it in perspective, the earth's surface temperature has increased approximately 1.4° F in the last 150 years and as much as 5° F in certain areas, such as the Arctic region.[26] More pertinent to the issue, though, is the rapidity of the current temperature increases; most recent scientific studies on Arctic melting highlight that earlier models were much too conservative. In fact, an April 2007 news release from the National Center for Atmospheric Research (NCAR) reported that "September ice actually declined at a rate of about 7.8 percent per decade during the 1953–2006 period."[27] This was contrasted with earlier model projections from the IPCC that showed a 2.5 percent average decline per decade for this time period (appendix B).

The NCAR news release emphasized that "the shrinking of summertime ice is about 30 years ahead of the climate model projections. As a result, the Arctic could be seasonally free of sea ice earlier than the IPCC-projected timeframe of any time from 2050 to well beyond 2100."[28] More recently, within the *Global Environment Outlook: Envi-*

ronment for Development (GEO-4) report, the IPCC revealed observations showing an average decline of 8.9 percent per decade.[29] The
point is that the global climate is changing more rapidly than anticipated, particularly in the Arctic. As a result, the warming climate in
the Arctic is drastically altering the stability of the Arctic's natural
environment, as indicated in the 2004 *Arctic Climate Impact Assessment (ACIA)*, an international effort of hundreds of scientists assisted
by the knowledge of indigenous people:

> The increasingly rapid rate of recent climate change poses new challenges to
> the resilience of arctic life. In addition to the impacts of climate change, many
> other stresses brought about by human activities are simultaneously affecting
> life in the Arctic, including air and water contamination, overfishing, increas-
> ing levels of ultraviolet radiation due to ozone depletion, habitat alteration
> and pollution due to resource extraction, and increasing pressure on land and
> resources related to the growing human population in the region. The sum of
> these factors threatens to overwhelm the adaptive capacity of some arctic
> populations and ecosystems.[30]

The key findings of the *ACIA* are based on a moderate scenario of
warming. Nonetheless, these findings highlight the urgency of acting
now to prevent or slow potentially irreversible impacts. Beyond the
realization that changes are occurring rapidly in the region, a key
finding is that "Arctic warming and its impacts have worldwide implications."[31] These implications are diverse, ranging from the multiplying
effect of the albedo feedback loop to rising global sea levels and alteration of
biodiversity and migratory habits. Perhaps an area often neglected by
business-minded opportunists is the fact that thawing ground will
disrupt existing infrastructure and prospective building projects like
pipelines, airports, roads, industrial complexes, and so forth. The
findings further discuss the cultural and economic disruptions in indigenous communities, an issue that underscores the need to integrate indigenous inputs into evolving Arctic policies. Overall, the
ACIA states, "Multiple influences interact to cause impacts to people
and ecosystems," and "the total impact is greater than the sum of its
parts."[32]

These impacts on natural systems and societies are not mutually
exclusive; in fact, the opposite is true. When it comes to climate
change, the Arctic is the epicenter. Those who understand this are
raising the loudest alarms for action, but the general public is quickly
gaining awareness. The *GEO-4* report explains that the "polar regions
influence major environmental processes, and have direct impacts on

global biodiversity and human well-being."[33] This is why headlines like "Arctic Sea Ice at Lowest Recorded Level Ever" and "Arctic Land Grabs Could Cause Eco-Disaster" have become so commonplace in scientific journals and mainstream media.[34]

One expert in this field is Dr. James Hansen, director of the NASA Goddard Institute for Space Studies and adjunct professor of earth and environmental sciences at Columbia University's Earth Institute. In his opinion, "the greatest threat of climate change for human beings . . . lies in the potential destabilization of the massive ice sheets in Greenland and Antarctica."[35] This would represent an irreversible consequence of climate change. The *ACIA* reported that melting of the Greenland ice sheet increased 16 percent from 1979 to 2002, when it broke all previous records.[36] Hansen argues that we have reached the "critical tipping point" and that "we have at most ten years—not ten years to decide upon action, but ten years to alter fundamentally the trajectory of global greenhouse emissions."[37] This decision is of such magnitude that it will impact future generations, escalating the priority of adapting to climate change.

Recent IPCC reports demonstrate how the Arctic is a prime example of the challenges of adaptation: "Arctic human communities are already adapting to climate change, but both external and internal stressors challenge their adaptive capacities. Despite the resilience shown historically by Arctic indigenous communities, some traditional ways of life are being threatened and substantial investments are needed to adapt or re-locate physical structures and communities."[38] As Hansen predicts, "If human beings follow a business-as-usual course, continuing to exploit fossil fuel resources without reducing carbon emissions or capturing and sequestering them before they warm the atmosphere, the eventual effects on climate change and life may be comparable to those at the time of mass extinctions."[39] National security, therefore, is becoming subordinate to global security.

Economics

Economic policy decisions made in the near term will have lasting impacts on the sustainable development of the Arctic. Safe, secure, and responsible development in the Arctic demands cooperation, not competition.

Resources

Scientists have long suspected that the Arctic Ocean holds significant quantities of hydrocarbon and mineral deposits including oil, natural gas, gold, platinum, lead, magnesium, nickel, and zinc. Until recently, however, low energy prices and prohibitive costs of extraction effectively limited exploration in the extreme Arctic environment. Recently, climate change and energy scarcity have combined in a kind of "perfect storm" to alter the age-old Arctic economic paradigm. Rapidly receding sea ice and higher energy prices are eroding the historical impediments to development. Exploiting these resources is becoming increasingly viable economically as the likelihood of positive financial returns and accessibility both improve.

The undiscovered hydrocarbon resources locked away beneath the ice are thought to be substantial. The 2008 Circum-Arctic Resource Appraisal (CARA) from the US Geological Survey (USGS) estimates that "90 billion barrels of oil, 1,669 trillion cubic feet of natural gas, and 44 billion barrels of natural gas liquids may remain to be found in the Arctic, of which approximately 84 percent is expected to occur in offshore areas."[40] Similarly, the USGS and the Norwegian company StatoilHydro estimate that the Arctic holds as much as 25 percent of the world's remaining undiscovered oil and gas deposits.[41] Estimates of the dollar value of these resources run into the trillions. These are the best attempts to estimate what lies beneath the Arctic Ocean seabed, about which less is known than the surface of Mars.[42] The *CARA* report acknowledges this limitation: "Because of the sparse seismic and drilling data in much of the Arctic, the usual tools and techniques used in USGS resource assessments, such as discovery process modeling, prospect delineation, and deposit simulation, were not generally applicable. Therefore, the *CARA* relied on a probabilistic methodology of geological analysis and analog modeling."[43] Regardless of the actual quantity of hydrocarbon resources beneath the Arctic, deciding where to drill would be just the beginning of a difficult process in a foreboding environment:

> Drilling and extracting oil in deep, ice-covered waters, thousands of miles from any tanker port, poses enormous technical challenges. Special equipment and highly trained crews must be brought in and protected in a harsh environment. Thousands of engineering and technical hurdles must be overcome simply to bring the oil to the surface—to say nothing of building the thousands of miles of pipeline that must be laid to get the oil to market. What

is more, according to some geologists, once oil companies finally do tap into the Arctic, the formations are far more likely to hold gas than oil.[44]

A twisted kind of triple irony exists in regard to the Arctic's suspected energy riches. First, as Arctic ice recedes, it increases access to more of the culprits that precipitated the melting in the first place— fossil fuels. Secondly, for mankind to avoid a worst-case climate change scenario, a "bridge" fuel is needed to minimize carbon emissions in the near-term while transitioning to a long-term, sustainable, carbon-free energy economy—natural gas.[45] Lastly, governments seeking national security may have merging interests with energy companies and environmentalists, as the negative effects of climate change become increasingly dramatic. Environmentalists, a group that could grow to include a vast majority of humanity, will demand their energy from cleaner sources, including natural gas. Energy companies will respond in kind by transitioning to these less carbon-intensive forms of energy. Governments attempting to ensure national security will find it increasingly difficult and expensive to unilaterally provide this fundamental governmental function as global environmental security rapidly deteriorates.

To avoid this scenario, visionary governments must recognize that climate change has altered the existing national security paradigm. Long-term national security has become unattainable through unilateral action; multilateral effort to mitigate the effects of climate change will be essential. Wise governments will adopt policies that encourage transition away from carbon-intensive energy sources and build the international frameworks to achieve the required global response. In the Arctic, governments must build the apparatus now to maximize this collaboration while minimizing environmental damage.

Commerce

The retreat of Arctic sea ice could have dramatic near-term effects upon global commerce. The Arctic sea routes, sought in vain by nineteenth century explorers, are opening up. Specifically, maritime shortcuts known as the Northwest Passage (over North America) and the Northern Sea Route (over Eurasia) are fast becoming realities. The Northwest Passage first opened in 2007; in 2008 both passages were ice free simultaneously for the first time in recorded history.[46] The implications of this are profound. As shipping shortcuts, they could reduce ocean distances by thousands of miles, saving days of travel time and potentially a great deal of money. Use of the Northern Sea Route would reduce the distance between Japan (Yokohama) and Europe (Rotterdam) from 11,200 nautical miles (nm) to only 6,500 nm.[47] It would also avoid the time-consuming and politically tumultuous chokepoints of the Strait of Malacca and Suez Canal. The Northwest Passage would reduce a voyage from Seattle to Rotterdam from 9,000 nm to 7,000 nm, saving additional time and money by avoiding the Panama Canal's delays and fees.[48] Even greater benefits could be realized by megaships that are too large to use the Panama and Suez Canals and currently make the long treks around the Cape of Good Hope and Cape Horn. Some are merrily predicting a future that can only be described as a panacea of trans-Arctic transportation bliss:

> Trans-Arctic shipping will become commercially viable and begin on a large scale. In an age of just-in-time delivery, and with increasing fuel costs eating into the profits of shipping companies, reducing long-haul sailing distances by as much as 40 percent could usher in a new phase of globalization. Arctic routes would force further competition between the Panama and Suez Canals, thereby reducing current canal tolls; shipping chokepoints such as the Strait of Malacca would no longer dictate global shipping patterns; and Arctic seaways would allow for greater international economic integration. When the ice recedes enough, likely within this decade, a marine highway directly over the North Pole will materialize. Such a route, which would most likely run between Iceland and Alaska's Dutch Harbor, would connect shipping megaports in the North Atlantic with those in the North Pacific.[49]

Significant obstacles will have to be overcome, however, before this rosy future can be realized. First, Arctic ice retreat may not make transportation any easier in the near term. As thick multiyear ice breaks off from high polar regions, seemingly ice-free areas are likely to remain too dangerous for passage by non-ice-capable ships for years to come. Second, the myriad of critical support facilities and capabilities needed for safe oceanic transit are currently nonexistent in the Arctic Ocean. Current inadequacies include search and rescue, traffic management, vessel tracking, solid and liquid waste disposal, harbors of refuge for ships in danger, notices to mariners system, and training for captains and crews of these vessels.[50] Additionally, highly skilled "ice pilots" will likely require special training and certification for particularly harrowing sections of the Northwest Passage. Furthermore, codes and methods of code enforcement for more rigorous ship design are needed to ensure that vessels transiting the Arctic have thicker hulls, more powerful engines, and special navigation equipment. Lastly, environmental disasters such as oil spills will have dramatically more severe and long-lasting negative effects in the delicate Arctic environment. Likewise, aggressive spill response capabilities will be of critical importance. As stated in the Arctic Environmental Protection Strategy (AEPS):

> The Arctic is one of the areas most vulnerable to adverse impacts from chronic and acute oil pollution. This is due to physical environmental conditions such as low temperature, periods with little or no light, ice cover, etc. Low temperatures lead to reduced evaporation of the more volatile, toxic oil components. Dark, cold winters in the Arctic lead to reduced ultraviolet radiation and biological decomposition of oil. In areas of drift ice, oil dispersal caused by wave action is also reduced. Oil in iced areas will be trapped between ice floes or under the ice, and only partly transported to the ice surface. These factors result in a generally slower decomposition of oil in the Arctic than in temperate regions. The period in which a particular oil spill can be harmful to wildlife is thus comparatively longer in the Arctic.[51]

The private sector has recognized the potential commercial boom that Arctic shipping could provide. Billions of dollars are being invested to develop fleets of Arctic tankers with cutting-edge, "double-acting" ship designs that can sail bow first through open water and then turn around and proceed stern first to break through ice.[52] The US Arctic Research Commission (USARC) anticipates that "as Arctic seaways become a reliable venue for global trade, the number of ice-class ships, currently around 7,800, will likely grow from 4.5 percent of the world's shipping fleet to 10 percent. . . . Indeed, an accessible Arctic Ocean also means new or expanded routes for the US military sealift to move assets from one part of the world to another."[53]

Tourism is also on the rise as cruise ships are venturing farther north every year. Greater coordination by Arctic nations will be needed in the future to ensure that tourism policies help minimize impacts on environmental degradation.[54] Furthermore, governments must mobilize now to meet these future challenges in terms of safe shipping:

Research, policies, and coordinated investment in infrastructure will ensure safe, secure, and reliable Arctic shipping. Under the principle of freedom of navigation, global shipping can come to our doorstep whether we invite it or not. Whether you envision the Arctic Ocean as a new seaway, for trans-Arctic shipping, competitive with the Panama and Suez Canals, or only foresee an expansion of the current shipping in and out of the Arctic, the time to prepare is now.[55]

As stated by former assistant secretary of state Daniel S. Sullivan, "Having a safe, secure, and reliable Arctic shipping regime is vital to the proper development of Arctic resources, especially now given the extent of Arctic ice retreat. . . . We can have such a regime only through cooperation, not competition among Arctic Nations."[56]

Politics

Politics remains one of the greatest obstacles to a sustainable national strategy for the Arctic. Nonetheless, several conventions and frameworks exist to help regulate behavior and enforce agreements on Arctic concerns, including the UN *Convention on the Law of the Sea* and various organizations, such as the Arctic Council and the International Maritime Organization. With the proper focus, much progress can be made through cooperative politics among Arctic nations.

Psyche of Arctic Nations

Of the eight Arctic nations, only the five bordering the Arctic Ocean make up the "coastal states." These include Russia, Norway, Canada, Denmark, and the United States. Of these, the United States has shown the least interest toward the Arctic.[57] The United States became an Arctic nation in 1867 after purchasing Alaska from Russia for $7.2 million, or less than two cents per acre.[58] Just two years after the Civil War, many Americans failed to see wisdom in the transaction. Opponents of the deal viewed Alaska as a distant, useless piece of land, nicknaming it "Seward's Folly" and "Seward's Icebox" after then–secretary of state William Seward, who championed the deal.[59] Many Americans view Alaska as a remote place that merits little attention, despite it becoming the 49th state in 1959. Most Americans, by and large, consider the United States a bicoastal nation, while in reality there are four coasts—East Coast, West Coast, Gulf Coast, and the 1,000-mile Arctic Coast.

An exception to this pervasive American disregard for Alaska has long been the US military. In 1935, Brig Gen Billy Mitchell recognized Alaska's strategic potential, dubbing it "the most strategic place in the world."[60] World War II saw a massive military buildup in Alaska. By 1943, 152,000 out of 233,000 people living in Alaska were members of the US armed forces. Though the postwar population would drop to 99,000 in 1946, Cold War military expenditures quickly pushed it back up to 138,000 by 1950.[61] Alaska gave the United States a clear strategic advantage over the Soviets throughout the Cold War. Close to the USSR and distant from the continental United States, Alaska provided a priceless offensive and defensive buffer for ballistic missiles and ballistic missile warning systems. Alaska's remoteness, previously viewed as a liability, made it a prized strategic possession. Today, the Air Force's decision to station one of its newest aircraft in Alaska is no coincidence; C-17s were recently relocated to Elmendorf AFB in Anchorage. According to Lt Col Dave Alamand, commander of Elmendorf's 517th Airlift Squadron, C-17s "can reach any critical point in the world in less than 10 hours," including Germany in only eight hours by flying over the North Pole.[62] Surprising to some, this is roughly the same flight time to Germany as from bases on the US East Coast. In addition to this strategic lift capability, Alaska is one of just two locations outside the continental United States to host the Air Force's top-of-the-line fighter, the F-22A Raptor.[63] The military is not the only organization to recognize Alaska's importance, however.

Since the early twentieth century, energy companies have been interested in Alaska for its oil and natural gas reserves. However, the costs of transportation kept production limited until two key events occurred. First, in 1967 North America's largest known oil field was discovered in Prudhoe Bay on Alaska's Arctic North Slope. Second, the Arab oil embargo in 1973 provided the cost incentive and political environment necessary to overcome hurdles of native land claims and environmentalist objections to approve building the trans-Alaskan oil pipeline. The pipeline, which enables oil from the North Slope to be pumped to the ice-free port of Valdez, was completed in 1977 at a cost of over $8 billion and has since transported over 15 billion barrels of oil.[64]

Clearly, Alaska remains vital to US national security both militarily and economically. Despite this, most Americans still view Alaska as an icy and distant land with not much to offer but energy and polar bears. This mentality has been hardened by the highly publicized political debates between energy companies and environmentalists over drilling in the Arctic National Wildlife Refuge (ANWR), a 19-million-acre refuge on the Arctic Coast estimated by the USGS to hold between 5.7 and 16 billion barrels of technically recoverable oil.[65] This amount would optimistically provide two years of America's energy needs at the current annual usage rate of roughly 7.5 billion barrels of oil.[66] ANWR's potential resources, though not insignificant, are not a sustainable solution to America's long-term energy dependency woes.

Russia and Canada, the two coastal states with the largest amount of Arctic coastline, have deeply grounded national psyches as Arctic nations. Russians consider that a majority of the Arctic belongs to them. They believe the Lomonosov Ridge, an underwater Arctic mountain range thought to connect Siberia and Greenland, to be an extension of their continental shelf and thus have laid claim to 460,000 square miles of the Arctic including the North Pole.[67] In August 2007 celebrated Russian polar explorer Arthur Chilingarov declared, "The Arctic is ours and we should manifest our presence" after placing a titanium Russian flag on the North Pole seabed 13,200 feet beneath the frozen surface.[68] The flag-planting mission was more than just a publicity stunt. It involved a nuclear-powered icebreaker and a research vessel with two mini submarines on a mapping expedition of the Arctic continental shelf in hopes of bolstering Russia's 2001 continental-shelf extension claim. The UN Commission on the Limits of the Continental Shelf (CLCS) denied that claim, pending further geologic evidence. In fact, more recent Canadian scientific mapping from March 2009 suggests that the North Pole may belong to Denmark.[69]

Canadians too have a deeply ingrained sense of Arctic ownership. Canadian prime minister Stephen Harper has declared, "Canada has a choice when it comes to defending our sovereignty over the Arctic, we either use it or lose it. And make no mistake; this government intends to use it."[70] The Harper administration's new *Canada First Defence Strategy* makes repeated mention of the Arctic: "Canadian Forces must have the capacity to exercise control over and defend Canada's sovereignty in the Arctic" and to "conduct daily domestic and continental operations, including in the Arctic and through NORAD [North American Aerospace Defense Command]."[71] Canada has backed up this rhetoric with plans to open a new cold-weather military training center, acquire six to eight new Arctic/offshore patrol ships, and homeport them at a new deepwater Arctic port. Satellites, advanced radars, and remotely piloted vehicles are also being procured to "ensure the constant monitoring of Canada's territory and air and maritime approaches, including in the Arctic, in order to detect threats to Canadian security as early as possible."[72] Compare this to the *National Security Strategy*, *National Defense Strategy*, and *National Military Strategy* of the United States, none of which mentions Alaska or NORAD. In fact, the single mention of the Arctic is found in the *National Defense Strategy*, but only when referencing Russia's resurgence.[73]

Also part of the Canadian psyche is a strong spirit of cooperation with the United States in the mutual defense of North America. *Canada First* has a repeated theme of being "a strong and reliable partner in the defence of North America in cooperation with the United States, Canada's closest ally. Given our common defence and security requirements, it is in Canada's strategic interest to remain a reliable partner in the defence of the continent."[74] Canada and the United States share the longest nonmilitarized border in the world and more than half a trillion dollars of annual trade.[75] The two nations have an extensive history of peacefully resolving differences and working bilaterally for mutual benefit. Examples are too many to list, but both nations must work together to resolve their ongoing disagreement over the Northwest Passage.

Canada views this fabled waterway through the Canadian Arctic "Archipelago" as internal waters, while the United States and a majority of the international community see it as an international strait, and thus the right of innocent passage should apply. This divide may result from Canada's self-image as an Arctic nation and America's self-image as the universal defender of the high seas, ensuring freedom of navigation for all nations. This deeply rooted sentiment dates back as early as 1801 when the nascent US Navy defeated the Barbary pirates who were controlling access to the Mediterranean Sea.[76] The United States and Canada should be aware of the passions on both sides of this issue as they work toward a peaceful solution.

According to the NDU report, one of the greatest challenges in the Arctic is that the United States "simply doesn't understand we are an Arctic Nation. We're a landowner in the Arctic with unique obligations, environmentally and strategically."[77] Today, the US Navy is as powerful as that of the next 17 largest navies combined, yet the United States has only one operable Arctic icebreaker.[78] In contrast, Russia has 18 icebreakers, of which seven are nuclear powered and capable of breaking through ice twice as thick as the US diesel-powered icebreaker.[79] US government officials have recognized that this deficiency of icebreaker capabilities has begun to limit US operations in the polar regions. This includes Alaska governor Sarah Palin, USARC chairman Meade Treadwell, and recent commanders of US Northern Command, US Transportation Command, and US Pacific Command.[80] As a case in point, USNS *Gianella* recently required a rescue from a leased Swedish icebreaker, after having spent 50 hours in pack ice.[81] On a positive note, this rescue could indicate the type of future cooperation that could become the norm for Arctic nations operating in the challenging polar environment.

The Scandinavian countries (Norway, Denmark, and Sweden) have traditionally viewed the Arctic holistically, especially in terms of environmental and indigenous factors. The psyches of Denmark and Norway as coastal Arctic nations are particularly relevant. For Denmark, this is because of its extended claims through Greenland. Once again indicating that America has historically lacked a strategic interest in the region, the United States ceded portions of disputed Greenland territory to Denmark in 1917. This settled claims resulting from American expeditions by Robert Peary in the late 1800s. Instead, the United States purchased the Danish Virgin Islands, which it considered a more strategic acquisition. More recently, Danish crown prince Frederik Andre Henrik Christian has outwardly demonstrated interest and concern for the Arctic. For example, he participated in the *Sirius 2000* expedition, a 2,795-kilometer dog-sledge journey in northern Greenland from Qaanaq to Daneborg, showing his commitment to understanding the region and its indigenous peoples.[82]

Understanding indigenous cultures is a key piece to the psyche of Arctic nations. The region contains a multitude of different indigenous groups spanning territory held by each Arctic nation (appendix C). According to Dr. Natalia Loukacheva of the Munk Center for International Studies in Toronto, "The evolving security perspective in Greenland and Nunavut is formed by the Inuit tradition which demands cooperation and peaceful conflict resolution rather than military actions."[83] Danish foreign policy emphasizes the key areas of common security, democracy and human rights, economic and social development, and the environment.[84] Environmental security, defined by the Danes as "the reasonable assurance of protection against threats to national well-being . . . associated with environmental damage," stands as a unifying concept for Greenland and Denmark even in light of possible future independence of Greenland.[85]

Norwegian security policy in the Arctic can be understood historically by its bilateral disputes with Russia, particularly over national interests in Svalbard, and its commitment to the "extended security" concept. Former foreign minister of Norway, Bjørn Tore Godal, summarized this post–Cold War Norwegian concept as follows: "Our security rests on many more pillars than the military. This is what the concept of extended security is all about. . . . Our security today cannot not be attended to by military means alone. A comprehensive and composite number of security challenges demand a much broader set of political and institutional measures."[86] Late Norwegian foreign minister Johan Jørgen Holst also spoke of a grander "common security" concept: "The most pressing challenges in the Arctic are not confined to military issues, but include also environmental problems, management and utilization of natural resources, and jurisdictional issues. The end of the Cold War has eliminated many of the obstacles to a common security approach to the challenges of the Arctic."[87]

Finally, the *Norwegian Government's High North Strategy* spells out specific areas of emphasis in the Arctic today. These themes are the backbone of this strategy: leadership of international efforts for building knowledge and capacity; stewardship to the natural environment, resources, and wildlife; strengthening cooperation, on a people-to-people basis and internationally, with Russia in particular; safeguarding the livelihoods, traditions, and cultures of indigenous peoples; and overall value creation through the appropriate framework, education, utilization, and management. The strategy also clearly articulates where Norway will stand on Arctic issues:

> The last large wilderness-like areas in our part of the world are to be found in the High North. The natural environment and cultural heritage of the region together make up a unique heritage that must be protected for future generations. This is why the environment and natural resources in the north must be protected against pollution and over-harvesting. It is also important to prevent developments from causing damage to the environment, and to prevent wear and tear and disturbance from increased traffic.[88]

International Frameworks

There is growing international interest in the framework of future Arctic governance. Arctic nations have increasingly articulated their respective economic stakes in the region's untapped resources in order to delineate the boundaries of territorial claims before new discoveries are realized. At the same time, the international community has expressed the need to cooperate in responsible environmental management of the fragile resources in the Arctic. Despite calls for new international frameworks in the Arctic, existing frameworks are well established. The new paradigm of Arctic governance may simply be to implement these frameworks with environmental cooperation in mind.

Harkening back to the days of colonial imperialism and the glory days of *Sputnik*, Russia's symbolic flag planting sparked a wave of sensationalist literature ripe with Wild West imagery of a "lawless Arctic Gold Rush" with nations making an "armed mad dash" to "carve up" resources. Similar to *Sputnik*, the act may have served as a wake-up call for the United States. "In spite of the exaggerated coverage, many were pleased the Russian 'media stunt' had reminded the US it was an Arctic nation with an important stake in the region."[89]

Contrary to these portrayals of chaos, the process of submitting territorial claims to the UN has thus far been deliberate and orderly. Norway submitted its claim in 2006; Canada and Denmark are gathering the data to submit their claims prior to their submission deadlines of 2013 and 2014 respectively. "In fact, the international community has maintained a relatively collegial atmosphere of negotiation in the region based on an effective framework of bilateral and multilateral agreements," according to an NDU report.[90] This is not to say that there are not any territorial disputes, however. In fact, six such disputes are known to exist, and three involve the United States.

US/Canadian disputes involve how to legally define the Northwest Passage and the demarcation of a 100-square-mile portion of the maritime border in the Beaufort Sea. The United States has also not resolved a disagreement with Russia over the status of an 18,000-square-mile area of the Chukchi Sea.[91] Canada has a dispute with Denmark over the status of Hans Island, located in the Nares Strait, between Canada's Ellesmere Island and Greenland. Russia and Norway have yet to resolve their maritime boundary in the Barents Sea, and Norway and Denmark have a similar disagreement in the East Greenland Rift Basin.[92]

A perfect historical analogy for resolving sovereignty disputes in the Arctic does not exist. Nonetheless, despite the unique characteristics of the Arctic Ocean, UNCLOS provides an important piece of a suitable international framework to resolve territorial issues and regulate commerce:

> The convention provides mechanisms for states to settle boundary disputes and submit claims for additional resources beyond their exclusive economic zones. Furthermore, UNCLOS sets aside the resources in the high seas as the common heritage of humankind, it allows states bordering ice-covered waters to enforce more stringent environmental regulations, and it defines which

seaways are the sovereign possessions of states and which international passages are open to unfettered navigation.[93]

Written in large part by the United States with its own national interests in mind, this comprehensive international law has not been ratified by the US Senate due to concerns over yielding US sovereignty. A small group of senators has been able to stall the ratification process for about 15 years by keeping it tied up in committee and preventing a full vote on the Senate floor. When former US secretary of state Hillary Clinton was asked if ratifying UNCLOS would be a priority for the State Department, she responded emphatically, "Yes it will, because it's way overdue."[94] Coalter G. Lathrop, president of Sovereign Geographics, counters predictions of chaos:

> There exists a comprehensive legal regime that defines the rights and obligations of states in, over, and under the world's oceans. It comes complete with customary rules, framework and subsidiary conventions, and dispute-settlement mechanisms and institutions. It applies to the Arctic Ocean. Whether such a regime stinks of world government or rings of international cooperation, it is far from a "legal vacuum." . . . If the Arctic descends into anarchy, it will be despite the rules that are already in place.[95]

Presently, Arctic governance is formed by UNCLOS, along with the International Maritime Organization (IMO) and the Arctic Council. In this regime, the five coastal states have the primary responsibility for managing activities in the region, including both development and environmental protection. On 28 May 2008, representatives meeting in Ilulissat, Greenland, adopted the *Ilulissat Declaration of the Five Arctic States* (appendix D). The declaration reaffirmed the responsibilities and challenges faced by the coastal states under the established legal regime. It also recognized the right of other states to participate in development and protection under the provisions of international law and through the IMO, the Arctic Council, and other relevant international forums. Furthermore, it specifically stated that there is "no need to develop a new comprehensive international legal regime to govern the Arctic Ocean."[96] As such, it recognizes the effectiveness of, and pledges a commitment to, the frameworks already in place. Likewise, it rejects the notion of an alternative regime for the Arctic Ocean as contrary to the existing and effective frameworks.

Maritime governance can be dated back to the first international treaty adopted in 1914, following the Titanic disaster of 1912. This treaty, the *International Convention for the Safety of Life at Seas*, is still the most important treaty for maritime safety today.[97] The IMO was established in 1948, following the foundation of the UN. The IMO's main task has been to "develop and maintain a comprehensive regulatory framework for shipping and its remit today includes safety, environmental concerns, legal matters, technical co-operation, maritime security and the efficiency of shipping."[98] The mission statement of the IMO emphasizes cooperation and preparedness for maritime accidents, including distress and safety communications, search and rescue, and oil pollution response.

Arctic governance also has deep roots in the AEPS of 1991, an initiative of Finland signed by all eight Arctic nations. The broad recognition of the strategy is that "only through careful stewardship by Arctic countries and Arctic peoples can environmental damage and degradation be prevented. These are the challenges which must be taken up in order to secure our common future."[99] The AEPS identified many areas of emphasis still direly needed in a sustainable strategy today, including scientific cooperation, assessment of environmental impacts, pollution control measures, and a commitment to international implementation.[100] It also established programs to foster this future cooperation: Arctic Monitoring and Assessment Programme; Protection of the Marine Environment in the Arctic; Emergency Prevention, Preparedness, and Response in the Arctic; and Conservation of Arctic Flora and Fauna.

Building on this strategy, the Arctic Council has been a strongly influential intergovernmental forum since its establishment in 1996 by the Ottawa Declaration. It serves as a "means for promoting cooperation, coordination and interaction among the Arctic States, with the involvement of the Arctic Indigenous communities and other Arctic inhabitants on common Arctic issues, in particular issues of sustainable development and environmental protection in the Arctic."[101] It includes all members of the eight Arctic nations and currently has six indigenous organizations as permanent participants. In addition, the council offers observer status to non-Arctic states, as well as other intergovernmental and nongovernmental organizations that have a stake in its purpose. Denmark took over the two-year rotating Arctic Council chairmanship role from Norway in April 2009. This rotation does not indicate a change in major focus areas of the council over the long term. The Norwegian, Danish, and Swedish chairmanships, spanning from 2006 to 2012, have cohesively identified common objectives in the Arctic, including following up on the ACIA report for climate change findings; improving the integration of resource management for sustainability and environmental protection; enhancing relations with the international Arctic science community, to include the massive *International Polar Year* project; improving the living conditions of local indigenous peoples; and continual assessment of its progress and international processes.[102]

One example of the effective use of established international processes is the close cooperation in the Straits of Malacca and Singapore. The agreement resulting from the Jakarta Initiative provides a recent model for a multilateral approach relevant to the Arctic sea routes. Over a two-day meeting in Jakarta ending on 8 September 2005, Malaysia, Indonesia, and Singapore launched a joint effort with the IMO, which respects the integrity of UNCLOS and directly promotes sustainable development and environmental protection. During opening remarks to the session, Efthimios Mitropoulos, secretary-general of the IMO, spoke of a global imperative of the safety and security in the straits, and affirmed that genuine progress could be made without delay using existing international frameworks:

> Today and tomorrow we will take stock of existing agreements and endeavour to reach convergence on the perception of likely threats to the safety of navigation in the Straits of Malacca and Singapore and, subsequently, identify the actions necessary to contribute to the building of confidence among the various stakeholders to address the demands of safety, security and environmental protection throughout while, at the same time, respecting the sovereignty and territorial integrity of the three littoral States and the relevant provisions of international law, in particular the United Nations Convention on the Law of the Sea.[103]

A key piece of the initiative in Jakarta is the "Eye in the Sky" program that established combined maritime patrol to ensure continuous coverage over the 805-kilometer Straits of Malacca. At the meeting in Jakarta, Col Suryo Wiranto, assistant chief of operations for Western Fleet Command of the Indonesian navy, stated that "this multilateral initiative will help optimize air surveillance of the participating countries by providing intelligence and information aimed at enhancing the immediate action of the naval patrolling units along the Malacca Straits."[104] According to Mitropoulos, this combined force is critical to building capacity for monitoring the straits, as a shared responsibility, for threats like piracy, armed robbery, and terrorism. It also enhances training to prevent or suppress unlawful acts and enacts cooperation in the areas of search and rescue and response to marine pollution incidents.

Overall, the Jakarta model stands as an international precedent for employing existing frameworks for better control of the seas and management of environmental risks. Again, Mitropoulos emphasized that "nowadays, safety, security, and environmental protection are, within the maritime domain and the work of the IMO, intertwined and inseparable."[105] As he further explains, the pathway to success is paved by a spirit that recognizes the need to work cooperatively: "For I am convinced that it is only through working together that we will be able to better address the multi-faceted and interconnected challenges and threats confronting our world nowadays and achieve progress in all areas of concern such as those that brought us here in Jakarta."[106] James Kraska, oceans policy adviser for international negotiations on the joint staff in Washington, DC, agrees that UNCLOS and the IMO are crucial pieces to a comprehensive package of international agreements necessary to regulate the Northwest Passage in the Canadian Arctic. He views the Malacca Straits model as ideal for the environmentally sensitive strait that is gradually becoming more accessible. In his words, "In the era of globalization, the multilateral successes in the Straits of Malacca and Singapore provide a framework for promoting Canada's goals of preserving the fragile Arctic environment, maintaining maritime domain awareness in Arctic waters and exercising appropriate jurisdiction and oversight over the Northwest Passage."[107]

Shifting Emphasis

Despite an apparently clear path to success in the Arctic, much progress is needed to ensure cohesive politics. Perhaps the most significant impact of climate change awareness stemming from the Arctic is a shift in viewing the world as an interconnected global community. Politically, in the words of Dr. John Ackerman, "the consequences of global warming could initiate replacement of the dominant international relations paradigm."[108] At the current crossroads of the international community, it seems that the tendency has been for a traditional response. Here is a case in point: *Discover* magazine released the top 100 scientific discoveries from 2008, listing the melting Arctic as its number five story. Ironically, the focus of the story is not that sea-ice coverage last year was one-third smaller than the 1979–2000 average, but that new sovereignty maps have been proposed.[109] Specifically, the story highlights that the International Boundaries Research Unit at Durham University in England "produced an online map of the Arctic maritime jurisdictions and boundaries that in a mere three days had been downloaded more than 42,000 times" (appendix E).[110]

The NDU report, while discussing the US strategic climate, lists American priorities in this order: security, economics, and environment.[111] The common mind-set consistently places environmental concerns second or third in line, rather than in the same first-tier category of security interests, on par with sovereign territorial claims and balance of power politics. This was the prevalent American strategic position under the Bush administration. Simply recognizing that climate change exists does not mitigate its consequences. Until the strategic communication at the national level places environmental security in line with national security, each individual nation will continue contributing to, and suffering from, the impacts of climate change in the Arctic.

President Bush released National Security Presidential Directive (NSPD) 66, *Arctic Region Policy*, on 12 January 2009. This effectively "updated" the existing US policy on the Arctic dating back to Presidential Decision Directive 26 from 1994. The six principal objectives in the Arctic region remain unchanged with the new policy, with the exception of referring to "homeland security needs" instead of "post-Cold War national security."[112] The clear undertone in the new policy, however, is one of national sovereignty and control of potential resources and future Arctic exploitation. This appears to be a conscious shift away from the 1994 policy, which spoke of an "atmosphere of openness and cooperation with Russia" and "unprecedented opportunities for collaboration among all eight Arctic Nations on environmental protection, environmentally sustainable development, concerns of indigenous peoples and scientific research."[113]

The push for international cooperation on the Arctic has been driven not just by those nations with sovereignty claims, but by others who see the issue from an environmental aspect. Their stakes are clear: the entire global community in the broadest sense consists of "Arctic nations" when coupling the fragility of the natural environment with the global impacts of climate change. In December 2008 the UN held a conference on climate change in Poland, where there was an aura of great expectations for the 15th conference of the UN

Framework Convention on Climate Change (UNFCCC) to be held in Copenhagen in December 2009. On the website for Conference of the Parties, Michael von Bülow says it is a matter of urgency for the members to come to a clear direction and appropriate burden sharing to put plans into action from the conference. He writes, "From a historical point of view, the UN Climate Conference in Copenhagen is one of the most significant gatherings ever. The world has precious little time to reach an agreement which will secure the future habitability of the planet."[114] He places the event higher in magnitude than the peace accords after the world's greatest wars as they were of only temporary impact. In contrast, "Copenhagen will be dealing with something fundamental to life on Earth: the stability of the biosphere."[115]

UN Secretary-General Ban Ki-moon highlighted the importance of cooperation during his opening statement in Poland, stating, "Today we need a global solidarity on climate change, the defining challenge of our era."[116] His speech came across as a call to arms by the UN to face the challenge of climate change. A fundamental aspect of his speech was that much success could be created by facing this challenge in conjunction with the failing global economy. In his words, "These crises present us with a great opportunity—an opportunity to address both challenges simultaneously. . . . An investment that fights climate change creates millions of green jobs and spurs green growth. We need a Green New Deal."[117] He praised the efforts of countries already embracing the spirit of the new green economy: green development conferences like those held in Qatar and Warsaw, investments in green energies like Denmark and even China, and active green economies like Brazil. "We must keep climate change at the top of our national agendas," he stated.[118] Furthermore, he said the world looks for leadership from the European Union (EU) and the United States, speaking with great optimism on the "incoming administration's plan to put alternative energy, environmentalism and climate change at the very center of America's definition of national security, economic recovery, and prosperity."[119]

The response of the EU and the United States to calls for cooperation like those expressed by Ban Ki-moon has been one of reciprocity. The EU wants to do its part, and the United States has begun to set the stage for bold action and clear statements as the world leader on the issue. János Herman, principal advisor for regional cooperation of the European Commission, states that the EU is a "natural and legitimate player" in the Arctic based on its members with Arctic claims, its proximity to the Arctic Circle, and its strategic relationship with the United States, Canada, and Russia.[120] The commission's core objectives in the Arctic are (1) the protection and preservation of its environment, (2) the sustainable husbandry of its resources, and (3) the development of its governance.[121] The general outlook in these three objectives, from the EU point of view, is to mitigate the effects of climate change, exploit resources with caution, and build on existing governance provided by UNCLOS.[122] Among the steps for improved governance is a push for EU observer status on the Arctic Council, with hopes to gain a seat at the table for discussion on Arctic development and to ensure that "exploration or exploitation activities would be carried out in accordance with the highest environmental standards."[123] The sustainable use of the region's resources is of highest concern for the EU according to Oda Helen Sletnes, ambassador and head of the mission of Norway for the EU. She uses the analogy of the "canary in the coal mine" to describe the Arctic because it warns the rest of the world of the looming dangers of climate change.[124]

The United States has begun speaking with increased commitment to working as a world leader on the current global problems of climate change and the suffering economy. The Obama administration has echoed the spirit of Ban Ki-moon in official speeches, in the selection of its highly influential positions, and in its first policy actions. During his inaugural address, the president spoke of the need to navigate the icy waters ahead, referring to the tough times and hard choices ahead for the United States. He specifically talked about building a new green economy with climate change mitigation in mind.[125]

Likewise, Secretary of State Hillary Clinton highlighted America's lead on this issue as a high priority when she addressed a crowd welcoming the appointment of Todd Stern as a new special envoy for climate change:

> As should be evident by now, the President and I believe that American leadership is essential to meeting the challenges of the 21st century. And chief among those is the complex, urgent, and global threat of climate change. From rapidly rising temperatures to melting arctic icecaps, from lower crop yields to dying forests, from unforgiving hurricanes to unrelenting droughts, we have no shortage of evidence that our world is facing a climate crisis. And let's be clear. A world in crisis goes well beyond the air we breathe, the food we eat, the water we drink. It is at once an environmental, economic, energy and national security issue with grave implications for America's and the world's future.[126]

Indicative of the political commitment to this problem, Stern then addressed the same crowd and spoke of the opportunity of "transforming the global economy."[127] He stated, "We need partnerships and joint ventures among countries, collaborations between governments and the private sector, new technology and new financing. And we will need, above all, political will."[128]

The president also sent a strong message by appointing Dr. Steven Chu, Nobel-Prize-winning physicist, as the US secretary of energy. Clearly, the administration plans to remain true to its promise to base response to climate change and efforts to build a green economy on sound science. At the same time, the political will to act was demonstrated by raising the federal corporate average-fuel-economy standards to encourage incentives for improving fuel efficiency in American vehicles. This legislation replaces standards that have been effectively frozen at 1986 levels. This is part of the administration's strategy to "Deploy the Cheapest, Cleanest, Fastest Energy Source—Energy Efficiency."[129]

Ackerman's suggestion that a political paradigm shift could be spurred by climate change may be unattainable in a timely manner without strong political will. This shift also requires a change to an ecologically based economy that is not only necessary for America's security, but also for global security. Furthermore, this shift requires a broader awareness of human impacts on the world around us. Professor Simon Dalby of Carleton University suggests that we now exist in an "Anthropocene" geological period where human interactions with the environment produce ecological disruptions and vulnerabilities that outweigh nature's ability to absorb them and heal itself.[130] "Thus," he states, "security planning needs to emphasize the importance of reducing the total throughput of materials and energy in the biosphere to limit disruptions while simultaneously building resilience and habits of international cooperation into human societies to better cope when disaster strikes."[131] He depicts the harsh reality that faces the human security of all nations based on scientific evidence suggesting the prospect of "peak oil," the interconnectedness of the earth's biosphere, and the corollary impacts on global economics and politics. In addition, he suggests a fresh look on mitigation efforts and the preservation ethos traditionally flagged as "environmentalism." He suggests that "adapting to new ecological circumstances . . . is not about parks and protection; it is about changing the modes of production and consumption to reduce total ecological throughput in the biosphere for sustainable human existence."[132]

This suggests that a paradigm shift has monumental implications for policy makers charged with developing an appropriate national strategy in the Arctic. Dalby emphasizes that while "state-based politics and spaces are appropriate paradigms for the human side of environmental matters . . . political leaders must move from mitigation and regulation after the fact to thinking seriously about design and construction of artifacts, technologies, and societies that minimize ecological throughput."[133] He lays out a new framework for a global environmental security that must (1) decrease ecological disruptions, (2) refocus military capabilities on providing short-notice aid and assistance, and (3) "extend the habits and institutions of international cooperation so that aid and trade—rather than confrontation and conflict—are the responses to ecological disruptions."[134] A better understanding of the biosphere system through natural science drives sound policy, as the two are inextricably linked.

Science

Collaboration harvests its benefits from differences in perspectives, knowledge and approaches, solving problems while at the same time offering benefits to all those involved in the process.

—Zinaida Fadeeva
United Nations University

The theory of climate change comes from the successful observations of numerous international programs of scientific study. The importance of science driving policy for climate change appears rather obvious. The need for continued research programs is clear, but what may be less easy to coalesce is the extent of scientific efforts and information sharing across national and international organizations. A strong national strategy for the Arctic should incorporate the collaborative spirit seen in the international scientific community. Furthermore, the national effort should merge military and civilian assets for synergistic response to climate change.

International

The International Polar Year (IPY) is a prime example of this collaborative spirit to understand regional changes and global links. The fourth IPY, covering two full annual cycles, spanned from March 2007 to March 2009 and involved over 200 projects with thousands of scientists from more than 60 nations using state-of-the-art technologies to explore physical, biological, and social research topics in both the Arctic and Antarctic.[135] Among the urgencies of the IPY are the changing snow and ice, rising sea levels, permafrost degradation, and health challenges of northern people. These studies represent an enormous effort. According to the International Council for Science and the World Meteorological Organization, the IPY is "one of the most ambitious coordinated international science programmes ever attempted."[136] These studies are not blind natural science efforts because the IPY recognizes the relationship between the physical and social sciences. The opportunity to draw the proper conclu ions from the studies is assisted by these mutual efforts. The IPY describes the spirit of discovery and the scope of science as follows:

> Many scientific frontiers in the polar regions are at the intersection of disciplines, and progress will be achieved not only through the use of new observational techniques, but also by the interdisciplinary cross-analysis of existing databases, taking advantage of outstanding strides made recently in computing capability and communication on the Internet. New polar scientific advances will occur on a tremendous range of spatial scales, from the previously inaccessible realms of the genome to vast areas of the Earth's crust beneath the ice and polar oceans.[137]

Interagency

Scientific collaboration at the national level is also not without precedent. US programs dedicated to the Arctic continue to make headway in understanding the Arctic problem. For example, USARC was established in 1984 by the Arctic Research and Policy Act. Its seven commissioners report to the president and Congress on goals and priorities for the US Arctic Research Program. The program is coordinated by the Interagency Arctic Research Policy Committee and chaired by the National Science Foundation (NSF) director.[138] In conjunction with the IPY, USARC helped develop an Arctic observation network (AON), a system of atmospheric, land- and ocean-based monitoring capabilities designed to advance Arctic environmental observations. AON data, in addition to furthering the efforts of the IPY, enables the US government interagency initiative to "get a handle on the wide-ranging series and rapid changes occurring in the Arctic."[139] This initiative is aptly called the Study of Environmental Arctic Change.

US interagency efforts have had varying degrees of success in information sharing, but interagency use of assets and methods is inevitable. One such effort was the cooperation of the Central Intelligence Agency (CIA) with Medea, a program initiated in 1991 by then–Senator Al Gore. Medea scientists worked to study trends in environmental science—such as global warming and the condition of polar ice caps—while benefiting from some of the data collected from CIA satellites, aircraft, ships and sonar arrays. The intent of this information-sharing program was to declassify certain information gathered for military intelligence purposes to use it for science. According to Dr. Jeffrey Richelson in *Scientific American*, "Never before has the intelligence community worked with a group of scientists outside the government with the kind of scale, trust and intimacy that will be required if the scientists are to make the fullest use of the government data and assets."[140]

Information sharing helps tackle two main pillars of the scientific method: the ability to replicate findings and to verify their validity through experimentation and observation. Skeptics of sharing classified information are concerned about the sensitivity of national security capabilities and data sets and question the usefulness of information declassified too late in the game for scientists to benefit. The overall experience of the Medea program was mutually beneficial since Medea scientists helped intelligence community analysts to process and fuse data from multispectral inputs. For example, their methods were crucial to understanding the effects of a series of oil spills in the Komi region of Russia and of Russia's chemical weapons disposal in the Arctic.[141] Other critics who feared that environmental observations would overwhelm shared intelligence assets have been disproven by the Medea experience, where "environmental collection effort occupies less than 1 percent of the time of reconnaissance satellites."[142]

Options Comparison

The NDU report, *The Arctic Circle: Development and Risk*, lays out three potential options for a national Arctic strategy without recommending a best course of action. While the report suggests a lower risk for each successive option, the implications of individual components are assessed here. Option 1 is "status quo": retain current levels of an international framework. This is considered a high-risk option because of the expanding Arctic mission area, insufficient Arctic infrastructure, and unsatisfied diplomatic agreements.[143] Option 2 is labeled as "limited enhancement" and is assessed as a medium-risk option with the following steps:

- Ratify UNCLOS.
- Articulate an Arctic Strategy which positively defines US interests and priorities.
- Arm the USCGC *Healy* (sole US ice-breaker) for defensive purposes.
- Create an Arctic combatant command able to manage and lobby for DOD assets in the region.
- Initiate a DOD working group to assess the feasibility of improving US Navy Arctic operations.
- Act to resolve border disputes with the Russian Federation and Canada on a bilateral basis.
- Develop a plan to safeguard the Bering Strait (the future trans-Arctic gateway for shipping).
- Review plans for establishing a base on Little Diomede Island [in the Bering Strait off the Alaskan coast] or improving Kivalina Lagoon [slightly further north in the Kotzebue Sound].[144] (See appendix F for map.)

Finally, option 3 lays out a presumably low-risk option with the following priorities:

Short Term

- Ratify UNCLOS.
- Submit US claims for extended territorial boundary.
- Conduct a comprehensive DOD review of Arctic exigency plans.
- Establish an interagency working group on Arctic scenarios.

Long Term

- Improve, upgrade, and expand the American icebreaker fleet (but begin process now).

- Review feasibility of a new Arctic combatant commander.
- Act to resolve border disputes with Russia and Canada.
- Begin fundraising campaign for US infrastructure improvements that will also serve Arctic clients (i.e., improved "ports of refuge," navigation and communication satellites, search and rescue operations, cartographical measurements, etc.)
- Arctic armaments treaty that restricts weapons in the region.[145]

The following analysis illustratively compares these options and their components with the research criteria, namely that the optimal strategy must:

1. Peacefully resolve territorial sovereignty issues and promote free trade economics.

2. Mitigate risks to human and environmental security in the region and around the globe.

3. Provide a long-term solution to the sustainable development of the Arctic.

4. Include a mechanism for enforcement and monitoring compliance.

The matrix summarizes the viability of these options with respect to the criteria (table 5.1). A traffic-light analogy expresses the quality of each option. Note that only options 2 and 3 receive a "green light" assessment. Overall, none of the three options constitute an acceptable comprehensive strategy.

Table 5.1 Criterion Matrix

Criterion	Option 1	Option 2	Option 3
1	Red	Yellow	Green
2	Yellow	Yellow	Yellow
3	Red	Red	Yellow
4	Yellow	Green	Yellow
Overall	Red	Yellow	Yellow

The first criterion is to peacefully resolve sovereignty issues and promote free trade. While progressing from option 1 to option 3, the strategy becomes more viable. Current policy is insufficient due to the unacceptable ambiguity over US claims and existing disputes with Russia and Canada. With ratification of UNCLOS in option 2, however, the

United States would legitimize its claims under international law and would gain leverage in negotiation with other nations that have ratified the convention. Under option 3, there is more substantial support to meet the first criterion because it recommends submitting US claims for its extended boundary. Scientific evidence and ocean mapping efforts could provide empirical data required to substantiate these claims and make sovereignty resolution more objective.

None of the options successfully meet criterion 2 for environmental security because the NDU report acknowledges the climate change problem but falls short of suggesting strategy options that incorporate steps to mitigate it. Since no option discusses how to protect the Arctic's fragile environment or consider the social and human welfare impacts of capitalizing on new resource and transit opportunities, a new option should address this core issue. Effectively, the status quo is just as good for this criterion since no new approaches are offered. A newly articulated strategy should emphasize environmental security as a high priority. The suggestion of a nonmilitarized Arctic, though respectable, is actually irrelevant and possibly even counterproductive to safeguarding the Arctic and controlling harmful interactions from an enforcement point of view.

Again, the options fall short with criterion 3, which is to provide long-term sustainability. Option 1 represents the worst option in some respects since it does not allow the United States to lawfully claim its offshore resources. Ratification of UNCLOS, on the other hand, only begins the process of exercising economic options from a traditional point of view. This step would need to be incorporated into an adaptive economy that benefits from activities like ecotourism and port services rather than oil drilling and mineral extraction. Long-term sustainability could be more at risk if these endeavors are not approached with measured caution. Option 3 suggests improvements to the icebreaker fleet and infrastructure projects, which could be positive steps toward sustainability.

Finally, the enforcing and monitoring criterion, a capstone to the other three criteria, is perhaps the greatest challenge of all due to the substantial size of the region and the potentially competing interests of state and nonstate actors. Military assets would probably play a significant role in this regard, giving teeth to international agreements and providing the best observation and response capabilities. Better monitoring could be achieved through satellite assets as proposed in option 3, but the suggestion to restrict weapons in the Arctic takes enforcement agencies out of the picture if those not in compliance with international law choose to arm themselves. Assets like the US Coast Guard cutter *Healy* and proposed basing in the islands and lagoons of northern Alaska could provide the required leverage for proper enforcement. Because option 2 suggests arming the *Healy* for defensive purposes, it receives the highest mark for this criterion.

Arctic Policy Comparison

Beyond the options proposed by the NDU report, the *Arctic Region Policy*, released 12 January 2009 by President Bush, has shortcomings when matched against the proposed criteria (table 5.2). In fact, this revision of the 1994 *United States Policy on the Arctic and Antarctic Regions* seems to regress in the fundamental area of environmental security. It appears the new policy was a final effort of the Bush administration to boldly state that the United States is an Arctic nation with rightful claims to offshore resources and the Northwest Passage. However, the new policy strikes out the idea of "openness and cooperation with Russia" and "environmentally sustainable development."[146] On a positive note, the 2009 policy endorses continued international scientific cooperation and states that "Arctic environmental research, monitoring, and vulnerability assessments are top priorities."[147] The policy recognizes that the "Arctic environment is unique and changing" and that additional stressors to its environment have "potentially serious consequences for Arctic communities and ecosystems."[148] It directs the Senate to promptly ratify UNCLOS, which would help resolve territorial disputes and "give the United States a seat at the table when the rights that are vital to our interests are debated and interpreted."[149]

Table 5.2. Criterion Shortcomings

Criterion	1994 policy	2009 policy
1	Red	Green
2	Green	Yellow
3	Green	Red
4	Yellow	Yellow
Overall	Yellow	Yellow

The downside of the 2009 policy lies in the sustainable development criterion as it ignores the new Arctic paradigm by intentionally placing higher emphasis on potential energy resources and traditional national security interests over global security. When referring to economic issues, it seeks to use cooperative mechanisms with other nations mainly because "most known oil and gas resources are located outside of United States jurisdiction."[150] Furthermore, it denies the possibility of an expanded role of the Arctic Council, suggesting that it "not be transformed into a formal international organization, particularly one with assessed contributions."[151] This misses a key step in achieving a three-prong Arctic strategy, as proposed by Scott Borgerson, international affairs fellow at the Council on Foreign Relations. His first two steps are effectively accomplished with the new policy. He suggested that President Bush make a final attempt to pass UNCLOS through the Senate and to unilaterally update its Arctic policy.[152] However, the updated policy makes no mention of ramping up US Coast Guard icebreaker capabilities.

Finally, the third prong of investing real diplomacy in the Arctic is unfulfilled. Borgerson's suggestion to empower the Arctic Council by creating a security institution of Arctic nations has merit. The 2009 *Arctic Region Policy* acknowledges long-standing boundary issues with Canada and Russia without offering diplomatic efforts for better cooperation.

Conclusion

Collaborative approaches require that countries and citizens choose their strategic decisions considering those of others, in such a way that the system's solution reaches the optimum.

—Rodrigo Lozano
Cardiff University

Achieving an adaptive national strategy for the Arctic poses a fundamental challenge to the United States. Such a strategy demands awareness of the dire environmental signals from climate change observations in the Arctic region and around the planet. A business-as-usual approach fails to ensure future US security because impacts observed in the Arctic are intrinsically linked with the rest of the global biosphere as one interconnected system. The conclusions of this research support the idea that there are holes in both the current US Arctic policy and recent proposals from the NDU conference on

Arctic climate change. The recommendations below bridge the gap for a sustainable, responsible Arctic strategy.

Findings

The findings indicate the need for a new national security paradigm due to the global consequences of climate change if the United States continues on the traditional course of competition for resources and fossil fuel energy. The melting Arctic has brought increased interest in the region's resources—especially oil and natural gas reserves—despite the complications of their extraction and the questionable long-term benefit of their use. Prospective commercial use of the Northwest Passage and Northern Sea Route to dramatically reduce shipping distances is also desirable from the traditional point of view. However, the negative impacts on Arctic people and ecosystems may outweigh the benefits of newfound shortcuts and port economies. Furthermore, the nature of climate change impacts on the global environment may make the movement of certain goods irrelevant as major shifts occur in local resources, agriculture, and human health.

On a positive note, the research also revealed that significant international frameworks are firmly established in both the political and scientific arenas. Scientific understanding of climate change through studies by organizations such as the Arctic Council and the UNFCCC provides awareness to facilitate the current discussion for political change. Most nations have officially accepted the idea of global warming and are working under the agreement of the Kyoto Protocol to decrease greenhouse gas emissions. Collaboration has been most significant in the international scientific community, to include major projects like the recent IPY for improving Arctic observations. For resolving territorial disputes and standardizing maritime law, UNCLOS provides a proven universal framework that is relevant in the Arctic.

The options analysis compared three possible strategic approaches proposed by the NDU report against four criteria. Of these, only criteria 1 and 4 are met, meriting a "green light" assessment. Criterion 1, peaceful resolution of sovereignty disputes and promotion of free trade, is satisfied through the recommendation to ratify UNCLOS and submit territorial claims to the CLCS. The fact that all other Arctic nations have already taken this step enhances the potential for resolving US disputes in the Arctic. Criterion 4, providing a monitoring and enforcement mechanism, is satisfied through the recommendation to provide capable military assets and basing options in the Arctic, including more US icebreakers.

A look at the 2009 US Arctic region policies shows that criteria 2 and 3 were actually best addressed under the 1994 version. This is mainly because the environmental concerns and spirit of cooperation, especially in the case of Russia, were paramount in that policy. The biggest concerns of the newer policy are the clear message of heightened national security in the region and the desire to claim and exploit hydrocarbon energy reserves.

Recommendations

The most appropriate national strategy for the Arctic is to pursue a combination of the status quo with enhanced capabilities and frameworks. The context of the new presidential administration provides a tremendous opportunity to make the right choices for climate change, at a time when the world sees itself at a critical decision point for sustainability. This national Arctic strategy could be summarized by three overriding themes for the United States: (1) homeland security, (2) being a good neighbor, and (3) world leadership.[153] Together, these themes produce a layered effect that is palatable for national security advocates, while leveraging the globalization and environmental security concepts that have become virtually indivisible from national security in the modern world.

Unilaterally, the United States should foster a true homeland security mind-set that incorporates environmental security concerns with national security assets. The United States should continue with collaborative scientific programs through the NSF and USARC while promoting interagency information and asset sharing through Medea. The United States should ratify UNCLOS, continue the process of Arctic geological surveying and ocean-floor mapping, and promptly submit the scientific evidence of its territorial claims to the CLCS. Through responsible time-sharing of intelligence satellites, more specific collection requirements should be addressed for key Arctic climate change indicators and environmental disaster monitoring. The US Coast Guard should immediately acquire a polar-capable icebreaker fleet, expanded to include armed, Arctic-capable ships that can provide enforcement and port protection services.

Bilaterally, the United States should continue its strong relationship with Canada and work more openly with Russia to find common ground on Arctic sovereignty disputes in the spirit of cooperation and environmental protection. The United States should work with Canada to strengthen a common continental defense and combine Coast Guard training exercises with a focus on controlling transit of the Northwest Passage, responding to oil spills, and conducting search and rescue operations in the Arctic environment. The United States and Canada should also expand NORAD mission sets to include routine Arctic monitoring from the sea, air, and space. An equivalent arrangement should be established with Russia emphasizing improved cooperation in Arctic scientific research. A more level-headed diplomacy with Russia should emphasize shared responsibilities to track toxic pollutants in the ocean, reduce greenhouse gas emissions, and respond to environmental disasters.

The United States should set the example of a climate change conscience by reshaping its energy infrastructure into a greener, more responsible one. It should continue international efforts that study and respond to climate change and encourage multilateral talks that address environmental security. The United States should influence the Arctic Council to accept members of the EU in observatory status to voice environmental concerns and provide useful data and research methodologies. It should reverse its current *Arctic Region Policy* in two main areas: propose expanding the role of the Arctic Council to an enforcing organization, and express the importance of increased cautiousness with Arctic drilling.

An expanded Arctic Council is the proper venue for improved Arctic governance. The Arctic Council was founded on sound principles from the AEPS that are relevant to a sustainable Arctic strategy. A strong cooperative working relationship for issues in the region is well-established through the council, and the ability to reach consensus on future governance in the Arctic is most promising with this framework. Models like the Jakarta Initiative and the Ilulissat Declaration confirm that continued governance in accordance with the IMO and UNCLOS is sufficient to regulate sovereignty and basic behavior in the Arctic. The Arctic Council should provide the specific oversight for responsibilities in protecting the Arctic environment and ensure safe and secure transit of vessels through the northern sea lines.

The concept of creating a new political alliance or adopting a new military geographic combatant commander (GCC) specific for the region, as suggested in the NDU report, seems unnecessary and possibly counterproductive. It is true that the United States will need to determine jurisdiction for the GCC overlap in the Arctic, with the US European, Pacific, and Northern Commands currently sharing responsibilities in the Arctic. Nonetheless, the United States should pursue more military cooperation with other Arctic nations to ensure common security in the region. A standing multinational force comprised of equitably shared resources should be established and mutually trained to ensure compliance of Arctic agreements and protect the region. A combined force, acting as an arm of the Arctic Council, would promote sharing military assets and information to better monitor, assess, and respond to human and environmental emergencies. It would also ensure gap coverage by time-sharing with mutually responsible nations, such as the successful efforts in the Straits of Malacca.

The United States should be the first to suggest a temporary moratorium on drilling in the Arctic. This would set the tone for the international community and give clear guidelines on scientific support for suspected impacts over the long term. This moratorium period should heavily focus on international collaborative research to include inputs from indigenous peoples on economic, social, and environmental impacts of energy exploitation in the Arctic.

Finally, the Obama administration should rewrite the current *NSS*. The 2006 *NSS* is founded on two pillars: (1) promoting freedom, justice, and human dignity; and (2) confronting the challenges of our time by leading a growing community of democracies.[154] A new pillar should reflect the urgency of responding to climate change, increasing general awareness of the impacts in the Arctic. It should incorporate the same spirit of leadership, collaboration, and stewardship expressed throughout this study. This third pillar of the *NSS* would express values of leading the world in a spirit of collaboration for a common environmental security and stewardship of a sustainable planet. We will lead by actively pursuing cleaner energy sources and protecting fragile ecosystems like those in the Arctic. America will work with other nations to improve the scientific understanding of our interconnected biosphere and ensure safe, secure, and responsible transit on our oceans.

Notes

1. NDU, "Arctic Circle," 3.
2. Bush, *National Security Strategy*, 3.

3. Ibid., 47.

4. Ibid., 3.

5. Ibid.

6. Nye, *Paradox of American Power*, 8–12.

7. NDU, "Arctic Circle," 3.

8. Ibid., 11.

9. Ibid., 11–12.

10. Hansen, "Threat to the Planet," section 1.

11. Marian Wilkinson, "Voyage into the Arctic as Summer Ice Vanishes," *Sydney Morning Herald*, 4 August 2008, http://www.smh.com.au/news/environment/a-voyage -into-the-great-arctic-meltdown/2008/08/03/1217701855502.html.

12. Tomczak and Godfrey, *Regional Oceanography*, 83.

13. Collins et al., "Physical Science behind Climate Change," 69.

14. Ibid., 66.

15. NOAA, *Arctic Report Card 2008*, 7.

16. Ibid.

17. Wilkinson, "Voyage into the Arctic," 2.

18. Intergovernmental Panel on Climate Change (IPCC) Working Group I, Technical Summary, 37.

19. NSIDC, "Education Center."

20. Wilkinson, "Voyage into the Arctic," 2.

21. Schwartz and Randall, *Abrupt Climate Change Scenario*, 9.

22. Ibid., 12.

23. Ibid., 6.

24. Ibid.

25. Wilkinson, "Voyage into the Arctic," 2.

26. Farrar, *Global Warming*, 7.

27. NCAR, "Arctic Ice Retreating."

28. Ibid.

29. UNEP, *Global Environment Outlook*, 279.

30. ACIA, *Impacts of a Warming Arctic*, 5.

31. Ibid., 10.

32. Ibid., 11.

33. UNEP, *Global Environment Outlook*, 199.

34. "Arctic Sea Ice at Lowest Recorded Level Ever," *ScienceDaily*, 16 September 2008, http://www.sciencedaily.com/releases/2008/09/080915162428.htm; and Westly, "Arctic Land Grabs."

35. Hansen, "Threat to the Planet," section 2.

36. ACIA, *Impacts of a Warming Arctic*, 3.

37. Hansen, "Threat to the Planet," section 4.

38. IPCC Assessment Report 4, *Climate Change 2007*, 15.

39. Ibid.

40. USGS, *Circum-Arctic Resource Appraisal*, 1.

41. Borgerson, "Arctic Meltdown," 67.

42. Ibid., 67.

43. USGS, *Circum-Arctic Resource Appraisal*, 1.

44. Roberts, *End of Oil*, 64.

45. Ibid., 313–14.
46. International Ice Charting Working Group, "National Ice Services Advise."
47. Borgerson, "Arctic Meltdown," 69.
48. Ibid.
49. Ibid., 70.
50. Ibid., 76.
51. Arctic Environment Protection Strategy (AEPS), 14.
52. Ibid., 71.
53. USARC, "Congress Hears Needs."
54. Dhanapala, "Arctic Security Problems," 12.
55. Ibid.
56. NDU, "Arctic Circle," 7.
57. Ibid., 3.
58. Gislason, "Brief History of Alaska."
59. Ibid.
60. Schanz, "Strategic Alaska," 49.
61. Gislason, "Brief History of Alaska."
62. Schanz, "Strategic Alaska," 49.
63. Ibid.
64. RDC, "Alaska's Oil and Gas Industry."
65. USGS, *Arctic National Wildlife Refuge*, 4.
66. Roberts, *End of Oil*, 155.
67. Scott G. Borgerson, "An Ice Cold War," *New York Times*, 8 August 2008, http://www.nytimes.com/2007/08/08/opinion/08borgerson.html?_r=2&oref=slogin.
68. Ibid.
69. "North Pole May Belong to Denmark."
70. Ibid.
71. Department of National Defence (DND), *Canada First*, 3, 8.
72. Ibid., 7.
73. DOD, *National Defense Strategy*, 4.
74. DND, *Canada First*, 8.
75. Scott G. Borgerson, "No Time for Chest Thumping," *International Herald Tribune*, 9 September 2007, http://www.cfr.org/publication/14169/no_time_for_chest_thumping.html.
76. US Department of State, "Barbary Wars."
77. NDU, "Arctic Circle," 6.
78. Borgerson, "No Time for Chest Thumping."
79. NDU, "Arctic Circle," 9.
80. Renuart, Memorandum.
81. Ibid.
82. "Crown Prince's Background."
83. Loukacheva, "Security Challenges and Legal Capacity," 3.
84. Østreng, *National Security and International Cooperation*, 233.
85. Ibid.
86. Ibid., 136.
87. Ibid.

88. *Norwegian Government's High North Strategy*, 45.
89. NDU, "Arctic Circle," 6.
90. Ibid.
91. Russell, "Carpe DIEM," 97.
92. Borgerson, "Arctic Meltdown," 74.
93. Ibid., 72.
94. US Senate, *Secretary of State Confirmation*.
95. Lathrop, Letter to the Editor.
96. *Ilulissat Declaration*, 1.
97. International Maritime Organization (IMO), "Introduction to IMO."
98. Ibid.
99. AEPS, 7.
100. Ibid., 2.
101. Arctic Council, "About Arctic Council."
102. Arctic Council, "Norwegian, Danish, Swedish Common Objectives."
103. Mitropoulos, Opening Remarks for Jakarta.
104. Yusoff, "Eye-in-the-Sky."
105. Mitropoulos, Opening Remarks.
106. Ibid.
107. Kraska, "Law of the Sea Convention," 281.
108. Ackerman, *Global Climate Change*, xvi.
109. Gosnell, "Top 100 Stories of 2008," 26.
110. Ibid.
111. NDU, "Arctic Circle," 7.
112. Bush, *Arctic Region Policy*, 2; and Clinton, *Presidential Decision Directive/ NSC-26*, 2.
113. Clinton, *Presidential Decision Directive/NSC-26*, 2.
114. Bülow, "Countdown to Copenhagen."
115. Ibid.
116. Ki-Moon, Opening Statement, 4.
117. Ibid., 1–2.
118. Ibid., 3.
119. Ibid., 2.
120. "EU and the Arctic."
121. Ibid.
122. Ibid.
123. "Environment Pushes EU."
124. "EU and the Arctic."
125. Obama, Inaugural Address.
126. US Department of State, Announcement of Appointment.
127. Ibid.
128. Ibid.
129. White House, "The Agenda."
130. Dalby, "Ecology, Security, and Change," 155.
131. Ibid.
132. Ibid., 159.
133. Ibid., 161.

134. Ibid., 162.

135. "About IPY."

136. *Scope of Science for IPY 2007–2008*, 1.

137. Ibid, 11–12.

138. Treadwell, *Is America Prepared?*, 1.

139. National Science Foundation, "Fact Sheet: The Arctic Observation Network (AON)."

140. Richelson, "Scientists in Black."

141. Ibid.

142. Ibid.

143. NDU, "Arctic Circle," 11.

144. Ibid., 11–12.

145. Ibid., 12.

146. Clinton, *Presidential Decision Directive/NSC-26*, 2.

147. Bush, *Arctic Region Policy*, 9.

148. Ibid., 8.

149. Ibid., 4.

150. Ibid., 8.

151. Ibid., 4.

152. Borgerson, "Russia's Other Front."

153. Maj Kevin B. Ferdinand, Canadian Forces, ACSC instructor, interview by the author, 28 January 2009.

154. Bush, *NSS*, ii.

Chapter 6

Catastrophe on the Horizon: Future Effects of Orbital Space Debris

Lt Col Jack Donahue

Orbital Space Debris Defined

Orbital space debris can be defined as dead satellites, discarded rocket parts, or simply flecks of paint or other small objects orbiting the earth. It is simply space "junk," but junk that can be extremely dangerous to space assets. Most of the debris concerns are associated with satellites and manned space missions in low Earth orbit (LEO). LEO extends out to about 5,000 kilometers (km) from the earth's equator.[1] There are two other bands of orbits that contain satellites. The first, geosynchronous Earth orbit (GEO), is the outermost band and extends out to approximately 35,888 km. The second is the medium Earth orbit (MEO), which is located between LEO and GEO in the approximate range of 10,000 to 20,000 km. Typically, satellites in GEO and MEO are shielded (hardened) from the harmful effects of space, such as radiation, and are more resilient.[2] However, there are roughly 300,000 small objects that are too small to be tracked (4 millimeters [mm] in size) but large enough to do potential harm to any object they could strike, given the enormous speeds of collision implied by orbiting objects.[3] Nevertheless, the current debris population in the LEO region has reached the point where the environment is unstable and collisions are becoming the most dominant debris-generating mechanism.[4]

Of the nearly 100,000 pieces of debris larger than a marble in orbit, those at altitudes above 1,000 km will remain in orbit for centuries, and those above 1,500 km will remain for millennia.[5] Currently, there are approximately 900 active satellites in Earth orbit and roughly 10,000 pieces of space debris longer than five inches traveling at approximately 11,000 miles per hour. Even a small piece of debris that is less than one-half inch is capable of doing serious damage, like depressurizing a spacecraft (exposing the crew to decompression sickness from lowering of environmental pressure).[6] A space launch can potentially create more space debris from pieces of the rocket or from the satellite being put into orbit. If any of these pieces come into contact with an active space asset, it could not only be catastrophic for the asset but also result in adversely affecting television, cell phones, Global Positioning System (GPS) signals, national security, intelligence (reconnaissance and imaging), and weather forecasting.

Research Questions and Thesis

The main question of this research is, Should the United States have an increased concern about orbital space debris? The supporting question is, If so, what futures could result from the driving forces and effects of this debris?

Space debris continues to accumulate every year, and this trend should be alarming. Therefore, this research paper's thesis is that if the United States does not resolve the orbital space debris problem, it will lead to a catastrophic collision between debris and satellites or manned spaceflight missions that will in turn adversely impact global communications, the economy, safety (danger to space crew), or US national security.

Research Purpose

This research brings some much-needed attention to the growing problem of space debris and highlights the driving forces behind the orbital space debris problem. An examination into the effects debris may have in the future sheds some light on the situation and puts into perspective how serious this issue has become and what impact it could have on our society and the world. This research is intended to identify some potential futures as a result of orbital debris and highlight potential solutions for consideration. Hopefully, this will spark some debate, and policy or legislative changes can be considered to avoid a potential space catastrophe in the near future.

Background Information

Today, spacecraft follow a carefully synchronized orbit using signals from ground controllers, who track known objects, to avoid the debris.[7] Countless man-hours and millions of dollars are spent cataloging space debris to prevent disastrous collisions with US space assets. Space operators do this by getting a rough fix on the trajectory of debris and craft from the US Air Force (US Space Surveillance Network [SSN], managed by US Strategic Command), which provides radar data on spacecraft trajectories.[8] As the amount of orbital debris continues to rise, operators find it increasingly difficult to monitor all the objects.

Previous Space Debris Incidents

Monitoring objects in space is only part of the answer. The sheer volume of space debris will soon make it difficult to maneuver spacecraft without risking an accident.[9] In fact, there have already been numerous logged incidents with orbital debris. For example, in 1983, a paint speck only 0.2 mm in diameter made a 4 mm dent in the Challenger space shuttle's windshield.[10] In September 1991 a space shuttle mission was interrupted to allow the shuttle Discovery to avoid debris from a decaying Soviet-era satellite.[11] In July 1996 the first recorded orbital collision occurred between a discarded rocket stage and a French spy satellite, damaging the satellite's stabilization system and sending it tumbling, although it was able to recover.[12] On 12 March 2009 debris came alarmingly close to the International Space Station, forcing crew members to take refuge inside a Russian-built Soyuz lifeboat.[13]

Studies have shown that operational spacecraft infrequently collide with other objects. These collisions increase over time as the small fragment population increases; this could prove to be mission ending for the spacecraft.[14] Without the United States taking steps to remove orbital debris, collisions resulting in the destruction of spacecraft could create clouds of new debris objects, compounding the problem and raising the probability of new collisions.[15]

Reducing and Clearing Orbital Debris

Scientists and space agencies around the world are working to come up with ideas for clearing orbital debris. One idea is to use robotic trash collectors that push large pieces of junk through the atmosphere where they mostly burn up in Earth's atmosphere before hitting the ground.[16] However, fuel expenses for these trash collectors might be too costly.[17] Other ideas include attaching electrodynamic tethers to new satellites or fitting satellites with aerobrakes so that at the end of their mission, they can enter Earth's atmosphere and burn up harmlessly.[18]

Others are considering various ways of reducing orbital debris proliferation, in particular, preventing the production of orbital debris in LEO. These ideas include various international space policies, treaties, and agreements between the United States and other countries that would ban tests in space that produce debris. In addition, satellites could be hardened before being launched into space, making them less vulnerable to the harsh environments of space. This would significantly increase their chance of survival from a debris collision.

Methodology

Scenarios enable new ideas about the future to take root and spread across an organization—helping to overcome the inertia and denial that can so easily make the future a dangerous place.

—Eamon Kelly
CEO of GBN

Description of Scearce and Fulton's Scenario-Thinking Model with Five Phases

Scenarios show how the future might unfold for our organizations, our issues, our nations, and even our world.[19] Scenarios are not predictions; they are stories about diverse ways in which relevant issues might evolve, such as future political environments, social attitudes, regulations, and the strength of the economies.[20] They are designed to stretch our thinking about the opportunities and threats that the future may hold, as we weigh them carefully when making short- and long-term strategic decisions.[21] Done well, scenarios are mediums where great change can be envisioned and actualized.[22] Scenario thinking is a process through which scenarios are developed and used to inform strategy.[23] After that process is complete, scenario thinking becomes a posture toward the world—a way of thinking about and managing change and exploring the future so the world might be better prepared.[24]

A scenario-based methodology will be used to examine this thesis, guided by the scenario-thinking approach described in *What If? The Art of Scenario Thinking for Non-Profits* by Diana Scearce and Katherine

Fulton of the Global Business Network (GBN). Scearce and Fulton's scenario-thinking model consists of five phases: orient, explore, synthesize, act, and monitor.

Phase One: Orient. The *orient* phase clarifies the focal issue at stake and uses that issue as an orienting device throughout the remaining four phases. The process begins by learning more about the challenges that a particular organization, community, or nation faces and understanding the underlying assumptions about the nature of those challenges and how they will play in the future.[25] Typically, the most effective way to understand these assumptions is to ask key stakeholders questions through structured interviews. However, the assumptions for this research paper will be generated from a variety of books, journals, scholarly periodicals, websites, and magazines.

The focal issue for this research is a catastrophic collision from orbital space debris. This phase also includes establishing a time frame for the possible futures. Most scenarios that are developed to inform strategy look five to 10 years into the future.[26] The time frame should always reflect how rapidly the issue in question is likely to change.[27] Currently, the volume of space debris will soon make it difficult to maneuver spacecraft without risking an accident; therefore, it will not be necessary to look too far into the future. Thus, the year 2015 was selected for the possible futures.

Phase Two: Explore. The *explore* phase consists of examining the issue in greater depth and identifying the "driving forces" that could shape the focal issue (catastrophic collision from orbital space debris). Driving forces are the changes outside normal control that will shape future dynamics in both predictable and unpredictable ways.[28] Driving forces include factors and shifts in the environment such as social, technological, economical, environmental, and political changes. These forces can be either predetermined elements or uncertainties.[29] Predetermined elements are forces of change that are relatively certain over a given future time frame, and uncertainties are unpredicted driving forces.[30]

Phase Three: Synthesize. In the *synthesize* phase researchers synthesize and combine the driving forces to create scenarios.[31] Likely, individuals have identified several driving forces, but some are not as important as others. Therefore, phase three is a narrowing phase in which one will cull and refine the driving forces to just a handful.[32]

The synthesize phase contains three elements: (1) Select the critical uncertainties from the driving forces that were classified by importance and degree of uncertainty. (2) Construct the scenario framework using each critical uncertainty as an axis for a two-dimensional matrix, with the range of uncertainty representing the polar extremes of each axis (fig. 6.1). Each quadrant of the matrix will represent a possible scenario or a potential future. (3) Create a short, distinctive, yet descriptive name for each notional future (based on the synthesis of the two poles that comprise that quadrant), and write a brief supporting narrative.

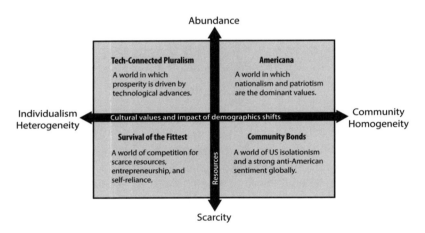

Figure 6.1. Scenario framework example. (*Adapted from* Diane Scearce and Katherine Fulton, *What If? The Art of Scenario Thinking for Non-Profits* [Emeryville, CA: GBN, 2004]: 37).

Phase Four: Act. In phase four researchers use scenarios to inform and inspire action.[33] The *act* phase consists of developing scenario implications and a strategic agenda. Imagine living in each scenario, learning how to prepare if the scenario is the future, and asking what actions are needed to avoid or mitigate a negative scenario. The answers to this question are the scenario implications.[34] The patterns and insights that emerge from the scenario implications are the building blocks of the strategic agenda—the set of strategic priorities that help make progress on the long-term goals.[35] The predetermined elements identified during the scenario development process can be used to decide if any of them figure prominently in the strategic agenda.[36]

Phase Five: Monitor. The last phase identifies specific warning signals or other leading indicators that could forecast the emerging reality of a particular future and monitors them. Leading indicators are signs of potential or significant change and can be obvious or subtle.[37] Leading indicators can serve as powerful signals to adapt strategy to the changing environment.[38] Once identified, strategies can be put in place to respond to the emerging reality.[39]

Method Justification

In order to gain more insight into ideas of how to handle the debris problem, along with the driving forces and effects of debris over the next five years, I describe four future scenarios based on consequences of orbital space debris in the year 2015. These scenarios are not predictions of the future; they simply analyze the challenges and potential solutions to the orbital debris dilemma that the United States must consider to protect our vital space assets.

Application of Scenario Five-Phase Model

Orient Phase

The *orient* phase clarifies the focal issue at stake and uses that issue as an orienting device throughout the remaining four phases. The focal issue of this paper is a catastrophic collision from orbital space debris in the year 2015. To better understand the situation, the issue must be characterized based on the challenges, facts, and assumptions associated with orbital space debris—the launching of satellites and the subsequent abandonment at end of life have been major contributors to the growth of orbital debris in LEO. Explosions of satellites (either by accident or by design) have also made a significant contribution to the current orbital debris situation.

Orbital debris concerns have captured the attention of nations worldwide. Thus, there are several international programs studying orbital debris through testing and modeling of space asset impacts and the debris environment. This has led to cooperation in the study of space debris through the Inter-Agency Space Debris Coordination Committee (IADC) and the United Nations (UN).[40] Studies have shown that orbital debris in LEO continues to grow at a rate of approximately 5 percent annually.[41] At that rate LEO will be so saturated with debris in the near future that the threat to space assets will be overwhelming.

One study that shows this alarming trend is the National Aeronautics and Space Administration (NASA) long-term debris environment model called Legend. The Legend model looks at projected future launch traffic based on historical data and sources of debris. The sources of debris include spent upper stages and spacecraft, mission-related debris (MRD) released during spacecraft deployment or operations, explosion and collision fragments, and sodium potassium droplets that have been tracked since the 1990s (caused by Soviet space vehicle's nuclear reactor ejections through the 1980s).[42] The model also uses the industry-standard Monte Carlo simulation method due to the statistical nature of future collision events. Some interesting assumptions can be made about the future of orbital debris based on the results of Legend. First, collisions between objects larger than 10 centimeters (cm) will increase from the current average of approximately 1.4 times per year to an average rate of 5.3 times per year by 2035, which is an increase of about 9.5 percent per year. Second, "collisions between small objects (<10 cm) and large objects (>10 cm) average nearly 95 percent of all events."[43] Of those events about 98 percent are noncatastrophic.[44] The modeling evidence presents an argument that "the statistics for catastrophic collision events are low in the historical period."[45] However, the catastrophic collision events begin to increase to an average of 5 percent by the end of the study period.[46] The chance of one catastrophic event should be a cause for concern, but "even a non-catastrophic impact on an operational spacecraft could compromise a mission."[47]

Explore Phase

The *explore* phase examines the issue of catastrophic collision of orbital debris in greater depth and determines the driving forces over the next five years. These forces can be predetermined elements or uncertainties.

The predetermined elements (relative certainties in the future) of orbital debris are that (1) launches will continue to occur worldwide, adding to the debris problem, and (2) current international space law will remain in effect for the foreseeable future.

Currently, the United States is the undisputed leader in space operations, averaging approximately 30 launches per year.[48] Even with the cutbacks in manned missions, the "US will continue to launch assets in space at its current pace in order to replace or upgrade aging satellites due to the US's growing reliance on space assets in LEO for ocean reconnaissance, weather forecasting, communications, and ground imaging."[49] Russia, the world's second space power, is launching satellites at an impressive rate, averaging more than 25 launches per year.[50] China (averaging six launches per year), Japan (averaging one to two launches per year), and the European Space Agency (averaging 10 launches per year) are expected to maintain or slightly increase their launch rates.[51] Other active space programs such as Canada, India, Israel, Thailand, South Korea, North Korea, Brazil, Argentina, Australia, Spain, and Ukraine are expected to slightly increase their current sporadic launch rates.[52]

International regulations continue to exist and are refined for space. Current international space law relevant to orbital space debris, such as the Limited Test Ban Treaty of 1963, will remain in effect for the near future. This treaty bans the testing of nuclear weapons in the atmosphere, in outer space, and underwater.[53] Therefore, states will not conduct nuclear weapon tests or other nuclear explosions in outer space or assist/encourage others to conduct such tests or explosions.[54]

The next space law currently in effect is the UN's Outer Space Treaty of 1967, which establishes basic legal principles and prohibitions related to space.[55] There are five main articles of this treaty related to orbital space debris. The first is Article IV, which states that "nuclear weapons and other weapons of mass destruction may not be placed in orbit, installed on celestial bodies, or stationed in space in any other manner."[56] The second is Article VI, which says that states are responsible for all governmental and private space activities and are required to supervise and regulate private activities.[57] The third is Article VII, which says that states are internationally liable for damage to states (and their citizens) caused by their own space objects (including privately owned ones).[58] The fourth, Article VIII, says that states retain jurisdiction and control over space objects in space or on celestial bodies.[59] The fifth and final article is Article IX, which says that states are required to conduct international consultations before proceeding with activities that would cause potentially harmful interference with activities of other parties.[60] This article also says that states must carry out their own use and exploration of space in a way that avoids harmful contamination of outer space, the moon, and other celestial bodies, as well as avoiding the introduction of extraterrestrial matter that could adversely affect the environment of the earth.[61]

Another treaty that is related to orbital space debris is the Antiballistic Missile (ABM) Treaty (1972) between the United States and the Soviet Union. This treaty prohibits the development, testing, or deployment of space-based ABM systems or the systems' components.[62] The next space law applicable to orbital space debris is the Liability Convention of 1972, which makes a launching state liable for damage by its space object to people and property on Earth, its atmosphere, or to another state's space object.[63] The last space law applicable to orbital space debris is the Convention on Registration of 1974. This law requires a party to maintain a registry of all objects launched into Earth orbit or beyond, and the information on orbital parameters and general function of the object must be furnished to the UN as soon as practical.[64]

There are numerous uncertainties (unpredictable forces) in store for the world over the next five years. Those concerning orbital debris are (1) technology, (2) exploitation of space vulnerabilities via cyberspace, (3) economic developments, and (4) natural disasters.

Currently, the configuration of global space technologies and assets is highly desirable from a US perspective.[65] The United States relies heavily on space assets for a myriad of capabilities. Some have voiced worries that the United States will lose its lead as the global innovator in technology or that an enemy could make technological leaps that would give it significant advantages.[66] That is possible, but by no means a foregone conclusion.[67] However, one thing is clear: "technology will proliferate."[68]

Space technology has become increasingly available to any country or multinational corporation with the ability to fund the research or acquire the technology and place it in orbit.[69] The increasing proliferation of launch and satellite capabilities, as well as the development of antisatellite (ASAT) capabilities, has begun to level the playing field.[70] Technological advances in kinetic-energy weapons by adversaries could cause structural damage by impacting the target with one or more high-speed masses, by ground- or air-based directed-energy weapons never getting close to their target, and by nuclear weapons detonating at an empty point in space, potentially putting our space assets at risk in the near future.[71] Kinetic-energy weapons are of growing concern. For example, in 2007 China successfully tested a direct-ascent, kinetic-kill ASAT vehicle that destroyed an inactive Chinese weather satellite. This test generated thousands of pieces of space debris that threatened many operational spacecraft.[72]

Another kinetic-energy weapon is microsatellites (microsats). Currently, at least 40 countries have demonstrated some ability to design, build, launch, and operate microsats.[73] Microsats can maneuver to observe and disrupt operations of orbiting assets and may soon be capable of harassing or destroying larger satellites at virtually any altitude.[74] Because these satellites are so small, they may not be easily detectable as part of a payload or when maneuvering in space.

Directed-energy weapons are laser, radio frequency, and particle beam weapons. Lasers operate by delivering energy onto the surface of the target. Gradual or rapid absorption of this energy leads to several forms of thermal damage.[75] Radio frequency (RF) weapons such as the high-power microwave have either ground- or space-based RF emitters that fire an intense burst of radio energy at a satellite, disabling electronic components.[76] Nuclear weapons are perhaps the technology of most concern to US space assets. Some argue, though, that adversaries would not use nuclear weapons in space out of fear of retaliation.[77] Others say, "What better way to use nuclear weapons than to destroy a key military capability of an enemy country without killing any of its population?"[78] Regardless of the arguments, a nuclear detonation would have three huge environmental effects in space: electromagnetic pulse (EMP), transient nuclear radiation, and thermal radiation.[79]

EMP from a nuclear detonation will induce potentially damaging voltages and currents in unprotected electronic circuits and components, virtually rendering space assets inoperative.[80] Increased radiation from such a detonation would also have profound effects on the space environment. This would severely damage nearby orbiting satellites, reducing the lifetime of satellites in LEO from years to months or less and making satellite operations futile for many months.[81] The risk of this potential threat is significant. To execute this mission, all one needs is a rocket and a simple nuclear device.[82] Iran, North Korea, Iraq, and Pakistan possess missiles that could carry warheads to the necessary altitudes to perform such missions.[83] Technological advances in adversary weaponry are certainly hard to predict even in the near term. However, if this weaponry matures and is successfully used, it will create additional space debris from the orbiting satellites being rendered inoperative (space junk), which will become potential hazards to other satellites.

Another unpredictable driving force is adversary exploitation of space vulnerabilities via the cyber domain. Through cyberspace, enemies (both state and nonstate actors) will target industry, academia, government, and the military in the air, land, maritime, and space domains.[84] One of the easiest ways to disrupt, deny, degrade, or destroy the utility of space assets is to attack or sabotage the associated ground segments through cyberspace.[85] The ground segments includes telemetering, tracking, and commanding space assets and space-launch functions. Ground stations are an extremely critical piece of a satellite's continued operation. However, many satellite tracking and control stations are lightly guarded, and many satellite communications, launch, data reception, and control facilities are described in numerous open-source materials, making the ground segment extremely vulnerable to cyber attack.[86] An attack on a fixed-ground facility can stop data transmission, render launch facilities unusable, and prevent control of satellites.[87] A single incident or a small number of incidents could significantly impact space systems for years.[88]

The next unpredictable driving force is economic developments. The recent economic downturn has been felt worldwide, but the US dollar is still the primary unit of international trade, allowing for borrowing at relatively low rates of interest.[89] However, the increased trend of borrowing creates uncertainty about the ability of the United States to repay the ever-growing debt and the future of the US dollar.[90] Plus, any lending stop would push the dollar down and drive inflation and interest rates up.[91] This dynamic could encourage the establishment of new reserve currencies as global economic actors search for alternatives to the dollar.[92] These changes in global economic conditions could have important implications for global security. The changes could decrease the United States' purchasing power and the ability to allocate resources, especially for defense purposes, causing power shifts around the world that could adversely affect global stability. Considering these economic challenges and the relatively high cost of launching satellites, this could impact requests for space services worldwide and potentially slow the rate of newly generated orbital debris.

The last unpredictable driving force is natural disasters. If large-scale hurricanes, tornadoes, earthquakes, or other natural disasters occur in the United States, particularly when the nation's economy is in a fragile state and US military bases or key civilian infrastructure is affected, these disasters could adversely impact US security.[93] Areas of the United States where there is great potential to suffer large-scale effects are the hurricane-prone areas of the Gulf and Atlantic coasts and the earthquake zones on the West Coast.[94] These two areas also happen to be the locations where the majority of US space launches occur at Vandenberg AFB, California, and Cape Canaveral AFS, Florida. If a natural disaster occurred in these two areas, the United States could be forced to rely on other countries to provide launch services. Also, if any of these natural disasters were to occur at any of the satellite tracking and control stations located throughout the world, they would disrupt communications with active satellites, forcing the United States to switch to an alternate station. However, due to the loss of satellite control, other space assets in close proximity could be at risk of a potential collision with that satellite.

Synthesize Phase

The *synthesize* phase combines the driving forces to create scenarios. Two driving forces—the most important and most uncertain to the focal issue of a catastrophic collision from orbital space debris in the year 2015—must be selected. These two driving forces are technology and future conflicts. These critical uncertainties are placed on two separate axes called "axes of extremes representing a continuum of possibilities ranging between two extremes."[95] These two axes are then crossed to create a rough scenario framework, which can be used to explore the four possible scenarios for the future.[96] Each quadrant of the matrix represents a possible scenario or a potential future.

Next, a short, distinctive yet descriptive name for each notional future is created, and a brief scenario narrative is provided for each. The four future scenarios are (1) enemy of mine, (2) space Pearl Harbor, (3) eyes wide shut, and (4) lost in space in the year 2015 (fig. 6.2).

"Enemy of mine" is an adversary's deliberate attack on space assets using kinetic- or directed-energy weapons. This scenario is driven by an adversary's advanced technical ability to launch an ASAT or a microsat (such as a space mine) into space to destroy or disable a satellite. It is also driven by an adversary's advanced ability to use a ground- or air-based system from a distance (such as a laser) to disable a satellite. If an adversary is willing to use these weapons in a sneak attack and wants to remain somewhat hidden, there is a high probability that he or she would also be willing to conduct other attacks, such as cyber, in the same way. In this scenario, the use of these weapons renders the targeted satellites inoperative, resulting in another piece of orbital debris that puts other operational satellites at risk.

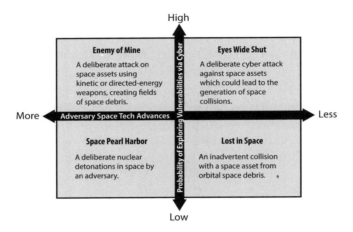

Figure 6.2. Complete scenario framework. (*Adapted from* Diane Scearce and Katherine Fulton, *What If? The Art of Scenario Thinking for Nonprofits* [Emeryville, CA: Global Business Network, 2004]: 72.)

"Space Pearl Harbor" is a deliberate nuclear detonation in space by an adversary (such as North Korea or Iran). This type of future is driven by the adversary's technical ability to possess a nuclear weapon and a missile to carry it and the ability to remotely detonate the device. Even though several countries possess these capabilities independently, technological advances in systems engineering are required to pull all the capabilities together to be successful. This scenario would not only wipe out nearby satellites from the blast and radiation, but also create huge amounts of additional orbital debris, increasing the likelihood of catastrophic collisions with other space assets. Since the United States has numerous nuclear detection satellites orbiting the earth, the adversary's location would likely be readily identified before satellites were rendered inoperative. Therefore, considering that an adversary is willing to launch an attack of such magnitude, this adversary is not worried about conducting sneak attacks and is unlikely to wage a cyber attack.

"Eyes wide shut" involves an adversary's deliberate cyber attack against space assets, specifically ground stations. This scenario is driven by an adversary's high probability to conduct cyber attacks. Because many countries have developed these capabilities, space technology advances are not required to conduct such an attack. Some countries even have "hackers that routinely probe DOD networks and computers."[97] In this scenario, communication to satellites and data transmission from the satellites to the ground stations are completely severed. Without the communication link, satellite control is lost, and the satellites become large masses of hurling orbital debris, putting other satellites at risk of a collision.

"Lost in space" is an inadvertent collision of a space asset with one of the thousands of pieces of existing orbital debris. This scenario is very real, and because it is attributed to the current debris situation, it isn't driven by either adversary technological advances or the probability of cyber attacks. The ISS has had several documented near misses with space junk. In each instance the ISS was maneuvered out of harm's way to avoid the objects. However, this scenario features a direct hit. A small piece of debris (no more than 20 mm in diameter) is detected without time to instruct the ISS to take evasive measures. The debris, traveling at about 10 times the speed of a rifle bullet, strikes the ISS, creating a massive hole in the huge structure. The collision is so severe that it knocks out the on-board communication and life support system, and the ISS is sent tumbling out of control. The ISS and crew are lost.

Act Phase

The *act* phase identifies the scenario implications and a strategic agenda (a set of priorities to help make progress on long-term goals). What would it be like living in one of these scenarios? Is there anything one could do to avoid or mitigate these scenarios for the future? The answers to the first question identify scenario implications in global communication, the economy, safety, and US national security. The answers to the second question identify a strategic agenda in order to mitigate the orbital debris problem.

The world has become increasingly reliant on satellites to provide information for such uses as communications, Internet access, navigation, military surveillance, environmental research, and banking. A loss of one or several satellites that facilitate these services (from a deliberate act by an adversary) could affect nearly everyone on the planet, especially if it was a nuclear detonation in space. The first implication is the disruption of global communications. People would not be able to communicate via cell phones or the Internet. The world banking industry would shut down, crippling an already fragile economy. US and coalition military forces around the world would not have the ability to use space assets for surveillance and GPS navigation to track friendly forces or target/destroy enemy forces, leaving US and coalition forces vulnerable to attack and potential fratricide. In fact, a similar situation on a much smaller scale already occurred when a single satellite, *Galaxy IV*, lost its bearing in 1998.[98] Forty-five million people, including hospital personnel, were disconnected from their paging service.[99] Also, local affiliates of media such as National Public Radio ceased broadcasting; Reuters was unable to send wire stories to media outlets; and Chinese Television Network couldn't transmit any of their news feeds.[100] Automated teller machines experienced service interruptions, as did credit card systems at gas stations and grocery stores.[101]

A second implication deals with world safety. As in the scenario "Lost in space," the loss of a costly space asset (the ISS) and the death of an international crew would be devastating to all countries affected. The threat of this particular incident is very real. In fact, the preliminary results of a recent NASA risk assessment of the decommissioned space shuttle put the risk of a manned spaceflight mission into perspective. The study concluded that "space debris accounts for 11 out of 20 of the most likely scenarios that could lead to the loss of another shuttle."[102] Another safety issue of concern, which could be the result of any of the four stated scenarios, is the reentry of space debris into the atmosphere and its possible impact on Earth. Over the years, the world has, fortunately, not had any major incidents, primarily due to the fact that large amounts of debris burn up harmlessly in the earth's atmosphere before impact. However, the possibility remains, especially with the growing amount of debris in LEO.

The third implication is the effect on US national security. Imagine the potential ramifications from scenarios "enemy of mine" or "eyes wide shut" "if space debris destroyed an early-warning satellite of an adversary nuclear-armed nation."[103] The United States may not get any advanced warning of a launched nuclear attack against us or our allies.

What strategic agenda should be prescribed to avoid or mitigate the possible scenarios for the future and implications from orbital debris? Author Michael O'Hanlon offers up some very good suggestions. These include (1) hardening and defending US satellites, (2) improving space monitoring, and (3) providing backup/alternatives to satellite capabilities. In addition to these strategies, the United States must continue to work with other countries to come up with solutions for clearing and reducing the proliferation of orbital debris.

First, hardening and defending US satellites would "require the continued hardening against nuclear effects, and where practical, more satellites should employ radio transmission frequencies and signal strengths capable of penetrating a nuclear disturbed atmosphere."[104] These measures ensure at least minimum l vels of bandwidth shortly after a nuclear attack.[105] LEO satellites should also have sensors to detect laser illuminations and other attack mechanisms, as well as the means to temporarily protect themselves against such attacks through shutter controls, which would shield their optics.[106]

Second, improved space monitoring would allow the United States "to know if its satellites are under attack or likely soon to be under attack."[107] Sensors could trigger the deployment of shields or other protective measures against certain types of threats, such as lasers.[108] They could also allow ways for a satellite to identify approaching microsats in order to maneuver away from a kinetic or explosive attack.[109]

Third, backup satellite capabilities would allow the United States to have "some additional satellite capability in its inventory at all times, together with the ability to launch and make operational such satellites quickly to mitigate vulnerabilities to ASAT weapons."[110] Alternative satellite capabilities, especially from a military standpoint, would be a good idea as well. Numerous airborne assets, such as those for imaging, signals intelligence, targeting, guidance, and communications, should be part of the force inventory.[111] Fiber-optic lines and undersea lines should be retained in many regions of the world to permit high-volume intercontinental communications even if satellites are lost.[112] Naval fleets, ground-force units, and aircraft should retain the ability to communicate internally through line-of-sight and airborne techniques to function as single entities if satellites are disrupted.[113]

Finally, the United States must continue partnering with other countries to implement solutions to reduce and prevent orbital debris. There are several potential ideas, such as using robotic trash collectors or attaching electrodynamic tethers to new satellites so that when they reach the end of their mission, they can be sent into Earth's atmosphere to burn up. A UK technology to clear clouds of debris in

LEO was introduced to the world on 26 March 2010. Scientists have designed and engineered a 3-kilogram miniature satellite fitted with a solar sail, called *CubeSail*.[114] *CubeSail* can be fitted to satellites or launch vehicles being sent into orbit and can be deployed to de-orbit assets at the end of their mission.[115]

Also, the United States and other countries must reach more space policies, treaties, and agreements to ban tests in space that produce debris and mandate the hardening of satellites being launched into space. Recent international cooperation has shown some very promising steps toward making this a reality. The formation of the IADC between the United States, the European Space Agency, the National Space Development Agency of Japan, the Russian Federal Space Agency, and space agencies from Britain, France, India, Germany, Italy, and the Ukraine has certainly promoted an awareness of the orbital debris problem. This group began making presentations to the UN Committee on the Peaceful Uses of Outer Space (COPUOS) in 1997.[116] Several technical debris mitigation guidelines were submitted to COPUOS in 2002 and officially endorsed by the UN General Assembly in 2007.[117] However, the endorsement wasn't legally binding, so implementation of debris-mitigation guidelines still lies in the hands of the different nations' governments.[118] Therefore, there is much work yet to be done in this area.

Monitor Phase

The *monitor* phase identifies the specific warning signals or other leading indicators that could forecast whether or not a future scenario is about to unfold. Unfortunately, the warning signs and leading indicators for a potential catastrophic collision between orbital debris and space assets are already upon us. The numerous recorded debris collision incidents, coupled with the expected increase in future launch rates, are very alarming. Also, the increasing availability of space technology to adversary countries and the rise in cyber conflicts, coupled with the current vulnerabilities of US space assets, could be a recipe for a catastrophe within the next five years. China's successful ASAT test in 2007 and the ISS near-miss collision with debris in 2009 are certainly two big wake-up calls to the world that now is the time to do something about the orbital debris situation.

Conclusion

The warning signs and leading indicators for a catastrophic collision between orbital debris and satellites or manned spaceflight missions are all around us. If significant strides are not made within the next five years to clear and remove orbital debris, a loss of satellites and the death of space crews could be the result. Furthermore, if something isn't done to better protect space assets now, it could lead to adversaries exploiting vulnerabilities through various kinetic, nuclear, and cyber attacks, causing satellites to become inoperative. This would lead to the generation of new debris, which would further compound the orbital debris problem. The effects of this would be felt worldwide with the disruption of communications, Internet access, navigation, military surveillance, environmental research, and the banking industry. The best way to avoid these consequences is to continue to harden satellites, improve space monitoring, and develop backups/alternatives to satellite capabilities. As mentioned, the United States must also continue to partner with other countries to implement solutions of clearing and reducing the proliferation of orbital debris. The world can change the potential alarming future of a catastrophic collision from orbital debris. The time to act is now.

Notes

1. O'Hanlon, *Neither Space Wars nor Sanctuary*, 30.
2. Ibid., 69.
3. Ibid., 42.
4. Liou and Johnson, "Risks in Space," 340.
5. O'Hanlon, *Neither Space Wars nor Sanctuary*, 42.
6. Robson, "Calling Occupants of Interplanetary Craft," 24.
7. Ibid.
8. Ibid.
9. Ibid.
10. O'Hanlon, *Neither Space Wars nor Sanctuary*, 42.
11. Ibid., 24.
12. Ibid.
13. Malik, "Debris Scare," 12.
14. Krisko, "Predicted Growth of the Low-Earth Orbit," 983–84.
15. Robson, "Calling Occupants of Interplanetary Craft," 24.
16. Than, "Orbital Cleanup," 30.
17. Ibid.
18. Ibid.

19. Scearce and Fulton, *What If?*, 7.
20. Ibid.
21. Ibid.
22. Ibid.
23. Ibid., 8.
24. Ibid.
25. Ibid., 24.
26. Ibid., 25.
27. Ibid.
28. Ibid., 27.
29. Ibid.
30. Ibid.
31. Ibid.
32. Ibid.
33. Ibid., 30.
34. Ibid.
35. Ibid., 31.
36. Ibid.
37. Ibid., 33.
38. Ibid.
39. Ibid.
40. Krisko, "Predicted Growth of the Low-Earth Orbit," 975.
41. O'Hanlon, *Neither Space Wars nor Sanctuary*, 42.
42. Krisko, "Predicted Growth of the Low-Earth Orbit," 976.
43. Ibid., 981.
44. Ibid.
45. Ibid., 982.
46. Ibid.
47. Ibid., 983.
48. O'Hanlon, *Neither Space Wars nor Sanctuary*, 53.
49. Ibid., 51.
50. Ibid., 53.
51. Ibid., 54–57.
52. Ibid., 57–58.
53. AU-18, *Space Primer*, 57.
54. Ibid., 57.
55. Frey, "Defense of Space Assets," 76.
56. AU-18, *Space Primer*, 57.
57. Ibid.
58. Ibid.
59. Ibid.
60. Ibid.
61. Ibid.
62. Ibid., 58.
63. Ibid.
64. Ibid.
65. O'Hanlon, *Neither Space Wars nor Sanctuary*, 62.

66. *JOE 2010: Joint Operating Environment*, 54.
67. Ibid.
68. Ibid., 55.
69. Ibid., 36.
70. Ibid.
71. AU-18, *Space Primer*, 276–79.
72. Ibid., 276–77.
73. Ibid., 277.
74. O'Hanlon, *Neither Space Wars nor Sanctuary*, 65.
75. AU-18, *Space Primer*, 277.
76. Ibid., 278.
77. O'Hanlon, *Neither Space Wars nor Sanctuary*, 67.
78. Ibid.
79. AU-18, *Space Primer*, 279.
80. Ibid., 280.
81. Ibid.
82. Ibid.
83. Ibid.
84. *JOE 2010, Joint Operating Environment*, 36.
85. AU-18, *Space Primer*, 273.
86. Ibid., 274.
87. Ibid.
88. Ibid.
89. *JOE 2010, Joint Operating Environment*, 19.
90. Ibid.
91. Ibid.
92. Ibid., 20.
93. Ibid., 33.
94. Ibid.
95. Scearce and Fulton, *What If?*, 28.
96. Ibid.
97. AU-18, *Space Primer*, 274.
98. David, "Clutter Above," 33.
99. Ibid.
100. Ibid.
101. Ibid., 33–34.
102. Ibid., 33.
103. Ibid., 34.
104. O'Hanlon, *Neither Space Wars nor Sanctuary*, 123.
105. Ibid.
106. Ibid.
107. Ibid.
108. Ibid.
109. Ibid., 124.
110. Ibid., 128.
111. Ibid., 129.
112. Ibid., 129–30.

113. Ibid., 130.
114. Wheeler, *Mission to Clear Dangerous Debris*, 1.
115. Ibid.
116. Black and Butt, "Growing Threat of Space Debris," 2.
117. Ibid.
118. Ibid.

Chapter 7

Waste to Watts and Water

Lt Col Amanda S. Birch

The year is 2030. At a major US expeditionary base, the power grid has failed, and limited fuel is available for purchase. Water reservoirs are nearly empty, and now fear is spreading that militants have contaminated available water resources. Health concerns take center stage as the sewage treatment plant and waste disposal systems stop working. Thankfully, the USAF has a powerful weapon that can save the day. After 20 years of research and development, the microbial fuel cell (MFC) gives expeditionary and home station commanders a capability to produce clean energy and clean water while using only wastewater and other organic wastes as fuel.

The USAF should invest in MFC research because this technology gives life to sustainable facilities decoupled from the infrastructure network, a key capability for national security in the 2030 environment. MFC capabilities, however, will not find success via research and development (R&D) investment alone. The USAF must collaborate within the Department of Defense (DOD) and beyond while taking a holistic systems approach to bring MFC capability to fruition. A successful strategy for MFCs will address not only the technological barriers but also the key social, industrial, and political hurdles that will bring about significant monetary and resource savings for the USAF.

The research methodology applied to capture all of these potential hurdles in MFC technology is the relevance tree. According to a report from The Futures Group International, this analytic technique ensures comprehensive exploration of a problem by breaking the system into increasingly smaller subsystems. The aim is to break the problem into enough detail so that the issues can be resolved by exploring potential options at key nodes.[1]

Relevance tree methodology is a natural fit to explore future development and use of MFC technology. It allows consideration of a larger context than mere technical feasibility. Books such as *Megamistakes: Forecasting and the Myth of Rapid Technological Change* and *Forecasting: An Appraisal for Policy Makers and Planners* make it clear that technological feasibility alone plays only a small part in adoption of new technologies; social, industrial, political, and economic factors often have the decisive role.[2]

For a current example of why this system's approach is important to emerging technology analysis, look no further than biofuels. The European Union (EU) did not analyze biofuels using a systems approach prior to policy decisions. The EU issued policy "to replace 10 percent of transport fuel with biofuels . . . by 2020," but this "green" idea furthered global warming, deforestation, and food and water shortages.[3] If a relevance tree methodology had been applied to biofuels, the EU might have avoided a costly and embarrassing policy decision.

The relevance tree research methodology drives the structure of this chapter. First, the relevancy of MFCs is established for airpower, national security, the 2030 environment, and applications outside primary DOD interest. After relevancy is established, the chapter explores the concept of self-contained facilities. Since MFCs are a key capability that could enable self-contained facilities, the technology is explained from a technological perspective and then analyzed along with other significant issues surrounding the technology using the relevance tree. Once the relevance tree is defined, key-node analysis in the technological, social, industrial, and political realms facilitates conclusions about the feasibility of a strategic plan to enable this capability to enhance US national security by the year 2030.

Who Cares?

The problem that MFCs address is defined by looking at their relevancy. Relevancy is first described in terms of air, space, and cyber power. Next, the research looks at the broader relevancy to national security, the 2030 environment, and beyond the DOD.

Relevancy to Air, Space, and Cyber Power

Facilities have evolved from mere shelters to force projection platforms and command centers (such as the AN/USQ-163 Falconer Air and Space Operations Center weapon system) and will be critical to air, space, and cyber power as long as humans are involved with force projection.[4] What demands will be placed on future facilities as we enter the cyber age and beyond? Since current facilities must last *at least* 67 years, USAF leaders must define a strategic capabilities plan for future facilities that approaches the facility life cycle but is flexible enough to meet intermediate requirements.[5]

One capability the USAF will require in future facilities is the ability to operate apart from the infrastructure network and line of communications (LOC) in a clean and efficient manner, both in an expeditionary environment and within the United States. Today's facilities tie to a power grid, a water distribution system, and a wastewater disposal network, creating key nodes of vulnerability in both the physical and cyber realms.[6] Facility locations are limited to areas with developed infrastructure that exists or that must be built. What if a single technology could eliminate infrastructure dependency for all three of these services? MFCs hold this promise.

The MFC promise for the USAF extends beyond infrastructure decoupling both abroad and at home. For expeditionary facilities, airlift requirements are reduced for light, transportable, reusable, maneuverable cities that do not require heavy equipment to build, infrastructure to support, or fuels to sustain. Today's mobile electric power (MEP), for example, "requires . . . up to 4,000 gallons per day of fuel sustainment, placing a severe burden on an already stressed air fleet."[7] MFC technology's potential to reduce airlift requirements and build operating bases in any environment relates to the strategic principle of agility, as defined by the *National Military Strategy (NMS)*.[8] Additionally, fuel moving through ground LOCs creates exploitable vulnerabilities to equipment, supplies, and personnel that would be mitigated if facilities required less or no fuel and water to operate. For facilities in a homeland defense posture (which all USAF facilities must expect), decentralized utilities shift risks away from vulnerable physical and cyber infrastructure nodes, eliminating critical targets for the enemy. This is important because the first national military objective defined in the *NMS* is to protect the United States, and the *National Strategy for Combating Terrorism* calls for "defense of potential targets of attack" to include critical infrastructure such as energy and water.[9] Furthermore, the synergy of using the same MFC technology at home and abroad will reduce craftsmen's training requirements while increasing their competence.

As a final note on MFC relevancy to the USAF, I narrowed the scope of this research to facility applications, but MFC significance is not limited to facilities alone. MFCs could be used in any application that requires clean energy, clean water, or organic waste disposal. Some obvious benefits beyond facilities include power for micro air vehicles; power for space assets; clean water, power, and waste treatment for aircraft latrines; power for ground vehicles; and clean, low heat signature generators for flight-line use.[10]

Relevancy to National Security beyond Air, Space, and Cyber Power

While the link between MFCs and air, space, and cyber power is clear, it is even more important to understand the broader link to US national security. This link will be discussed under four main topics: (1) reducing natural resource consumption, (2) eliminating spark points for world conflicts, (3) prioritizing stability, security, transition, and reconstruction (SSTR) operations, and (4) accomplishing tasks outlined in the *National Security Strategy* (*NSS*).

Reducing energy consumption and natural resource dependency is a national security issue. The Whole Building Design Guide Sustainable Committee notes that "with America's supply of fossil fuel dwindling [and] concerns for energy supply security increasing, . . . it is essential to find ways to reduce load, increase efficiency, and utilize renewable fuel resources in federal facilities."[11] Lt Col John Amidon agrees: "The current world energy situation poses a national threat unparalleled in 225 years . . . [and] meeting this dilemma with a technical solution plays on America's greatest strengths, those of the inventor and the innovator."[12] The president codified this concern about natural resource dependency for both energy and water in Executive Order 13423, which requires agencies to reduce energy use by 3 percent a year (or 30 percent total) by 2015 and to reduce water consumption by 2 percent a year (or 20 percent total) by 2015.[13] The president launched goals that are even more aggressive in December 2007 by signing the Energy Independence and Security Act of 2007.[14] Considering that buildings in the United States consume 68 percent of electricity, facilities are a logical target to reduce natural resource dependency.[15] Former secretary of the Air Force Michael Wynn agrees with these goals: "The reliance on imported oil continues to threaten the economic, financial, and physical security of the nation while the use of domestic fossil fuels contributes to nationwide pollution problems. The Air Force believes that development of renewable energy sources for facility energy is one important element of our comprehensive strategy."[16] The DOD also understands the link of energy to national security and to the military instrument of power. The Defense

Science Board expressed this in a report linking fuel efficiency to six principles of war: surprise, mass, efficiency, maneuver, security, and simplicity.[17] A 2007 poll conducted for the Yale Center for Environmental Law and Policy shows that 63 percent of Americans also agreed that energy is a national security issue by confirming that energy issues threaten the United States more than terrorists.[18] In summary, natural resource consumption is a national security concern acknowledged by the president, confirmed by the USAF, and linked to the principles of war. Facilities are a logical starting point for reducing resource consumption.

While the focus of this research is on US national security, technologies that reduce water and energy dependency could contribute to a reduction in armed conflicts throughout the world—conflicts that the United States often attempts to resolve. Since water and energy resources spark conflicts, alternative solutions to obtaining these natural resources would prevent conflicts.[19] Three examples come to mind. First, in the Future Capabilities Game 2007 (FG07), the scenario's conflict concerned natural resources. If the natural resources were available through MFCs or other technologies, could the conflict have been prevented? The second example concerns the peaceful split of the Czech Republic and Slovakia in 1993. Could the "velvet divorce" that resulted in peace and good governance have occurred if resources such as oil or water were at stake?[20] The final example is the Jordan River Basin, which includes Israel, Jordan, Lebanon, Syria, and the West Bank. Since 1948, 18 "extensive war acts causing deaths, dislocation, or high strategic costs" and dozens more hostile acts have occurred in this region.[21] Would these conflicts be less likely to start or be more likely candidates for peaceful resolution if water resources were available through a technological breakthrough? Critics find that natural resource availability will not be a panacea for conflicts that also have deeper cultural roots. These examples establish the argument that water and energy resource availability, enabled by MFCs or other technologies, could contribute to future world stability by offering diplomats a tool to pursue a better state of peace.

The third link of MFCs to national security is in the growing priority of SSTR operations. Today such missions are not in vogue with the USAF's institutional infatuation with technology.[22] However, for the future, MFCs will provide capability that will be useful in all four quadrants of military challenges shown in the 2006 *Quadrennial Defense Review* (QDR)—irregular, catastrophic, disruptive, and traditional challenges.[23] Additionally, MFCs will provide capabilities that are essential to all six operation plan phases as described in Joint Publication (JP) 3-0, *Joint Operations*.[24] The broad applicability of MFC capability allows this technology to fill a niche outside the "seize and dominate" phases and traditional security challenges where USAF technological innovation attention is typically focused.

MFC technology moves the USAF toward the 2005 DOD Directive (DODD) 3000.05, *Military Support*, which states, "Stability operations are a core US military mission. . . . They shall be given priority comparable to combat operations."[25] Since stability is key to transferring power to civil authorities, and since facility and infrastructure construction are a large component of stability, the United States could use MFC technology to expedite this transition in areas with damaged or absent infrastructure. New USAF irregular warfare doctrine acknowledges this mission by a call to civil engineers to perform it.[26] Another stabilization role the US military performs is humanitarian relief. "Humanitarian relief has long been recognized as a mission of the American armed forces," and the massive response to the "most destructive tsunami ever recorded" in Indonesia in 2004 is an example of the need for a capability to produce clean drinking water in the absence of operational infrastructure.[27]

Whether the military likes to acknowledge this aspect of its mission or not, SSTR operations are a core mission. While assigned to Iraq, Army captain John Prior captured the sentiment that is prevalent in today's writing on SSTR and counterinsurgency efforts: "'Infrastructure is the key now,' Prior said more than once. 'If these people have electricity, water, food, the basics of life, they're less likely to attack.' Sewage, Prior realized, was the front line of nation-building."[28] The infrastructure provided by US military teams paves the way for winning the hearts and minds of the indigenous population by meeting its basic needs, which in turn adds legitimacy to stressed governments after war or disaster. In short, MFC technology adds capability across all phases of war and all types of challenges.

Using the military instrument of power (IOP) for nation building is a possibility based on DODD 3000.05, but the *NSS* links infrastructure development efforts to two essential strategic tasks that leverage the diplomatic and economic IOPs as well. The two essential tasks outlined in the *NSS* that relate to MFC technology are (1) to "ignite a new era of global economic growth through free markets and free trade," which includes "secure, clean energy development," and (2) to "expand the circle of development by opening societies and building the infrastructure of democracy."[29] The US Department of State (DOS) could support both objectives by helping developing nations become stable democracies using technology such as MFCs that enable modular, cost-effective, resource-savvy, low-maintenance, infrastructure-free facilities, especially in remote and impoverished areas. Furthermore, using MFC technology in impoverished areas provides clean water, combats disease, and helps states integrate impoverished nations lacking infrastructure into the global economy.[30] Nongovernmental organizations (NGO) could use MFCs in a similar manner to further these *NSS* objectives, but they could also use the technology as a baseline for establishing or supporting refugee camps or humanitarian relief efforts. The DOS and NGOs could use MFC technologies to accomplish essential strategic tasks specified in the *NSS*.

To recap, MFCs could enhance national security beyond air, space, and cyber power in four ways: (1) reducing natural resource consumption, (2) eliminating world conflict spark points, (3) prioritizing SSTR operations, and (4) accomplishing essential tasks outlined in the *NSS*.

Relevancy to the 2030 Environment

The relevancy of MFC technology for air, space, and cyber power, and the larger national security context in today's environment, is evident, but that relevancy will grow even more as we approach the year 2030. MFCs will be a key defense capability regardless of which future threat dominates in 2030. Four main threat scenarios could depict the 2030 environment, and each of these scenarios needs MFC technology to enable national security. If the United States faces a *conventional, major-theater* enemy in 2030, MFCs will be needed to enable expeditionary and homeland facilities from which to project traditional air, space, and cyber power. If the terrorist threat to the homeland dominates in 2030, MFCs will be needed to eliminate key nodes of vulnerability in the homeland infrastructure (such as the power grid, water, and wastewater systems). If counterinsurgencies, small wars, and humanitarian crises (such as those faced over the past 50 years in Vietnam, Iraq, and Afghanistan) characterize the next century, MFCs will be needed to provide critical infrastructure to "win hearts and minds" and legitimize nascent governments. If energy and water shortages or environmental concerns are the biggest national security concern in 2030, MFCs will be needed to provide green power and clean water.[31] No matter which scenario strategic planners assume is most important for 2030, MFCs could reduce the probability of strategic surprise if R&D investment begins now.[32]

The argument that follows looks more closely at the fourth scenario—water and energy resource shortages. Steven Schnaars, a marketing professor who specializes in future technologies, observes that "forecasters are imprisoned by their times."[33] Humans tend to look at today's crisis and project it into the future. Conventional threats, terrorism, small wars, insurgencies, and humanitarian crises are today's discernable threats covered extensively in the literature and the Air Command and Staff College curriculum. Energy and water resource shortages are tomorrow's strategic threats that are often overlooked, creating strategic risk.

Energy will continue to be a concern in 2030. In 2007 the US Department of Energy (DOE) forecasted international power demand to double by 2030.[34] Today's energy crisis is well-recognized and built into future national security strategy.[35] Projects to reduce consumption and to transition to green power sources are under way. The projected crisis for power, then, is not likely to be quantity and sources, but availability.

Today's facilities depend on a power grid that has both physical vulnerabilities (enemy actions, natural disasters, and demand saturation) and cyber vulnerabilities (control software). Distributing the network into smaller pieces reduces risk, with an ultimate goal of individual self-contained facilities with collocated production and consumption. Besides reducing risk, after initial capital investment, power costs would drop since 30 percent of most electric bills is for transmission costs, and 10 percent of electricity is lost in transmission.[36] Self-contained facilities would be more likely to survive physical or cyber terror attacks as well as natural disasters.[37] Consumers could also reduce vulnerability to brownouts that threaten productivity and the economy.[38] Self-contained facilities address the nonavailability threat.

Water availability will be a bigger natural resource crisis in 2030 than decision makers grasp today. Planning failures for this emerging shortage will result in a strategic surprise, forcing crisis action or emergency responses that will divert attention from the USAF's main goals.[39] A potential water shortage in 2030 is well documented, and the USAF must prepare for it today. Water shortage forecasts are available, for those willing to heed them, in future scenarios, futurists' predictions, and mainstream media.

Four credible future scenario projects highlight a future shortage of water. First, the United Nations (UN) Millennium Project scenarios lend credibility to the prediction of a global water shortage in the 2030 time frame. In its product *2007 State of the Future*, "providing sufficient clean water for everyone, without conflict" is one of the "15 Global Challenges" that need to be addressed "to improve prospects for humanity."[40] These futurists observe that today "more than 1 billion people do not have access to safe drinking water" and that "by 2025, 1.8 billion people could be living in water-scarce areas desperate enough for mass migrations, and another 3 billion could live in water-stressed areas."[41] They also note that "80 percent of diseases in the developing world are water-related. Many are due to poor management of human excreta. About 2.6 billion people lack adequate sanitation."[42] MFCs would address the water and sanitation challenges forecast by the UN Millennium Project.

Second, the Nobel Prize–winning Intergovernmental Panel on Climate Change predicts that by 2020 as many as 250 million Africans could experience water stress.[43] Third, Air Force planners looking at 2025 scenarios also expect future water shortages. The King Khan scenario predicts that "clean drinking water [will be] scarce and competition over water rights [will] become a source of conflict in Africa and Southwest Asia."[44] Finally, FG07 also reflects this same natural resource shortage. Future water shortages consistently appear in strategic planning scenarios.

Individual futurists also agree about the scarcity of future water. Peter von Stackelberg highlights the need for future water technology by predicting that "water is becoming increasingly scarce. . . . By 2025, about 3.4 billion people will live in regions that are defined by the UN as water-scarce."[45] The Futurist May 2008 magazine cover claims that "global demand for water has tripled in the past half century." The article's author expects this trend to continue and projects that since 70 percent of water consumption is for agriculture, water shortages will also lead to food shortages.[46] Professional futurists expect to see a water crisis by 2030.

Even popular media, which are generally not future focused, are reporting on the likelihood of water scarcity in 2030. The government estimates that, beginning in 2009, the demand for water will outstrip supply in La Paz-El Alto, Peru.[47] Even more surprising, the predicted water shortage in 2030 is not limited to places outside of the United States. Lake Meade, the main water source for Phoenix and Las Vegas, "has a 50 percent chance of becoming unusable by 2021."[48] Both cities host military bases threatened by the absence of water. The threat of a water shortage is on the horizon, not just in the Middle East but also in the Western Hemisphere.

Natural resources will be scarce in 2030, and networked infrastructure will carry unnecessary risks. Scenario planners, futurists, and popular media have issued the warnings—water and energy shortages will characterize the world, including the United States, in 2030. Sustainable technologies that minimize natural resource losses while producing beneficial by-products will be necessary to project air, space, and cyberspace power, regardless of the most likely threat.

Relevancy beyond the Department of Defense

While this research focuses on the applicability of MFCs to national security through the military IOP, MFCs also enable the diplomatic and economic IOPs. Understanding the larger impact of this technology allows the USAF to identify R&D partners. This study also paints a picture of how important MFCs could become for 2030. The figure in appendix G shows application and benefit areas.

Understanding Microbial Fuel Cell Technology

With the relevancy of the research established, this section explains MFC technology. First, the research explores the self-contained facilities concept and how MFCs enable it. Next, an overview of MFC components and their interaction provides a foundation for further analysis. Additionally, a short section addresses what MFCs are not. Finally, with technical details in hand, the last section summarizes the technology's maturity.

Self-Contained Facilities Concept

The genesis of this research is the self-contained facilities concept. A self-contained facility moves services and connections from outside infrastructure into the footprint of the building. Examples of infrastructure that facilities connect to include electricity, natural gas, water, wastewater, solid sanitary waste disposal, and roads. Ideally, self-contained facilities would also include self-maintenance, or at least self-monitoring, capabilities such as remotely adjustable climate controls, self-repairing wall and roof materials, and drain clearing capabilities. Furthermore, self-contained facilities should be light, reconfigurable, reusable, and maneuverable cities that do not require heavy equipment such as bulldozers and well-drilling rigs to build or sustain. These facilities leave no footprint when moved.

Since the topic of self-contained facilities is broad, this research focuses on the one technology that offers the most capability toward self-contained facilities—MFCs. MFCs are the most promising technology to explore for the self-contained facilities concept because they fold in several infrastructure and LOC dependencies—power, water, wastewater treatment, and waste disposal. For 2030's threats, self-contained facilities enabled by MFCs can reduce infrastructure and LOC vulnerabilities for facilities at home and abroad.

Microbial Fuel Cell Technology Overview

An overview of MFC technology is the starting point for exploring what MFCs can provide and the best way to move toward that goal. A brief study of figure 7.1 offers the best way to gain a basic understanding of MFC technology. Following the pictorial overview is a summary of how MFCs work as well as a description of the salient technology components for a more in-depth understanding of MFCs.

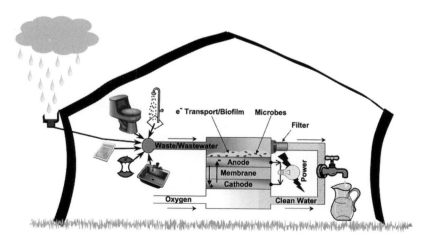

Figure 7.1. Microbial fuel cell technology overview

One type of biological fuel cell, the MFC, uses living microbes as a catalyst for an electrochemical reaction that can convert waste to power and water.[49] Microbes metabolize waste products in a process that frees electrons. This idea is not new. Wastewater treatment plants use microbes to degrade organic matter. The new twist is capturing released electrons as power. "Normally the electrons power . . . the bacterial cells. However, by depriving the bacteria of oxygen . . . the electrons can be wrested . . . and used to power a circuit."[50] Wastewater is cleaned, as it is in wastewater treatment plants today, and the by-products of the reaction are clean water and power.[51] With this understanding, the stage is set to discuss the primary components.

Fuel. Fuel is the substrate in which the microbes act. Examples of fuels for MFCs include wastewater such as gray water, black water, and storm water; kitchen scraps; industrial waste streams; agricultural waste streams; sugars such as glucose, fructose, lactose, and mamose; algae; or any other type of carbon-rich waste product such as wood, paper, or plastic.[52] The ideal mixture of the substrate is a key investigation area.[53]

Electrodes. Microbial fuel cells have an anode and a cathode. Flow of electrons between these two electrodes through an external resistance yields power. Electrode materials dictate how well electron transport can occur.[54] Electrode surface area also governs waste processing speed and power output density.[55]

Catalysts. Catalysts start the electrochemical reaction. They are necessary at both electrodes. A traditional fuel cell uses platinum as the catalyst, but in MFCs, "bacteria on the anode . . . can act as the catalyst instead."[56] The catalyst governs the reaction speed at both electrodes and therefore becomes a variable that dictates the speed of power and clean water production.[57] A robust mixture of microbes, such as Geobacter and Shewanella, in the anode chamber catalyzes the reaction and allows for fuel flexibility.[58] Several microbiologists are studying the genetic engineering involved with optimizing microbes for MFCs.[59]

Membrane. A membrane separates the two electrodes and allows protons to pass from the anode to the cathode. It also allows anions to pass from the cathode to the anode. This proton exchange creates a potential across the two electrodes that pulls electrons from the anode to the cathode, thus generating electricity. The protons then combine with the oxygen at the cathode to produce water. Proper design of the membrane is important because this exchange controls the potential available across the electrodes (which equates to power) and the rate at which the reactions can occur at both electrodes.[60] Membranes are a current research topic, and recent publications suggest that Nafion membranes should be replaced with a nanoporous filter or "fast proton conducting ceramic membranes" to optimize power output and reliability.[61]

Electron Transport. Mediators help move electrons in the anodic chamber to the electrode so that they may be captured to produce electricity. Many MFC publications report supplementing the solution around the anode with mediators that are toxic chemicals, such as methylene blue.[62] Microbes, however, synthesize and excrete mediators as they "breathe."[63] This natural method of transporting electrons to the anode, often referred to as a mediatorless MFC, allows electrons to be passed to the anode via direct contact between the microbe and the electrode surface. Two examples of mediatorless electron transfer appear in the MFC literature—nanowires and biofilms. Nanowires are hairlike appendages that bacteria use to move electrons to the electrode surface.[64] Biofilms enable electron transport by orienting cell surfaces so that the electron-transporting proteins are a certain distance from the electrode, allowing electron hopping.[65] Biofilms coat the anode and grow on a carbon-based fiber.[66]

What Microbial Fuel Cells Are Not

With these main components defined, it is now possible to refine the definition of MFCs by understanding what their technology is not. Since many competing and complementary alternative energy projects are in the spotlight, it is important to understand what differentiates these technologies. Some technologies that should not be confused with MFCs are biofuels and biomass, hydrogen fuel cells, protein- or enzyme-based fuel cells, solar power, wind power, and desalination plants. A brief explanation of these technologies is included in appendix I. Future MFC applications will likely be coupled with some of these complementary energy and water technologies to build fully self-contained facilities.

Microbial electrolysis cells (MEC), on the other hand, are a type of MFC, but they are not the focus of this research. MECs use an additional small voltage input (which could be provided by another MFC) to drive hydrogen production at the cathode. This hydrogen then drives a traditional fuel cell. MECs are more complex than the basic MFC idea explored here. Dr. Bruce Logan's group at Pennsylvania State University is researching this conceptualization.[67]

Technology Maturity

With a basic understanding of the concept of MFCs, how mature is the technology? Using MFCs on a large scale to dispose of wastewater, to clean water, and to generate electricity is a futuristic idea. Dr. Glenn Johnson, an MFC expert at the Air Force Research Laboratory, assessed MFC technology readiness level (TRL) as "two," which means that the basic concept or idea has just been formed.[68] In Johnson's assessment, in 10 years leaders will talk about MFCs as frequently as they discuss ethanol today.[69] Derek Lovley, an MFC researcher at the University of Massachusetts–Amherst, puts it this way: "One way to think of this technology is that it is currently at the state of development that solar power was 20 to 30 years ago—the principle has been shown, but there is a lot of work to do before this is widely used."[70] MFC technology is still in its formative stages—the perfect time for the USAF to envision future uses for this emerging technology and shape the research to meet that vision.

Microbial Fuel Cell Relevance Tree: A Systems Analysis Framework

With a basic understanding of MFC relevancy and technology, analysis is now appropriate. MFCs could make a significant contribution toward self-contained facilities, but how could they contribute and what must be addressed to achieve it? To answer these questions, this research used a relevance-tree systems analysis. The relevance tree was first defined and then analyzed at key nodes. From this analysis, some capabilities and limitations emerged. Finally, a brief cost analysis showed the practical feasibility of implementing MFCs.

Defining the Microbial Fuel Cell Relevance Tree

A relevance tree breaks the problem into successively smaller parts so that individual issues can be identified and addressed. A graphical representation of this research is presented in appendix G and shows what it will take to move MFC technology from concept to capability.

Key-Node Analysis

The MFC relevance tree is a detailed, systematic sketch that captures the salient concerns surrounding MFC R&D and implementation.

Because the tree has over 100 branches, this research cannot detail concerns at each node. The key-node analysis, therefore, seeks to highlight the most important nodes that leaders must address to advance MFC technology. This analysis looks at four tree branches: technological, social, industrial, and political challenges.

Key Technological Nodes. The first of these branches has three main categories: basic science, engineering, and military suitability. This analysis highlights the biggest challenges in each of these areas.

Basic science challenges exist for all the major MFC components: fuels, electrodes, catalysts, membranes, and electron transport. Fuel mixtures and sources must be determined.[71] Electrode size, shape, and materials must be optimized.[72] Catalytic microbes must be better understood to determine power output limits and optimal mixtures for fuel flexibility.[73] Nanotechnology breakthroughs will enable high-integrity membranes that transport protons quickly without fouling.[74] For electron transport, hairlike structures on the microbe surface that form nanowires must be investigated.[75] Finally, microbiologists must advance biofilms to learn the mixtures, the inoculation methods, and the best materials to grow microbial catalysts.[76]

Beyond these challenges, engineering issues must be identified early and addressed in parallel with the basic science. Configuration issues such as modularity and stacking, energy storage, and coupling with other power- and water-generation equipment must be considered now.[77] Manufacture will also bring challenges. Scaling laboratory experiments up to full-size systems capable of producing hundreds of thousands of watts of power and thousands of gallons of water will likely be problematic.[78] Mass manufacturing nanomembranes will also chart new territory. Of course, manufacturing puzzles are solvable if the physics are possible, but they may drive costs, size, or weight of the final product.

The final technological branch is military suitability. Like any biological system, microbes are fragile. On the positive side, they can thrive in a broad range of environments and can adapt to any niche over time.[79] They exist in permanently frozen lakes (though water flow stops in frozen conditions) and in high-temperature sea vents.[80] On the negative side, living organisms may not have a shelf life and may require lead time to form productive populations.[81] If addressed early in R&D, a procedure could be developed for "seed" generation. For example, inoculums could be introduced and could begin colonizing the system en route to an expeditionary location. Simple workarounds exist for the first few hours or days until the systems are fully operational and stable. For more details about the technological challenges, see appendix H.

Key Social Nodes. The "social" aspect is the second branch that leaders must consider to advance the MFC concept. The three key social nodes are operational transparency, resistance to change, and cost.

The first ke social node is operational transparency. In facilities, technologies that do not require occupants to change their lifestyle or business model will be most successful, so MFCs designed to be compatible with today's facilities are more likely to see widespread adoption.[82] For example, it would be easier to design technologies that capture household organic waste than it would be to train a whole society to feed sorted kitchen scraps into a basement MFC. Others might resist the change if they knew their toilet water was cleaned and recycled to their kitchen sink. Of course that is what happens today, but it is at a distant treatment plant rather than in the crawl space at home.

Operational transparency is related to the second key node—social willingness to change. In *The End of Oil*, Paul Roberts asserts that the success in hybrid vehicles sales might be an indicator of social readiness to accept revolutionary technologies that decrease dependence on traditional energy sources.[83] But social trends related to automobiles do not translate into a desire for change in American homes and businesses. Among other reasons, Americans change vehicles more frequently than homes.[84]

Second, modifying facilities built to last 100 years or more is different from changing features and infrastructure for vehicles that are replaced at least an order of magnitude more frequently. Roberts's book captures this idea: "If the auto industry is ripe for an efficiency revolution, it's not clear whether that revolution can spread to other sectors . . . . Industrial nations currently waste an extraordinary amount of energy through poorly designed homes, office buildings, and factories—all of which could be redesigned for dramatic energy savings. Yet the daunting and hugely expensive task of reengineering such large pieces of infrastructure will require more than the kind of snappy ad campaign that has worked for hybrid cars."[85]

Beyond operational transparency and social willingness to change, MFCs will not see widespread adoption unless the advantages outweigh the costs. Even if two concepts provide the same service for the same cost, human habit will choose the old over the new. Slow adoption of photovoltaics is an example of consumers deciding that advantages do not yet outweigh costs.[86] Yet a deliberate or subconscious cost-benefit analysis is influenced by politics. For instance, government regulations implementing child-restraint seats and fire alarms changed the cost-benefit analysis because breaking the law is now a cost.[87] The same could become true for MFCs if policies on security, energy, or water change.

While social inertia is daunting, change is always possible. This change might even be easier in the civilian sector than within government bureaucracy. The question is whether incentives are needed to change the cost-benefit equation to bring the idea to reality in the desired time frame.

Key Industrial Nodes. The third branch necessary to advancing the MFC concept is industry. Many industrial factors could affect MFC adoption and widespread use. This analysis considers two main industries: construction and utility. The construction industry, which accounts for 20 percent of the American economy, does not embrace innovation.[88] The United States Green Building Council (USGBC) states that "the building industry is characterized by relatively slow rates of innovation due to its size, diversity, fragmentation, and low investments in research."[89] In *Megamistakes*, technological change expert Steven Schnaars suggests that a precedent for lack of innovation may mean "leaders are napping."[90] This reflects lack of government interest, investment, incentive, and century-long facility life spans.[91] The utility industry may show similar resistance to adopting new sustainable technologies. Infrastructure such as high-voltage transmission lines, buried power lines, waterlines, and sewage pipes are costly investments that utility companies will not abandon quickly. However, the right incentives could allow innovative companies and municipalities to gracefully bridge a transition that could last as long as half a century. With the right leaders, R&D investment, and incentives, new technologies will be adopted.

Key Political Nodes. The final branch of the relevance tree to be analyzed is the political branch. Government investment, regulations, standards, taxes, and subsidies could all impact MFC success either positively or negatively. In fact, politicians wield the most power in shaping social and industrial demand for this capability. They even hold power over technology development since most academic R&D is funded through the government. If USAF leaders want

MFCs for the future, the political machine must be a primary point of engagement. Specific recommendations follow in the conclusion.

Microbial Fuel Cell Key Capabilities and Challenges

The application relevance tree and the key node analysis of the MFC relevance tree provide the framework to systematically investigate MFCs. Throughout this research, capabilities and challenges of MFCs have emerged. Some key MFC capabilities and challenges from a USAF perspective are shown in appendix J.

Basic Cost Analysis

MFC capabilities and limitations are clear, but will it cost too much to replace, build, operate, and maintain MFC facilities? No! Appendix K provides some estimates for a 1,100-person base. This section investigates how operational cost savings would quickly pay for capital investments, briefly explores maintenance and operations requirements, and, finally, highlights a few benefits that are difficult to translate into dollars.

Operations costs will quickly pay for capital investments. According to this research's calculations, organic waste has the potential to provide up to 25 percent of the power at an expeditionary base. While it is still uncertain how much of this potential energy MFCs could capture (alone or in combination with other technologies), scientists are optimistic that the technology would be much more efficient than combustion engines that peak at about 50 percent efficiency.[92] If MFCs and complementary technologies could capture 90 percent of the potential energy available (energy efficiencies have already been recorded at 65 percent and electron capture efficiencies at 96 percent), they could replace one of the four MEP-12 generators during a 1,100-person deployment.[93] This would save $69,000 per day in fuel and fuel delivery costs at a single 1,100-person location (see appendix K for details). Translated into major theater operations, during a 150,000-person deployment, MFCs could save as much as $50 million each day. The capital costs of an MFC (even if double the cost of today's generators) would quickly be recouped because of the reduced fuel requirements.

As a first step, if only the shower and latrine units became self-contained (power for lights, hot water, and water pump) using their own black water and gray water, the USAF would still save $2,500 per day at a single 1,100-person base. On top of these fuel cost benefits, the USAF would be able to capture and recycle 15,000 gallons of water each day at a 1,100-person installation. Even if MFCs cannot turn 90 percent of the potential energy of organic waste into energy, and even if significant R&D investments and capital costs are required, it is clear that the USAF would benefit from reduced costs and increased capabilities.

Maintenance would be less as well. Microbial fuel cells do not have moving parts like gas-fired generators. Maintenance requirements would be similar to today's sewage treatment plants. Primary maintenance tasks include filter cleaning and periodic electrode replacement. Pumping sewage from expeditionary latrines and transporting it to the sewage treatment location could be eliminated, cutting maintenance hours, reducing truck traffic and inspections at base entries, and improving quality of life for both residents and craftsmen. Furthermore, personnel would not have to maintain fuel levels in storage bladders or bury as much infrastructure. Overall, maintenance requirements would be similar to or less than existing systems.

Beyond the cost savings, decision makers must also account for other benefits not reflected in this basic cost estimate. Because of the reduced airlift requirements for fuel and water, some mobility aircraft could be freed for other missions. Additionally, ground LOCs would become less burdened, minimizing improvised-explosive-device risk to personnel, equipment, and supplies. Similar benefits in reduced shipping requirements would ease the demand on sea LOC throughput as well. Although reduced LOC demand from a risk perspective is not quantitatively calculated here, the potential to save lives and assets by reducing fuel and water demands during combat has merit.

This systems analysis quantified MFC capability and identified major obstacles in bringing MFC technology online. After building a relevance tree as an analysis framework, key technological, social, industrial, and political nodes emerged. Understanding these key factors resulted in conclusions about capabilities and limitations. After quantifying potential capabilities and limitations, a basic cost analysis revealed that MFCs could yield savings of up to $50 million per day in operating costs for a major theater deployment.

Conclusions

This research began by asking if the USAF should invest in MFCs. To answer this question, this research explored "who cares," explained the technical aspects of MFCs, and used relevance tree methodology to analyze capabilities, limitations, obstacles, and costs. With this analysis, the conclusion emerges: yes, the USAF should invest in MFC R&D, but investment alone is insufficient. This section explains this conclusion by discussing MFCs for self-contained facilities, strategy suggestions, and future research.

Microbial Fuel Cells—The Grail for Green, Self-Contained Facilities?

MFCs hold great promise to meet future waste disposal, water, and power requirements with significant cost savings, but they are a component required for success—not a panacea for all self-contained facility needs. MFCs are primarily a wastewater treatment capability and will likely meet 100 percent of that requirement. The fundamental capability that distinguishes MFCs from other sustainable facilities technologies is their ability to process sewage, kitchen scraps, and storm water for sanitary waste disposal and to restore water to potable quality. It is a bonus that MFCs also provide potable water and power as chemical reaction by-products.

While MFCs are likely to meet 100 percent of the waste disposal requirements, expecting MFCs to meet 100 percent of facility power and water requirements is unrealistic.[94] For power and water, MFCs must be coupled with demand reduction through both technology and conservation efforts. Roberts predicts that "no matter what energy technologies we end up using twenty or thirty years from now, we still won't have enough energy for everyone if we haven't found ways to use much less of it. Efficiency remains our greatest hope."[95] Even with increased efficiencies, MFC power densities will not meet forecasted power demand alone. MFCs may meet only 25 percent of full power requirements, so MFC technology should be coupled with other sustainable power sources such as hydrogen fuel cells, solar power, wind, and thermal technologies.[96] These are promising energy sources with capability gaps that MFCs could fill (e.g., to produce hydrogen at night, on cloudy days, on low-wind days, or in places where thermal technologies are not viable).

For water supplies, MFCs can capture and recycle water, but the by-products of the chemical reaction will not produce large quantities of water itself. The main water benefit of MFCs is the ability to recapture the 70 percent of water used that now moves into the sewage treatment process and evaporates (in an expeditionary setting).[97] The water cleansing and reaction by-product capabilities must be augmented by tapping industrial waste streams or through water collection technologies such as rainwater and dew harvesting.[98]

MFCs are not a silver bullet, but they will fill gaps in existing sustainable technologies, and they provide power, water, and waste treatment while enabling self-contained facilities.

Strategy Recommendations and Future Research

Though MFCs cannot meet 100 percent of power and water requirements, they can augment production and dispose of all wastes while filling gaps in other power and water technologies. In light of the relevance-tree analysis, this section recommends strategy and future research to address technological, social, industrial, political, and business case considerations.

Technological Considerations. First, leaders must decide to invest in facility research and development, including MFCs. The USGBC highlights that "the design, construction, and operation of buildings account for 20 percent of US economic activity and more than 40 percent of energy used, . . . yet far less than 1 percent of the federal research budget is allocated to buildings."[99]

Next, the USAF must develop a road map for MFC technology to vector the R&D funds. The road map should include basic science milestones, but it should also outline envisioned systems, manufacturing techniques, and schemes for components working together up to the level of complete self-contained facilities. For example, if a target is expeditionary self-contained facilities, all component technologies such as MFCs, solar power, rainwater collection, and self-monitoring/self-maintaining systems must be identified, investigated, integrated, and set as deliverables. Deliverable interim milestones, such as an expeditionary self-contained shower and latrine facility by 2015, must be incorporated into the plan as well. Often systems engineering and manufacturing challenges are as difficult as basic science. Early conceptualization could identify the toughest obstacles that could be addressed in parallel with the basic science development to optimize research time and dollars. Appendix H is a starting point for science, systems integration, manufacturing, and military suitability challenges that should be addressed in the road map.

In addition to the road map, the technology investment strategy should be collaborative. Collaboration must first begin with the pursuit of academic partners by the USAF and the DOD, but it should ultimately become a cross-agency plan since this technology has the potential to contribute to areas of interest beyond the DOD. The DOD has initiated several notable energy projects, but no unified, concerted effort exists yet across the services.[100]

The technology strategy and future research recommendations are (1) USAF R&D investment in MFC technologies, (2) development of a road map to spend those investment dollars, and (3) improvement of a collaborative technology approach.

Social Considerations. The social barriers to widespread use of MFCs are perhaps the most vexing challenges from the perspective of a USAF engineer.[101] Yet the impediments must be addressed because "enabling the rapid adaptation of new energy technologies to civilian use is required for the Nation's long-term physical and economic security."[102] Scientists and engineers can solve the technology problem, but if society does not adopt the technology, costs will increase, homeland security benefits will not be realized, and synergies between expeditionary and permanent facilities will be lost. Social obstacles must be the subject of further investigation. The USAF must hire outside expertise (like psychologists, consumer and marketing experts, or futurists) or rely on collaborative partners like the DOE to gauge the magnitude of social challenges that might occur, possible solutions, and their impact on national security goals.

Industrial Considerations. This research identified many industrial challenges in bringing MFCs to fruition; however, with a deliberate plan, these obstacles are surmountable. Incentives are powerful change agents, and specific recommendations should be the focus of future research. A good starting point for this research might be lessons learned from ethanol infrastructure.[103]

Political Considerations. First, policy makers must deliberately decide if a free market can effectively shape the future energy and water economy or if government intervention is necessary to protect the economy and ultimately national security. In *The End of Oil*, Roberts argues that a free-market economy could bring about a new energy economy if energy prices gradually increase, but he worries that world events could lead to catastrophic spikes in oil prices.[104] He says that "improving efficiency . . . must begin in the political sphere with a new consensus by policy makers that the energy system must change in fundamental ways—and, above all, real leadership to ensure that such change actually happens."[105] One of the primary functions of government is to provide collective security for the nation. Risks in today's energy volatility suggest that government intervention may be necessary. Ultimately, policy makers must decide if, when, and how to intervene, but the important thing is that they make an intentional decision to intervene or not intervene, rather than simply falling back to a default position resulting from indecision.

Second, policies must not dissuade military decision makers from doing the right thing when it comes to energy and water. Wing commanders, for example, see new technologies as risks without rewards since operational savings are not realized at the installation level. Furthermore, incentives such as tax credits or renewable energy credits penalize the government since no benefits can be gained. Scott Buchanan, in his article "Energy and Force Transformation," says that "the Services, combatant commanders, research laboratories, and other major DOD organizations should be allowed to keep a portion of the savings from innovative initiatives in material, procedures, and doctrine that significantly enhance energy efficiency."[106] The USAF should engage its attorneys and policy makers to find creative incentives that reward decision makers for taking sensible risks to implement microbial fuel cell technologies.

Beyond these two primary political recommendations, future research should investigate policies that could jeopardize or enhance bringing MFCs to fruition. Specific areas that should be addressed are investment policies and levels, incentives, regulations, standards, taxes, and subsidies. This future research should specifically consider how decisions in these areas directly and indirectly affect the social, industrial, technological, and government realms.

Business Case. No investment strategy or policy decision is complete without a supporting business case. This research included only a cursory cost analysis focusing on an 1,100-person expeditionary base, which clearly showed the advantages of MFCs for remote and expeditionary facilities. Future research should expand this business case, especially for permanent facilities that would require more extensive investments to update building systems to accommodate

MFC technologies and would have less organic waste (as a percentage of power required) on hand from which to generate power.

Summary

National security planners cannot know the exact threats for 2030, but the environment could be characterized by conventional, major theater threats; terrorist threats; small wars, insurgencies, and humanitarian disasters; or water and energy resource shortages. Which of these threats dominate the 2030 environment is irrelevant; they all require the capabilities that MFCs provide—distributed, secure, and sustainable power, water, and waste/wastewater treatment. MFCs are a guaranteed investment for the future. They are a flexible technology capable of enabling effects across the entire range of military operations, and, as a bonus, they will also quickly pay for themselves.

The USAF should invest in MFC research because this technology allows development of self-contained facilities decoupled from the infrastructure network, a key capability for national security in the 2030 environment. The USAF must develop facility energy, water, and wastewater capabilities to ensure future combat effectiveness of air, space, and cyberspace forces that rely heavily upon facilities. Leaders cannot assume that these enablers will be available in the future; they must plan for them. However, an MFC investment strategy must include more than R&D funds. The USAF must pursue a collaborative approach that addresses not only the technological barriers at the scientific and systems-integration level but also the key social, industrial, and political hurdles as well. Our national security depends on it.

Notes

1. This research methodology is described in detail in Futures Group International, "Relevance Tree and Morphological Analysis."

2. Schnaars, *Megamistakes*, and Ascher, *Forecasting*.

3. "Biofuels May Threaten Environment"; Harrabin, "EU Rethinks Biofuels Guidelines"; Biello, "Biofuels Are Bad for Feeding People"; and Rosenthal, "Biofuels Deemed a Greenhouse Threat."

4. Joint Publication (JP) 1-02, *Department of Defense Dictionary of Military and Associated Terms*, defines *facility* as "a real property entity consisting of one or more of the following: a building, a structure, a utility system, pavement, and underlying land." Throughout the rest of this paper, however, *facility* will refer to just the building

or structure while *infrastructure* will refer to the utility systems and pavement. The 2007 *Air Force Handbook* explains that the "AN/USQ-163 Falconer Air and Space Operations Center Weapon System (AOC-WS) is the senior element of the Theater Air Control System. The joint force air component commander /combined forces air component commander uses the system for planning, executing, and assessing theater-wide air and space operations. The AOC-WS . . . disseminates tasking orders, executes day-to-day peacetime and combat air and space operations, and provides rapid reaction to immediate situations by exercising positive control of friendly forces." The AOC-WS occupies approximately 70,000 square feet of space where 1,000 to 2,000 people work. US Air Force, *Air Force Handbook 2007*, 64–65.

5. DuBois, *Defense Installations Strategic Plan*, 8.

6. The Whole Building Design Guide Sustainable Committee explains in "Optimize Energy Use" that "increased security of energy supply and distribution systems have become an important component of national security after the 9/11 terrorist attacks. Today, power generation is still mostly handled by massive centralized plants, which are inevitable targets, and electricity moves on vulnerable lines." The vulnerability of infrastructure to attack in the cyber realm was confirmed by the Department of Homeland Defense and is reported in Meserve, "Sources."

7. "Logistics Fuel Reformer/Processor."

8. "Agility is the ability to rapidly deploy, employ, sustain and redeploy capabilities in geographically separated and environmentally diverse regions." Myers, *National Military Strategy*, 6.

9. Facilities will increase in importance as force-projection platforms for space, cyberspace, remotely piloted vehicles, and long-range bombers operate from facilities that are not near the battlefield. Myers, *National Military Strategy*, 8; and Bush, *National Strategy for Combating Terrorism*, 13.

10. The Army has already developed fuel cells (but not MFCs) for silent, low-heat signature generators. Holcomb et al., "Energy Savings for Silent Camp™ Hybrid Technologies," 134–37. Other examples of the low-heat-signature capability of fuel cells abound in the literature, including Lambert, "Fuel Cells."

11. Whole Building Design Guide Sustainable Committee, "Optimize Energy Use."

12. Amidon, "A 'Manhattan Project' for Energy," 76.

13. Bush, Executive Order 13423, Strengthening Federal Environmental, Energy, and Transportation Management.

14. "The Lighting Efficiency Mandate will phase out the use of incandescent light bulbs by 2014, and improve lighting efficiency by more than 70 percent by 2020. . . . The Federal Government Operations Mandate will reduce the energy consumption of Federal Government facilities 30 percent by 2015. Additionally, all new Federal buildings will be carbon-neutral by 2030." See "Fact Sheet: Increasing Our Energy Security."

15. Whole Building Design Guide Sustainable Committee, "Optimize Energy Use."

16. US Air Force, "U.S. Air Force Renewable Energy Program," 3.

17. Defense Science Board Task Force, *More Capable Warfighting*, 10.

18. Glenn, *Worldwide Emerging Environmental Issues*, 7.

19. For evidence that resources are a source of conflict, see "The Dark Side of Natural Resources"; Abbott, Rogers, and Sloboda, *Beyond Terror*, chap. 3; Klare, *Resource Wars*; and Renner, *Anatomy of Resource Wars*.

20. Morrison and Conway, *Kiss, Bow or Shake Hands*, 121.

21. Yoffe, "Basins at Risk," 71.

22. Carl Builder asserts that the altar of worship for the USAF is technology and that the enchantment with technological marvels, especially flying machines, characterizes USAF culture. Builder, *Masks of War*, 19.

23. Rumsfeld, *Quadrennial Defense Review Report*; and *National Defense Strategy*, 2–3. This array of four challenges—traditional, irregular, catastrophic, and disruptive— originally appeared in this document.

24. The six plan phases are shape, deter, seize the initiative, dominate, stabilize, and enable civil authority. JP 3-0, *Joint Operations*, iv-26.

25. DOD Directive 3000.05, *Military Support*, 19.

26. Air Force Doctrine Document 2-3, *Irregular Warfare*, 42–43.

27. Elleman, *Waves of Hope*, v.

28. Packer, "Letter from Baghdad"; and Meserve, "Sources."

29. Bush, *National Security Strategy*, 25–27, 31–34.

30. Logan, "Energy Diversity Brings Stability," 5161. Logan said that "modern wastewater treatments have accomplished more to protect human health and our environment than perhaps any single technology."

31. For a thorough analysis of environmental threats to national security and a sustainable security strategy, see Ackerman, "Climate Change," 56–96.

32. In a white paper, Gen T. Michael Moseley emphasizes that future fights will not be the same as today's fights and that the USAF must look ahead to make proper assumptions about the future to avoid unnecessary risk. Moseley, *Nation's Guardians*, 9.

33. Schnaars, *Megamistakes*, 63.

34. Energy Information Administration, *International Energy Outlook 2007*, 61.

35. See, for instance, National Energy Policy Group, *National Energy Policy*.

36. Amidon, briefing, subject: "Needed Now," slide 44.

37. Ibid.

38. Many power systems "have become overburdened in recent years, illustrated by the California energy brownouts in 2001." US Green Building Council, *Building Momentum*, 10.

39. Martino, "Technological Forecasting," 14.

40. Glenn and Gordon, *2007 State of the Future*, 10.

41. Ibid., 14.

42. Ibid.

43. Intergovernmental Panel on Climate Change, *Climate Change 2007*, 11.

44. Engelbrecht et al., *Alternate Futures for 2025*, 76.

45. Water technology is one of 12 technologies highlighted by von Stackelberg as essential to the future in "Future of Universal Water."

46. Brown, "Draining Our Future," 16–22.

47. "Loss of Andes Glaciers Threatens Water Supply."

48. Barnett and Pierce, "When Will Lake Mead Go Dry?" and Felicity Barringer, "Lake Mead Could Be within a Few Years of Going Dry, Study Finds," *New York Times*, 13 February 2008. http://www.nytimes.com/.

49. The other type of biological fuel cell is an enzyme or protein fuel cell. These are explained in appendix I.

50. Biever, "Plugging into the Power of Sewage."

51. Wastewater treatment efficiency will be less than current wastewater treatment plants because energy that would normally allow the microbes to metabolize more of the waste is being captured to produce electricity. Logan et al., "Microbial Fuel Cells," 5189.

52. Rodrigo et al., "Production of Electricity," 198–204; "Project to Turn Beer Wastewater into Power," *Fuel Cells Bulletin* 2007, no. 7 (2007): 11; Yokoyama et al., "Treatment of Cow-Waste Slurry," 634–38; Catal et al., "Electricity Production from Twelve Monosaccharides," 196; Rabaey et al., "Microbial Fuel Cell Capable of Converting Glucose," 2915–21; and Hatcher, "New Sources of Biomass Feed Stocks."

53. The maximum power density from MFC fuel found to date is one kilowatt of power per cubic meter of waste. Fan, Hu, and Liu, "Enhanced Coulombic Efficiency," 348.

54. Logan et al., "Graphite Fiber Brush Anodes," 3341.

55. Top power output based on electrode surface area is 5.8 watts per square meter. Rosenbaum et al., "Interfacing Electrocatalysis and Biocatalysis," 6810–13.

56. Angenent, "Microbial Fuel Cells Turn on the Juice."

57. Microbes are typically not used at the cathode, but the cathodic catalyst is still an important variable in power and water output. See Cheng, Liu, and Logan, "Increased Performance of Single-Chamber Microbial Fuel Cells," 364–69; and You et al., "A Microbial Fuel Cell Using Permanganate," 2721–34.

58. Lovley, "Bug Juice," 501–2.

59. Biffinger et al., "Biofilm Enhanced Miniature Microbial Fuel Cell"; and Logan and Regan, "Electricity-Producing Bacterial Communities," 517.

60. Proton exchange is governed by the surface area of the anode and the membrane. Oh and Logan, "Proton Exchange Membrane," 162.

61. Biffinger et al., "Diversifying Biological Fuel Cell Designs," 1672–79; and Tsui and Wiesner, "Fast Proton Conducting Ceramic Membranes," 79–93.

62. Walker and Walker, *Biological Fuel Cell*, 10.

63. Many microbes synthesize and excrete soluble redox-active molecules to enable anaerobic respiration. Stams et al., "Exocellular Electron Transfer," 371.

64. Gorby et al., "Electrically Conductive Bacterial Nanowires," 11358–63; and Reguera et al., "Extracellular Electron Transfer," 1098–101.

65. Biffinger et al., "Biofilm Enhanced Miniature Microbial Fuel Cell."

66. Angenent, "Microbial Fuel Cells Turn on the Juice."

67. For a nontechnical explanation of this concept, see Logan, "Microbial Electrolysis Cell Research." For a recent scientific publication on this configuration, see Cheng and Logan, "Sustainable and Efficient Biohydrogen Production."

68. TRL is a measure of the maturity of an emerging or desired technology. See Deputy Under Secretary of Defense for Science and Technology, *Technology Readiness Assessment (TRA) Deskbook*, ES-1, III-1–III-3; and Johnson, "Microbial Fuel Cell for Remote Power Generation," 5. The TRA Deskbook also observes that in TRL 2 "invention begins. Once basic principles are observed, practical applications can be invented. Applications are speculative, and there may be no proof or detailed analysis to support the assumptions. Examples are limited to analytic studies." 3–14.

69. Glenn R. Johnson and Robert Diltz, discussion with the author during visit to the Air Force Research Laboratory, Tyndall AFB, FL, 6 February 2008.

70. Biever, "Plugging into the Power of Sewage."

71. For a summary of different fuel sources matched with different microbes, see Kim, Chang, and Gadd, "Challenges in Microbial Fuel Cell Development," 487.

72. The "short diffusion lengths and high surface-area-to-chamber volume ratio utilized in the mini-MFC enhanced power density when compared to output from similar macroscopic MFCs." Ringeisen et al., "High Power Density," 2629. For cross section and area matter, see Ringeisen, Ray, and Little, "A Miniature Microbial Fuel Cell," 591. Angenent is studying "anode-cathode shapes, surfaces areas and distances to both increase power and reduce the resistance in the system so that less power is lost as it runs." "Fuel Cell Generates Electricity," 3.

73. Many microbes may still be awaiting discovery. Lovley, "Bug Juice," 506.

74. Biotechnology and nanotechnology are closely linked for MFC research. For example, see Morozan et al., "Biocompatibility Microorganisms," 1797–803.

75. For a visual depiction of biological nanowires from pili, see fig. 4 in Gorby et al., "Electrically Conductive Bacterial Nanowires," 11361.

76. "Power Boosted 10-Fold," 7; Rabaey et al., "Microbial Ecology Meets Electrochemistry," 9. Rabaey et al. note that "multiple populations within microbial communities can co-operate to achieve energy generation"; Ghangrekar and Shinde, "Microbial Fuel Cell," 8; and Logan et al., "Microbial Fuel Cells," 5184.

77. Aelterman et al., "Continuous Electricity Generation," 3388–94.

78. MFCs show promise in the lab, but substantial additional optimization will be required for large-scale electricity production. Lovley, "Microbial Fuel Cells," 327.

79. Rittmann et al., "Vista for Microbial Ecology," 1102. "The numbers of different microbial strains are enormous—de facto infinity. Furthermore, only a tiny fraction of the strains have been cultured and characterized. Second, microorganisms can evolve rapidly."

80. Johnson and Diltz, discussion.

81. "Electricity generation in a MFC was obtained after a short acclimatization period of less than 10 days." Of course, this is only the beginning of MFC research, so these numbers could go down. See figure 2 in Rodrigo et al., "Production of Electricity," 200.

82. Schnaars, *Megamistakes*, 117.

83. An Internal Revenue Service report indicates that Toyota alone has sold more than 60,000 hybrid vehicles in the United States, ending a federal tax credit incentive program for purchasing that company's hybrid vehicles. "2008 Hybrids Certified as Tax Credit"; and Roberts, *End of Oil*, 338–39.

84. The average American driver purchases a new vehicle every three to five years. Jones, "What Is a Hybrid Vehicle?"

85. Roberts, *End of Oil*, 338–39.

86. Schnaars, *Megamistakes*, 118.

87. Ibid., 121.

88. United States Green Building Council, *Building Momentum*, 4.

89. Ibid., 17.

90. Schnaars, *Megamistakes*, 153.

91. A lasting effect of the Cold War was a diversion of funds and intellectual talent away from "civil research and development and into military programmes." Abbott, Rogers, and Sloboda, *Beyond Terror*, 59.

92. Lindeburg, *Mechanical Engineering Reference Manual*, 29-11.

93. Energy efficiency measures how much of the energy input can be converted to output. Rabaey et al., "Microbial Fuel Cell Capable of Converting Glucose," 1533. The Coulombic efficiency measurement indicates how many of the electrons produced in the anodic chamber can be captured by the electrodes. Rabaey et al., "Tubular Microbial Fuel Cells," 8077.

94. "Electricity generation from wastewater will not by itself solve the need for power in the U.S. The energy in human, animal, and food-processing wastewater alone can provide at most only 5% of our current electricity needs and thus a small percentage of our total energy use. MFCs are just one part of a needed transition to a more diverse and stable energy portfolio." Logan, "Energy Diversity Brings Stability," 5161.

95. Roberts, *End of Oil*, 338.

96. See estimate calculations in appendix K, "Basic Cost Analysis"; and for potential synergistic technologies, see appendix I, "Competing and Complementary Microbial Fuel Cell Technologies."

97. See estimates calculated in appendix K.

98. Simonite, "Dew-Harvesting 'Web.' "

99. United States Green Building Council, *Building Momentum*, 2.

100. James, "Sierra Bravo."

101. Even experienced forecasters find social trends the most difficult aspect of future technologies to predict. Schnaars, *Megamistakes*, 100.

102. Buchanan, "Energy and Force Transformation," 54.

103. Johnson and Diltz, discussion.

104. Roberts, *End of Oil*, 340.

105. Ibid., 339.

106. Buchanan, "Energy and Force Transformation," 53–54.

Chapter 8

How to Fuel the Future of Airpower

Maj Yvonne Carrico Gurnick

Throughout history, energy has been the limiting factor in all military operations, whether it was Roman armies foraging for supplies, or General George S. Patton running out of fuel as he dashed across France, or the long military buildup in Desert Storm. The situation today is little different.

—Dr. Doug Kirkpatrick
Biofuels Program Manager
Defense Advanced Research Projects Agency

Oil's status as a cheap and plentiful resource and use as a primary fuel source across the globe have remained unchallenged for over a century. Only within the past few decades, amid increasing signs that the era of endless oil may be coming to a close, has the search for an alternative fuel gained momentum. This quest is especially significant for the United States. As the world's largest oil consumer, the United States uses over 20 million barrels of oil per day—an amount nearly three times that of the second largest consumer, China.[1]

This situation entails two fundamental problems. First, oil is a finite resource. As wells run dry, finding new oil reserves to satisfy the world's demand becomes increasingly difficult. Second, the United States cannot support its demand for oil with the present domestic supply as it imports nearly 60 percent of the oil needed to keep the country running.[2] This environment not only leads to problems on the domestic front (such as the recent climb in cost for a gallon of unleaded fuel) but also spells trouble for the US military, which must grapple with how to keep all of its vehicles supplied with fuel. The US Air Force consumes 73 percent of the oil used annually by the military and thus is particularly affected.[3] Amid decreasing stability in the Middle East and increasing volatility in the oil market, the United States is progressively more concerned about its dependence on oil and is becoming more involved in the search for an alternative fuel.

Unfortunately, the solution for aviation will take more than simply replacing oil with one of the other fuels available. Oil has many traits that make it a good fuel: stability, high energy density, and, until recently, a cheap and plentiful supply. Aircraft fuel is even more exacting, requiring thermal stability, a below-zero freeze point, a high energy-to-mass ratio, and a high flash point to avoid the danger of fire. Many of the alternative fuels being developed for cars, trucks, and other ground-based vehicles do not meet the stringent demands required of aviation fuels.

Two areas of alternative fuel research show promise for use in aviation. The first is synthetic fuels, created by converting a solid feedstock first into a gas and then into a liquid. The three synthetic fuels being explored are coal to liquid (CTL), natural gas to liquid (GTL), and biomass to liquid (BTL).[4] The second area of research starting to gain momentum in aviation is biofuels. Four alternative biofuels are being explored: biodiesel, biobutanol, ethanol, and algae-produced oils.[5] The prospects for all of these fuels will be further discussed.

In addition to cost and performance, environmental concerns continue to play a larger role in the alternative fuels debate. One aspect is the desire to find a renewable source of fuel. Developing another fuel on a nonrenewable source such as petroleum does little good, for even the most abundant nonrenewable resource will eventually run out. A second factor is the desire to reduce the carbon dioxide emissions created in the production and use of a fuel. It is for this reason that synthetic fuels have been put on hold—their production creates more carbon dioxide than today's oil refineries.[6] This fuel will remain sidelined until the environmental impact of its production can be resolved.

Within the military, the Air Force has taken the lead in the research and development of an alternative aviation fuel. Because the Air Force devotes more of its budget and has a greater need for jet fuel than the other services, it has the most to gain or lose by finding a suitable alternative. Once validated by the Air Force, any alternative fuel can be used across the Department of Defense. This paper focuses on the Air Force's role in finding an alternative.

Questions that must be addressed are which alternative fuels are now (or soon to be) available that can meet the Air Force's aviation fuel needs, and what aviation fuel options the Air Force should pursue that would be consistent with national security objectives. This paper describes two types of alternative aviation fuel available now with high prospects for success: coal- or natural-gas-based liquid fuel and biofuels created from algae. This paper maintains that CTL and GTL fuels should be exploited today to alleviate our immediate dependence on foreign oil; however, the Air Force should focus on biofuels derived from algae to permanently replace oil-based fuels.

Fischer-Tropsch (FT) fuels are the best alternative for aviation today. The Air Force is testing a blended synthetic GTL fuel in various aircraft, and this fuel has proven to be compatible with current jet fuel specifications and performance requirements. Moreover, the United States is believed to hold the greatest share of recoverable coal in the world.[7] Tapping into such a large domestic resource would improve dependability as well as alleviate many of the national security concerns regarding oil. However, these fuels are only a temporary solution, primarily because they are nonrenewable and do not meet performance specifications unless they are blended with traditional aviation fuel.

Biofuels, especially biofuels from algae, are poised to become the jet fuel of tomorrow. In contrast to FT fuels, biofuels would replace oil-based jet fuels completely (not as a blend) and offer the best prospects for meeting environmental concerns. While the research into this fuel is promising, scientists believe that large-scale production of biofuel from algae is still five to 10 years away.[8] The Air Force is on the right path pursuing an alternative aviation fuel in both FT fuels and biofuel since both of these options will provide an alternative to oil for today and tomorrow.

This paper uses an evaluation framework to identify and assess three of the alternative jet fuels under development. The next section describes how oil-based fuel became the fuel of choice and the specific traits oil exhibits that make it a good choice for aviation. Subsequent sections discuss which alternative fuels are available and being researched today, focusing on the most promising alternative fuels—coal- and natural-gas-based liquid fuels and biofuels synthesized from algae. Based on predetermined evaluation criteria, the potential benefits and shortcomings of these fuels are discussed, culminating in a recommendation on what course of action is best for the Air Force.

Historical Background of Aviation Fuels

US dependence on foreign oil is not a recent occurrence, and America's reliance on imported oil has steadily increased since the 1950s (fig. 8.1). The recent fluctuations in oil and gas prices are one aspect of this dependence. Although media coverage focuses on the commercial side of these price changes, the US military must also adjust its budget and spending to accommodate any increase in fuel costs. For the Air Force, every 1 percent rise in the price of jet fuel means an increase of approximately $23 million in annual fuel costs.[9] These price fluctuations impact budget planning, considering that in 2006 the Air Force spent 82 percent (or $5.8 billion) of its energy budget on aviation fuel alone.[10]

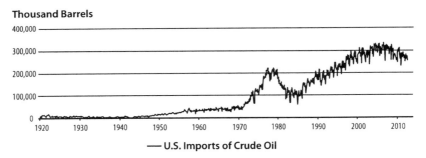

Thousand Barrels

— U.S. Imports of Crude Oil

Figure 8.1. Crude oil imports to the United States. (*Adapted from* US Energy Information Administration [EIA], "US Imports of Crude Oil," accessed 6 February 2009, http://tonto.eia.doe.gov/dnav/pet/hist /mcrimus1m.htm.)

Unlike the automobile, jet aircraft have used an oil-based fuel from their inception. Although alternative fuels have been considered over the years, previous alternatives could never match up to petroleum's combination of performance, energy content, availability, and price. At times, alternative fuels were used out of necessity, such as during World War I when illuminating kerosene (typically used for wick lamps) was used due to the short supply of gasoline.[11] The military first published specifications for aviation fuel in 1944, beginning with the kerosene fuel named JP-1.[12] After World War II the Air Force began experimenting with fuel mixtures called wide-cut fuels, which became JP-2, JP-3, and JP-4. These fuels are considered wide cut because they contain a mixture of various types of kerosene with other flammable liquids and were developed to increase the availability of jet fuel in case of shortages (such as in times of war).[13] However, these wide-cut fuels could never match the performance of pure kerosene. The Air Force began to move away from wide-cut fuels in the 1970s with the introduction of JP-8.[14] While several specifications of jet fuel are available today, the most prevalent is JP-8 and its commercial equivalent, Jet-A. These fuels are the benchmark for aviation; however, recent increases in cost have prompted both commercial and military aviation to look for an alternative.

The commercial airline industry may be motivated by cost to find an alternative, but for the military, cost is only one facet of the problem. Since the United States cannot feed its demand for oil domestically, it must import the majority of its oil from other countries—essentially exporting control over the fuel necessary to power the military. This lack of control over a primary energy source is a national security issue, one that requires intervention on all levels. A dependable and preferably domestic source of fuel is imperative for the Air Force to fly, fight, and win today's and tomorrow's wars. The future of American air superiority depends in part on the creation and implementation of a viable alternative jet fuel.

Another consideration is the continued availability of oil. As the demand for oil rises globally, supply will begin to fall short, leading to higher prices and increased conflict over this finite resource. How much longer oil will remain a viable American energy source is one of the most controversial questions being asked in the ongoing national dialogue on energy. The truth is that no one can accurately predict when demand will overtake supply; this issue is subject to constant speculation since the amount of oil still awaiting discovery is unknown.

The debate centers around a concept called peak oil—essentially the moment in time when half of the earth's supply of oil has been extracted.[15] Some geologists believe this point has already been reached, while others think it could still be decades away. However, once this point in time has passed, the diminishing supply of oil will make the remaining quantity increasingly difficult to find and extract. Whether or not peak oil has been reached, the volume of oil being discovered annually has been in decline since the 1960s, and existing fields are producing up to 8 percent less oil each year.[16] Waiting until the supply of oil is exhausted is not an option when a stable and secure future for the United States is at stake.

Discussion of Alternative Fuels

Alternative fuels are the way of the future, and aviation is no exception. Interest in alternative fuels is not new; in fact, both synthetic fuels and biofuels have periodically been researched and developed, and both alternatives are currently produced commercially, at least in small amounts. This section will focus on the development of synthetic fuels and biofuels and their promise as an alternative aviation fuel today. Since the Air Force is investigating both of these options, the state of military research will also be discussed.

Synthetic Fuels

Synthetic fuels offer the best alternative to oil today, and their ability to augment oil in blended fuel can immediately reduce the demand for oil in aviation by up to 50 percent. Synthetic fuels got their start in World War II, when Germany developed what is known as the FT process to create synthetic fuel from coal due to its lack of domestic or importable crude oil.[17] In simple terms, the FT process begins by combusting a carbon-based starting material to produce a gas. This gas is then fed into a reactor where it is mixed with various catalysts to produce a synthetic crude oil. This synthetic crude oil can then be refined and processed using the same systems used today for natural crude oil.[18]

Synthetic fuel production is currently limited to three primary feedstocks: CTL, GTL, and BTL.[19] These fuels can be used with minor or no modifications to today's aircraft engines and can be distributed using the existing fuel infrastructure. The FT process also yields identical fuel regardless of the starting material, meaning that fuels created from different feedstocks can easily be blended together.[20]

As of this writing, only one commercial-scale facility produces aviation fuel using FT CTL production methods. This facility, operated by the South African company Sasol, produces around 150,000 barrels of synthetic fuel a day.[21] In the United States, the Syntroleum Company has recently begun production of GTL fuel from natural gas.[22]

The Air Force's goal is to certify all of its aircraft on a 50/50 blend of JP-8 and synthetic fuel with an additional goal of flying half of the fleet on blend fuel by 2016.[23] The Air Force has already certified the B-52 and C-17 to use GTL synthetic fuel and completed testing on the B-1B, F-15, F-22, and KC-135.[24] Testing included the aerial refueling of an F-22 by a KC-135 as well as the flight of an F-15E at Mach 2.2.[25] So far, the test flights have used Syntroleum's natural gas–based fuel. However, the Air Force intends to test a coal-derived fuel later.[26]

One of the major obstacles standing in the way of full-fledged production of FT fuels is legislation passed under the Clean Air Act of 2007. Section 526 prohibits any government agency from spending taxpayer money on a fuel that emits more carbon dioxide than current fuels either during production or use.[27] Although FT fuels burn cleaner than their petroleum-based alternatives, their production yields up to twice as much carbon dioxide as compared to the production of JP-8.[28] This means that until the technology to capture or sequester carbon dioxide is improved (and the price of such technology is lowered), facilities to produce FT fuels cannot be built, and the government cannot purchase these fuels. This manufacturing problem is the biggest drawback to FT fuels. Nevertheless, these fuels have many traits that make them an appealing alternative for aviation fuel, and one that could be available today.

Biofuels

Biofuels are poised to become the alternative fuel of the future, and recent research indicates that algae possess the highest potential of any biofuel to date. Research into liquid biofuels goes back to the 1900s when the biofuel ethanol was used in the first Model T.[29] However, once large supplies of crude oil were discovered in Texas and Pennsylvania, biofuels fell out of favor with automakers, and gasoline became the cheaper fuel of choice.[30]

Three types of biofuels (defined as generations) are being explored. First-generation biofuels are the most common and include ethanol, biomass fuels, and biodiesel. These fuels are developed from any crop with a high sugar or starch content or from plant-based oils.[31] These fuels are not ideal for mass production since they compete directly with food crops for land and water.

The second generation of biofuel, called "cellulosic ethanol," comes from fibrous plant waste such as stems, leaves, or wood.[32] Unfortunately, the process for turning this plant waste into fuel, plus the amount of waste that would be required to meet our fuel needs, limits the value of this fuel.

The third generation, and the one showing the most promise, is fuel derived from algae. The idea of using algae as a fuel source is not new; in fact, the US Energy Department researched producing transportation fuel from algae in 1978. Unfortunately, this research was abandoned in 1996 with the conclusion that the cost of biofuel from algae would never be competitive with petroleum (which at that time was only $20 per barrel).[33] However, with increases in the price of oil and better technology for oil extraction, today oil from algae holds the most potential as a replacement for petroleum.

Biofuel from algae is a completely different fuel than its generation one and two counterparts. Generation one and two biofuels are created by processing the starches or sugars of plants (or plant waste) to make an ethanol-based fuel. In contrast, biofuel from algae is processed from the oil produced by microalgae organisms. These oils are lipids and triglycerides similar to what is in vegetable oil and are processed into a kerosene-type (not ethanol based) fuel.[34] This difference allows biofuel from algae to be used for more complex fuels, such as those required for aviation.

While the pursuit of synthetic fuels seems to be on hold, the Air Force is increasing its interest in biofuels. Recently, the Air Force announced its intention to acquire two types of biofuel for testing in Air Force aircraft, with the initial goal of certifying both types of fuel for use as a 50/50 blend by 2013.[35] The Air Force is not the only agency working to find an alternative aviation fuel; both Virgin Atlantic and Boeing are jointly researching the use of biofuels in commercial aviation.[36] Additionally, the Commercial Aviation Alternative Fuels Initiative was created in 2006 to work with organizations such as the Federal Aviation Administration and to research potential alternative fuels for commercial aviation, including biofuels.[37]

There is no single answer to this problem; however, it is clear that both the Air Force and commercial airlines need to develop substitutes for oil-based jet fuel—alternative fuel development and production are keys to future national security and economic stability.

Methodology and Explanation of Evaluation Criteria

Many traits have made oil the fuel of choice for aviation. Covering all of these qualities would be impractical; therefore, this paper focuses on six traits of oil-based fuels that any alternative must meet or exceed: performance capabilities, energy content, compatibility, low cost/low carbon, source, and storage/transport requirements (fig. 8.2). Although

JP-8 is used as the baseline for comparison, Jet-A (the commercial fuel of choice) is nearly identical and shares the same qualities as far as the examined traits are concerned.

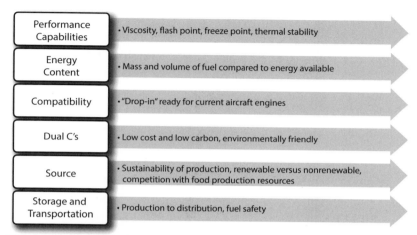

Figure 8.2. Aviation fuel traits

Performance

The first trait, and arguably the most important, is that any alternative fuel must match the performance capabilities of JP-8. While many factors encompass a fuel's performance capability, this paper analyzes four traits to determine any alternative fuel's suitability (fig. 8.3).

	GTL	CTL	Biofuel from Algae
Viscosity	√	√	√*
Flash Point	√	√	√*
Freezing Point	√	√	√*
Thermal Stability	√	√	√*

Figure 8.3. Performance analysis
√ = meets or exceeds requirements
≈ = partially meets requirements
X = does not meet requirements

Note: Performance standards for biofuel from algae have an asterisk to indicate this is the desired performance capability; this fuel is tested to verify results.

Viscosity. Viscosity is a liquid's amount of resistance to flow under pressure; this property increases as temperature decreases. If viscosity is too high, an engine cannot be relit in flight; therefore, an upper limit is specified for jet fuel.[38] The maximum viscosity for JP-8 is 8.00 centistokes at -20° Celsius (C).[39]

Flash point. Flash point is the lowest temperature at which a fuel's vapors will ignite. Due to handling and ground safety concerns, a minimum flash point of 38° C (100° Fahrenheit [F]) is specified for jet fuel.[40]

Freezing point. The freezing point for jet fuel is measured by determining the temperature at which the last solid crystal melts; therefore, this limit is much higher than the temperature at which it will completely solidify.[41] The maximum freezing point for jet fuel is -40° C.[42]

Thermal stability. The thermal stability measurement indicates a fuel's ability to absorb heat from other engine components (act as a heat sink) without breaking down into gums or particles that build up on engine components. Fuels are tested under extreme conditions to measure this property since it can take hundreds of hours of normal operation to determine inadequate thermal stability.[43] JP-8 is currently rated at 325° F for thermal stability.[44]

Energy Content

The second trait is energy content, as the primary purpose of any fuel is to provide a source of energy for power. Typically, this energy is released by breaking the bonds between carbon and hydrogen molecules within the fuel.[45] Fuel is measured for both gravimetric (mass or specific energy) and volumetric energy content, and it is desirable to have a low mass/volume compared to energy content.[46] This is important because any fuel with lower energy content would either require more fuel (more weight, decreased payload) or result in less range than an aircraft fueled with JP-8.

Compatibility

The third trait is the ability to use any new fuel in existing aircraft without changing engine or fuel system components or altering day-to-day operations. These fuels are classified as "drop-in," meaning they are interchangeable as well as mixable with today's aviation fuel.[47]

Low Cost / Low Carbon

The fourth requirement is actually two traits whose importance is intertwined. Cdr Jeffrey Eggers, in his journal article "The Fuel Gauge of National Security," calls this requirement "the dual C's: low cost and low carbon."[48] To succeed, a fuel must be similar in cost to and more environmentally friendly (less carbon emissions over the entire life cycle) than JP-8. Researchers estimate that to be competitive with current fuel costs, any replacement fuel needs to meet a two-to-three -dollars-per-gallon price frame. Fuel is required to have lower carbon emissions in accordance with the 2007 Energy Independence and Security Act. A provision within this law prohibits any government agency from purchasing an alternative fuel whose creation and/or use emits more greenhouse gases than conventional fuels.[49]

Source

The fifth trait of an alternative fuel is its source. Considerations pertaining to a fuel's source include whether production is sustainable, whether the resource is renewable or nonrenewable, and whether the fuel source competes with land or water resources used for food production.

Storage and Transport

Finally, the last traits that are important for any alternative fuel to meet are storage and transport requirements. These include requirements such as getting the fuel from production to distribution to aircraft and ensuring that the fuel is safe for ground personnel to work with.

Evaluation Results and Analysis

In this section, I analyze each of the three alternative fuels according to the six traits. Because GTL and CTL are created using the FT process, they are nearly identical fuels with the exception of their source (natural gas or coal, respectively). Both synthetic and biofuel aviation fuels are being developed using the current characteristics of JP-8. The closer they match these specifications, the more likely they will be adopted for use. With that in mind, the first three areas of evaluation (performance, energy content, compatibility) do not deviate far from the standards set by JP-8. It is in the last three areas (low cost/carbon, source, storage and transport) that the strengths and weaknesses of these future fuels can be determined. The initial production cost of these fuels is not being considered as a factor for the cost analysis portion of this paper. It would be unfair to compare these initial costs with the established mass-production costs of petroleum. The cost portion of this analysis assumes that once mass-produced, these fuels must be in the price range of two to three dollars per gallon to be competitive with the price of oil at approximately $90 a barrel.

Performance

The performance standards for synthetic fuels as well as biofuels are very close to those for JP-8. Measurements have shown that FT fuels (CTL and GTL) perform better overall than petroleum and that they have a higher flash point (less likely to catch fire on the ground), lower freezing point (can withstand colder temperatures), and better thermal stability (can handle more heat before breaking down).[50] One problem with FT fuels is that they contain no aromatics. While aromatic-free fuel is cleaner burning, these compounds allow the seals and gaskets in an aircraft's fuel system to swell and prevent fuel leaks.[51] Since FT fuels have only been used as a blend with conventional fuel, the lack of aromatics has not been a problem. If FT fuels are used alone, additives that simulate the role of aromatics should be included during the refining process. Such measures do not affect the performance of FT fuels and only ensure that engine and fuel system components continue to operate as they do with JP-8.

Less data exists about the performance capabilities of biofuels, although there are reports that the DARPA has recently manufactured a fuel identical to JP-8 using algae as the feedstock.[52] In the past, biofuels have not enjoyed much support in aviation due to their tendency to freeze close to 0° C and insufficient thermal stability. Initial research on biofuels developed from algae indicates that these problems have been solved and that a fuel matching the performance specifications of JP-8 (without blending) is possible with these biofuels.[53]

Energy Content

Second to performance, energy content is a critical factor for any replacement fuel. FT fuels are similar to jet fuel in energy content (the slightly higher gravimetric content and slightly lower volumetric content do not affect performance).[54] Biofuels typically do not have the same energy content of JP-8, falling between 10 to 50 percent short of jet fuel energy content.[55] The reason lies in the atomic structure of each fuel. Biofuels contain more oxygen bonds than their synthetic and petroleum counterparts, and unlike carbon and hydrogen bonds, these bonds yield no energy when broken.[56] Biofuel from algae shows more promise in this area since the oil from algae appears to be more similar to crude oil than what is typically extracted from a biofuel feedstock.

Compatibility

Both FT fuels and biofuel from algae are being developed so that they are drop-in ready and can immediately replace current aviation fuels (fig. 8.4). As discussed above, if FT fuels are used, aromatics must be added to avoid leaks from engine components. It is unclear if biofuel from algae would also require the addition of aromatics.

	GTL	CTL	Biofuel from Algae
"Drop-in" ready	√	√	√*

Figure 8.4. Compatibility analysis
√ = mee s or exceeds requirements
≈ = partially meets requirements
X = does not meet requirements

Low Cost/Low Carbon

The dual requirements of cost and carbon are at present the Achilles heel of alternative fuels. Both FT fuels and biofuels have certain limitations that may prevent the commercial marketplace from accepting them as alternative fuels (fig. 8.5). The cost to build a single FT refining facility is from $2 to $4 billion dollars, not including the additional costs for carbon capture and sequestration.[57] To produce enough biofuel from algae to meet today's aviation fuel demands would cost from $74 billion to $2.5 trillion (depending on what method is eventually selected to extract the oil from the algae).[58] While these amounts may seem astronomical, once mass-produced FT fuels and biofuels can likely compete with oil priced above $75 a barrel.[59] Because biofuels from algae have only been produced in small amounts and algae growth and extraction methods are still being developed, it is not possible to determine whether or not biofuel from algae can be competitively priced.

	GTL	CTL	Biofuel from Algae
$3 or less per gallon	≈	≈	X
Equal or less CO^2	X	X	√

Figure 8.5. Carbon and cost analysis
√ = meets or exceeds requirements
≈ = partially meets requirements
X = does not meet requirements

The carbon problem must also be addressed before committing to any alternative fuel choice. The European Union (EU) has proposed adding aviation emissions to existing mandatory cap-and-trade guidelines (where an airline would be responsible for purchasing carbon offsets based on the amount of carbon dioxide released); however, many non-EU commercial carriers are fighting this plan.[60] In the United States, Congress proposes to regulate the carbon dioxide standards for fuel producers instead of targeting the airlines directly.[61] In either case, carbon emissions may soon become a larger player in the cost of any aviation fuel.

FT fuels fail regarding environmental concerns due to the carbon dioxide released during their manufacture. While the prospects for carbon capture and sequestration are promising, this technology will add to the final cost of these fuels. On the other hand, biofuels not only produce 60 to 80 percent less carbon dioxide over their entire life cycle, they also feed on carbon dioxide and could be used to decrease carbon dioxide output from power plants and refineries.[62]

Source

Biofuels also outpace FT fuels when the source is considered (fig. 8.6). Both natural gas and coal are nonrenewable sources of fuel that will run out over time, much like oil. Although both coal and natural gas are sustainable today, once the US domestic supplies are exhausted, an alternative source would be required. However, biofuels are both renewable and sustainable. The supply of oil is limited only by our capacity to grow and harvest algae. Previously it was thought that the area required to grow enough algae to satisfy demand would be impractical. (In 2008 the Boeing company estimated that nearly 1 million square kilometers—an area the size of Belgium—would be required.[63]) However, scientists discovered that algae is a very flexible material and is able to grow and reproduce in sunlit tubes, below ground in total darkness, and in saltwater or sewage treatment facilities.[64] Another benefit is that algae do not compete directly with food or water resources like some other biofuels. It is this wide range of possibilities that scientists hope to exploit as they determine the best method of growing and harvesting oil from algae.

	GTL	CTL	Biofuel from Algae
Renewable	X	X	√
Sustainable	≈	≈	√

Figure 8.6. Source analysis
√ = meets or exceeds requirements
≈ = partially meets requirements
X = does not meet requirements

Storage and Transport

In all of the tests completed to date, both synthetic fuels and biofuels have met or exceeded the storage and transportation safety requirements that conventional fuels must meet. Moreover, once synthetic fuels or biofuels leave the refineries, they can be transported using the same network already established for petroleum products (fig. 8.7). Due to their similarities to jet fuel, both synthetic and biojet fuel can also be mixed with conventional aviation fuel in blends, such as the 50/50 JP-8 and GTL fuels undergoing certification by the US Air Force.[65]

	GTL	CTL	Biofuel from Algae
Safe to Store	√	√	√ *
Safe to Transport	√	√	√ *
Able to use current Infrastructure	√	√	√ *

Figure 8.7. Storage and transport analysis
√ = meets or exceeds requirements
≈ = partially meets requirements
X = does not meet requirements

Summary of Analysis

The summary chart (fig. 8.8) shows that biofuel from algae holds clear advantages over FT fuels in terms of low carbon emissions, renewability, and sustainability. The only relative advantage of FT fuels is that they may be cheaper than biofuel from algae; however, this benefit may vanish once the costs for carbon capture and sequestration are factored in. All three fuels meet performance, energy content, and operability requirements for use in both military and commercial aircraft. In addition, all of these fuels can be stored and transported using the current petroleum infrastructure. Finally, the four areas that are marginal for FT fuels (cost, carbon, renewable, and sustainable) are also marginal for oil. The one advantage FT fuels, especially CTL fuels, have over oil is the source: the EIA estimates that the United States has more recoverable coal than any other nation, and as a region, North America is second only to eastern Europe (including Russia).[66]

	GTL	CTL	Biofuel from Algae
Performance	√	√	√
Energy Content	√	√	√
Compatibility	√	√	√
Low Cost	≈	≈	X
Low Carbon	X	X	√
Renewable	X	X	√ *
Sustainable	≈	≈	√
Storage/Transport	√	√	√ *

Figure 8.8. Summary of analysis
√ = meets or exceeds requirements
≈ = partially meets requirements
X = does not meet requirements

There is one further area to discuss when evaluating these fuels—time. While biofuels appear to be the ideal petroleum replacement, we are just beginning to understand their production and development. The US Energy Department believes that lowering the price of fuel from algae to a competitive level will take from five to 10 more years; increasing levels of production to meet demand could take even longer.[67] FT fuels are capable of being produced today, but compliance with the emissions standards set by the 2007 Energy Independence and Security Act will take time to develop and implement. One of the biggest barriers to alternative fuels in aviation is that despite their capabilities and benefits, neither of these fuels are ready to take the place of oil today.

Conclusion and Recommendations

Oil, once plentiful and cheap, has become an unpredictable resource that can no longer be depended upon as the primary energy source for the world. In the United States, finding a domestic source of fuel is essential for economic and national security concerns. Today, the search for an alternative energy supply has expanded to include aviation. Although aircraft have used oil-based fuels from the beginning, the technology and motivation to develop an alternative aviation fuel are finally at hand.

The three alternatives showing the most promise for aviation are CTL, GTL, and biofuels from algae. Analyzing these fuels and comparing their common traits with those of JP-8 show that both synthetics and biofuel from algae meet or exceed the performance specifications expected of jet fuel. In addition, none of the fuels examined requires changes to aircraft engine components or the storage and transport methods already in place for aviation fuel. However, CTL and GTL face the same problem as oil in that they are nonrenewable and nonsustainable; additionally, they have a higher carbon dioxide footprint than does oil. Biofuels are low carbon, renewable, and sustainable but may require at least another decade before they are ready for commercial production.

The Air Force has been working to develop an alternative fuel for military aviation and until recently was focusing solely on FT fuels developed from coal or natural gas. However, the spotlight on the high carbon levels associated with the production of these fuels has halted the fuels' development, at least temporarily. Furthermore, the recent advances in developing biofuel from algae have garnered the military's attention, and plans to test this fuel are in the works. The Air Force must now decide which option is better: investing in the carbon capture technology required to bring FT fuels on line or remaining dependent on oil and placing all bets on biofuel from algae.

If the Air Force continues to pursue FT fuels, a higher initial investment will be required to cover the extra costs associated with carbon capture. As oil prices decrease, justifying this additional cost will become more difficult for the Air Force and commercial airlines. However, the long-term benefits of investing in FT fuels outweigh these initial costs, especially if the price of oil skyrockets. If the Air Force does not pursue FT fuels, oil will remain the only source of aircraft fuel for at least the next decade. With the volatility of today's oil market, it is impossible to calculate the costs of having no alternative to oil for another 10 years.

By continuing to pursue biofuels, the Air Force will increase the potential for moving completely away from oil-based aviation fuel. However, making this happen will take time and money. If the Air Force does not pursue biofuels, it will fall behind the alternative-fuels power curve; the civilian sector will continue to pursue these and other alternative aviation fuels. However, military involvement in biofuels means increased investment, higher product demand, and typically more stringent testing. Commercial airlines may not have the motivation or capital to develop biofuels without the investment and support of the military.

I recommend that the Air Force continue to pursue both FT fuels and biofuel from algae. While the initial costs of FT fuels may be high, these fuels are ready to be produced at a commercial level and can immediately decrease the oil required for jet fuel by 50 percent. Since these fuels have been certified for use in commercial aircraft, partnerships between the military and commercial airlines could help diffuse the initial costs of getting FT production up and running, as well as the investment costs of carbon capture and storage technology.

However, FT fuels are a temporary solution, and the goal of finding a permanent replacement for oil must continue. Biofuel from algae could be that solution. It is renewable and sustainable, and initial research indicates that biofuel from algae can be manufactured into a fuel identical to today's jet fuel. By remaining involved in both programs, the Air Force can utilize FT fuels to reduce aviation's reliance on oil today while simultaneously developing biofuels as the future of aviation fuel and a replacement for oil tomorrow. The Air Force has a unique role in this research, and unlike the commercial airlines, its decisions will extend beyond aviation and can impact both the future economic stability and national security of the United States.

Notes

1. EIA, "Petroleum Basic Statistics."
2. Ibid.
3. Eggers, "Fuel Gauge of National Security," 12.
4. Williams, "Military Planners Explore Options."
5. Ibid.
6. Altman, "Global Climate Change."
7. EIA, "World Estimated Recoverable Coal."
8. William Matthews, "From Algae to JP-8: Pentagon's DARPA Funds Efforts to Make a Green Jet Fuel," *Air Force Times*, 5 January 2009, http://www.defensenews.com /story.php?i=3885995.
9. Gayle S. Putrich and Vago Muradian, "Rising Fuel Prices Change Air Force Ops— Officials Look for Ways to Become More Efficient," *Air Force Times*, 28 July 2008, 10.
10. Ibid.
11. "History of Jet Fuel."
12. Ibid.
13. Ibid.
14. Hemighaus et al., *Aviation Fuels Technical Review*, 1.
15. Roberts, "Tapped Out," 87.
16. Ibid., 88.
17. Chandler, "Fueling the Future," 39.
18. Kopp, *US Air Force Synthetic Fuels Program*, 4.
19. Williams, "Military Planners Explore Options."
20. Hemighaus et al., *Alternative Jet Fuels*, 6.
21. Williams, "Military Planners Explore Options."
22. Kopp, *US Air Force Synthetic Fuels Program*, 10.
23. Upson, "U.S. Air Force Synthetic-Fuel Program in Limbo."
24. Price, "Flying the Coal-Fired Skies," 1.
25. Upson, "U.S. Air Force Synthetic-Fuel Program in Limbo."
26. Ibid.
27. Price, "Flying the Coal-Fired Skies," 2.
28. Ott, "Algae Advances," 66.
29. EIA, "Ethanol—A Renewable Fuel."
30. Smith, "Biofuels."
31. Ibid.
32. Ibid.
33. Matthews, "From Algae to JP-8."
34. Smith, "Biofuels."
35. Anselmo, "USAF Launches Major Biofuel Initiative."
36. Gaffney, "Fly the Eco-Friendly Skies," 40.
37. Altman, "Global Climate Change."
38. Hemighaus et al., *Aviation Fuels Technical Review*, 7.

39. ExxonMobil Aviation, *World Jet Fuel Specifications*, 8.
40. Hemighaus et al., *Aviation Fuels Technical Review*, 10.
41. Ibid., 7.
42. Hemighaus et al., *Alternative Jet Fuels*, 8.
43. Hemighaus et al., *Aviation Fuels Technical Review*, 5.
44. Ibid., 31.
45. Hemighaus et al., *Alternative Jet Fuels*, 2.
46. Ibid.
47. Altman, "Global Climate Change."
48. Eggers, "Fuel Gauge of National Security," 12.
49. Kauffman, "Pentagon's Plans Hit Turbulence," 4.
50. Chandler, "Fueling the Future," 40.
51. Hemighaus et al., *Alternative Jet Fuels*, 5.
52. Chandler, "Exotic No More," 50.
53. Ibid.
54. Ibid.
55. Chandler, "Fueling the Future," 41.
56. Hemighaus et al., *Alternative Jet Fuels*, 2.
57. Chandler, "Fueling the Future," 41.
58. Ott, "Algae Advances," 66.
59. Ibid.
60. Caruso, "Carbon in the Skies," 15.
61. Ibid.
62. Chandler, "Exotic No More," 52.
63. Ott, "Algae Advances," 66.
64. Chandler, "Exotic No More," 53.
65. Ott, "Algae Advances," 66.
66. EIA, "World Estimated Recoverable Coal."
67. Matthews, "From Algae to JP-8."

Chapter 9

Conclusion

Dr. John T. Ackerman and Dr. Kathleen Mahoney-Norris

The distinct and multifaceted future trends examined in this collection share the recurring theme of their potential effect on US national security. The authors investigated specific research topics thoroughly but with the clear insistence that their studies are not the last word and that more analysis of the topics—as well as monitoring of future warning signs—is needed. Forecasting what is possible and desirable, as the summaries below indicate, requires persistence, diligence, and foresight.

Maj Kelvin S. Fan's qualitative investigation into the future impacts of the "mercenarizing" of the US government clearly identifies this trend as a threat to US national security. The lack of private military company regulations, transparency, and accountability damages the US strategic image and hinders the accomplishment of key security objectives. His research succinctly identifies three negative trends that US government officials need to be cognizant of:

- Tactical but short-term successes of private military companies (PMC) have undermined strategic efforts; poaching practices can potentially weaken US military forces in the long term.

- Several recent high-profile PMC missteps have damaged the global opinion of the United States and undermined current and future activities to bolster freedom, justice, and human dignity internationally.

- The lack of legally enforceable regulation, accountability, and transparency undercuts the United States' overriding support for fairness, democracy, and the rule of law.

If decision makers within the US government recognize the negative trends Fan identifies and use those trends as starting points for a substantial and dedicated dialogue toward reversing them, then their selective use of PMCs may be productive and positive. However, if these leaders ignore trends and continue down the path of less regulation, transparency, and accountability, PMCs will become a "bane for national security" and a blight on US national interests around the world. Fan concludes that follow-up into how these trends are evolving requires consistent and detailed monitoring of PMC activity both at home and abroad.

Lt Col Kelly L. Varitz's evaluation of plausible Western European futures highlights many aspects of US-European security relations. As the population of Western Europe ages and European states become more reliant on external energy sources, those states will have to make some difficult choices. The challenging decisions will directly influence the security relationship between the United States and our European allies. Will Western European nations become more isolationist as their gross domestic products and cohorts of military-age youth shrink? Will massive influxes of migrant youths from cultures alien to Western European society assimilate rapidly and painlessly, or will Western European culture be forced to evolve toward the new norms and values of the migrants? Will Western Europe become wholly dependent on Russian energy sources, susceptible to Russian foreign policy impulses and eventually a vassal to Moscow's power? Irrespective of which future becomes reality, US national security professionals must be aware of the possible defense implications and consequences, monitor the trends, and prepare diligently for each uncertain future.

Lt Col Lourdes M. Duvall's in-depth look at key aspects of approaching developments in information technology reveals the critical prominence of human cognition and its relationships to Air Force command and control (C2) activities. She reviews the current USAF C2 vision and key capabilities required for future C2 operations, basic concepts of human information processing, and human-systems interaction. Her insightful recognition of the importance of these facets of situational awareness shines a necessary spotlight on how essential this area is to USAF C2 dominance on the battlefield. In addition, she illustrates the ongoing status of USAF C2 operations by using an air and space operations center (AOC) as an example. Duvall exposes the remarkable recent advances in C2 as well as the specific limitations of the current approach to C2 system design and integration with respect to human factors and human-computer interaction. She also crafts a plan for C2 system design, development, and implementation that seeks to enhance human cognitive strengths and mitigate inherent limitations. Duvall's recommendations are supported by human factors and human-computer interaction field research, including tactical flying operations. Finally, she proposes a forward-leaning conclusion that "to maintain and expand our advantage in C2, the human aspects of information processing, decision making, and human-system interaction must be understood and integrated in the USAF C2 vision."

The basic undertone of Lt Col Christopher S. Kean and CDR David C. Kneale's research is the necessity of vigilance. They conclude that climate change in the Arctic should be seen as a warning and should underpin future security policy decisions. They also stress that our current international relations paradigms are inadequate for informing Arctic security discussions and policy making. Kean and Kneale suggest that "the shared natural environment and its understanding through the scientific community may be the new drivers to shape the political response to climate change." As a consequence, they advise implementing ecologically grounded economic, political, technological, and security processes that enhance global cooperation and collaborative efforts, especially in the fragile and dynamic polar environments. US national security decision makers would do well to heed these warnings and recommendations.

Lt Col Jack Donahue's survey of impending threats to domestic and international security created by the growing quantities of orbital space debris should spur more intense global efforts to address this potentially catastrophic challenge. A collision between a manned spacecraft and one of the thousands of pieces of junk orbiting the planet could be deadly. Also, a marble-sized piece of space trash crashing into a commercial communications satellite could shut down global finance, banking, and Internet commerce for extended periods. Donahue documents these future threats, explores their ramifications, hypothesizes potential futures, and identifies plausible courses of action to meet the orbital debris challenge. Notably, his recommendations for effectively mitigating the debris threat provide a valid and credible starting point for reducing the risk of disaster today. In particular, Donahue maintains that coming changes in space technology will have huge consequences on the space debris challenge as new technological advances could rapidly decrease the amount of orbiting trash. But global cooperation and collaboration are needed to research, develop, and deploy the new technologies. He recommends hardening new satellites against collisions; building new, more robust space-debris-monitoring capabilities; and planning/implementing backup systems to current and future satellite systems/

competencies. Donahue also recognizes that the United States cannot alleviate the space debris problem alone and will need international assistance to meet this challenge. His final statement clearly highlights the urgency surrounding this threat: "The world can change the potential alarming future of a catastrophic collision from orbital debris. The time to act is now."

Lt Col Amanda S. Birch offers an in-depth analysis of an emerging technology that has utility across several security planning domains. Microbial fuel cells (MFC) can provide energy and clean water during conventional or major theater conflicts, when terrorists destroy or damage key energy or freshwater infrastructures, or when they strike at home or abroad after hurricanes, tornadoes, earthquakes, or other destructive natural disasters. She indicates that MFCs are "a flexible technology capable of enabling effects across the entire range of military operations and, as a bonus, they will also quickly pay for themselves." Conversely, she concludes that the development of MFC technology will require more than just an infusion of research and development funds. Widespread availability of MFC technology will become a reality in the future only if the Defense Department enables "a collaborative approach that addresses not only the technological barriers at the scientific and systems integration level but also the key social, industrial, and political hurdles as well." Birch convincingly argues that planning for our future national security challenges will always include the need for clean water and a nearly limitless energy supply, regardless if the threat is focused on combat operations or humanitarian disaster relief. She also cautions that now is the time to act.

Finally, Maj Yvonne Gurnick's inquiry into alternative fuel supplies for the Air Force begins and ends with a clear admonition: "Oil, once plentiful and cheap, has become an unpredictable resource that can no longer be depended upon as the primary energy source for the world." From her research, she finds that the USAF faces a fork in the road that will dramatically alter its future. "The Air Force must now decide which option is better: investing in the carbon capture technology required to bring FT [Fischer-Tropsch] fuels online or remaining dependent on oil and placing all bets on biofuel from algae." Gurnick offers FT fuels as a solution for today and as a bridge from current dependence on the volatile oil market to future employment of the newest technologies using algae. She emphasizes that for national security reasons, the USAF should remain engaged in fuels research now and in the near future.

The futures research presented in this text is orientated toward two audiences. Some researchers focused their efforts on understanding trends in light of their application to improving decision making in the US security policy arena. Others explored, in a rigorous academic fashion, critical technological trends that could most influence US national security in the near future. Decision-oriented futures research will help policy makers identify the most relevant and pressing critical factors or driving forces. The academic approach often exposes a range of technological trends, assessing their impacts against a specific set of assumptions or criteria.[1] Both methods have started dialogue on emerging trends that futures researchers as well as US national security leaders should continue. Together, these approaches should help decision makers "illuminate policy choices, identify and evaluate alternative actions, and, at least to some degree, avoid pitfalls and grasp the opportunities of the future."[2]

Notes

1. Glenn, "Introduction to the Futures Research," 8.
2. Ibid., 6.

Appendix A

Isotherm Arctic Map

(Courtesy of National Snow and Ice Data Center, Perry-Castañeda Library map collection.)

Appendix B

Sea Ice Melting

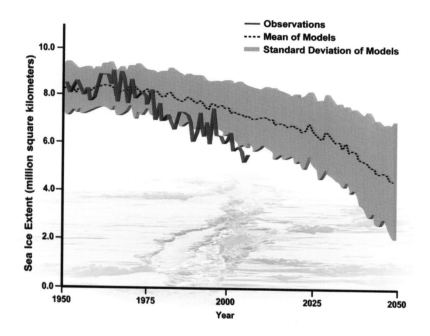

September sea ice extent: observations and model runs. (Courtesy of the University Corporation for Atmospheric Research, http://www .ucar .edu/news/releases/2007/images/arctic_sea_ice_extent6.jpg.)

Appendix C

Indigenous Arctic Populations

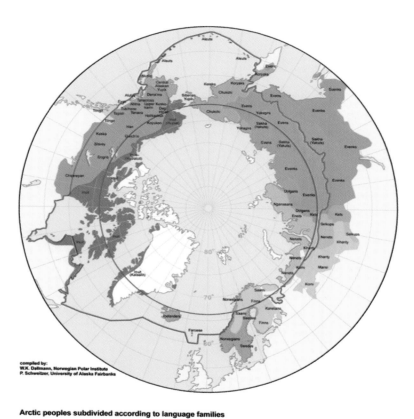

Arctic peoples subdivided according to language families

Indo-European family	
Germanic branch	
Uralic family	
Finno-Ugric branch	
Samoyedic branch	
Altaic family	
Turkic branch	
Tungusic branch	
Chukotko-Kamchatkan fam.	

Isolated languages	
(Ketic and Yukagir)	
Eskimo-Aleut family	
Inuit group (of Eskimo br.)	
Yupik group (of Eskimo br.)	
Aleut branch	
Na-Dene family	
Athabaskan branch	
Eyak branch	
Tlingit branch	

------- Arctic circle
------- Arctic boundary according to AMAP

Notes:

Areas show colours according to the original languages of the respective indigenous peoples, even if they do not speak their languages today.

Overlapping populations are not shown. The map does not claim to show exact boundaries between the individual language groups.

Typical colonial populations, which are not traditional Arctic populations, are not shown (Danes in Greenland, Russians in the Russian Federation, non-native Americans in North America).

(Map courtesy of Arctic Council, http://www.arctic-council.org/images/ maps/indig_peoples.pdf. Compiled by Winfried K. Dallmann, Norwegian Polar Institute.)

Appendix D

Ilulissat Declaration

The Ilulissat Declaration
Arctic Ocean Conference
Ilulissat, Greenland, 27–29 May 2008

At the invitation of the Danish minister for foreign affairs and the premier of Greenland, representatives of the five coastal states bordering the Arctic Ocean—Canada, Denmark, Norway, the Russian Federation, and the United States—met at the political level on 28 May 2008 in Ilulissat, Greenland, to hold discussions. They adopted the following declaration:

The Arctic Ocean stands at the threshold of significant changes. Climate change and the melting of ice have a potential impact on vulnerable ecosystems, the livelihoods of local inhabitants and indigenous communities, and the potential exploitation of natural resources.

By virtue of their sovereignty, sovereign rights, and jurisdiction in large areas of the Arctic Ocean, the five coastal states are in a unique position to address these possibilities and challenges. In this regard, we recall that an extensive international legal framework applies to the Arctic Ocean as discussed between our representatives at the meeting in Oslo on 15 and 16 October 2007 at the level of senior officials. Notably, the law of the sea provides for important rights and obligations concerning the delineation of the outer limits of the continental shelf, the protection of the marine environment, including ice-covered areas, freedom of navigation, marine scientific research, and other uses of the sea. We remain committed to this legal framework and to the orderly settlement of any possible overlapping claims.

This framework provides a solid foundation for responsible management by the five coastal States and other users of this Ocean through national implementation and application of relevant provisions. We therefore see no need to develop a new comprehensive international legal regime to govern the Arctic Ocean. We will keep abreast of the developments in the Arctic Ocean and continue to implement appropriate measures.

The Arctic Ocean is a unique ecosystem, which the five coastal states have a stewardship role in protecting. Experience has shown how shipping disasters and subsequent pollution of the marine environment may cause irreversible disturbance of the ecological balance and major harm to the livelihoods of local inhabitants and indigenous communities. We will take steps in accordance with international law both nationally and in cooperation among the five states and other interested parties to ensure the protection and preservation of the fragile marine environment of the Arctic Ocean. In this regard we intend to work together including through the International Maritime Organization to strengthen existing measures and develop new measures to improve the safety of maritime navigation and prevent or reduce the risk of ship-based pollution in the Arctic Ocean.

The increased use of Arctic waters for tourism, shipping, research, and resource development also increases the risk of accidents and therefore the need to further strengthen search and rescue capabilities and capacity around the Arctic Ocean to ensure an appropriate response from states to any accident. Cooperation, including on the sharing of information, is a prerequisite for addressing these challenges. We will work to promote safety of life at sea in the Arctic Ocean, including through bilateral and multilateral arrangements between or among relevant states.

The five coastal states currently cooperate closely in the Arctic Ocean with each other and with other interested parties. This cooperation includes the collection of scientific data concerning the continental shelf, the protection of the marine environment, and other scientific research. We will work to strengthen this cooperation, which is based on mutual trust and transparency, inter alia, through timely exchange of data and analyses.[1]

Note

1. Ilulissat Declaration, "Arctic Ocean Conference," Ilulissat, Greenland, 27–29 May 2008: 27-29.

Appendix E

Maritime Jurisdiction and Boundaries in the Arctic Region

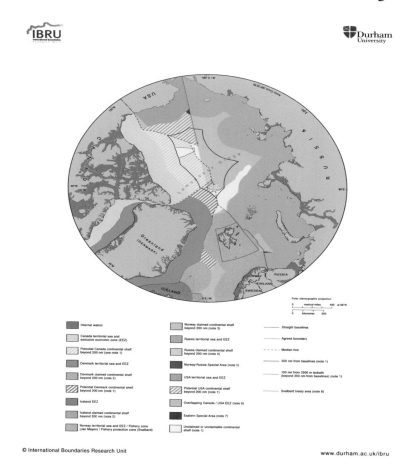

(Map courtesy of Durham University International Boundaries Research Unit, http://www.dur.ac.uk/resources/ibru/arctic.pdf.)

Appendix F

Bering Strait and the Chukchi Sea

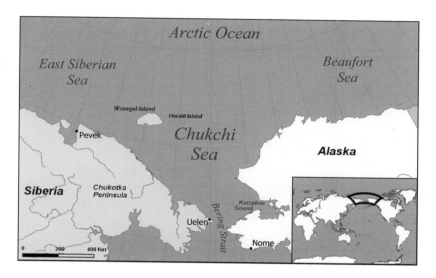

(Map courtesy of Wikipedia.com, http://en.wikipedia.org/wiki/Chukchi _Sea, Creative Commons Attribution-Share Alike 3.0 Unported license.)

Appendix G

Applications and Collaboration Partners

Microbial fuel cells (MFC) have many potential applications within DOD and beyond. The figure below lists some applications and the agencies that are potential collaboration partners.

Application relevance tree

Because of the broad applicability of MFCs, collaboration could provide synergy in bringing MFC capabilities to fruition. The following website provides an overview of research groups currently investigating MFCs: http://www.microbialfuelcell.org.

Appendix H

Microbial Fuel Cell Relevance Tree

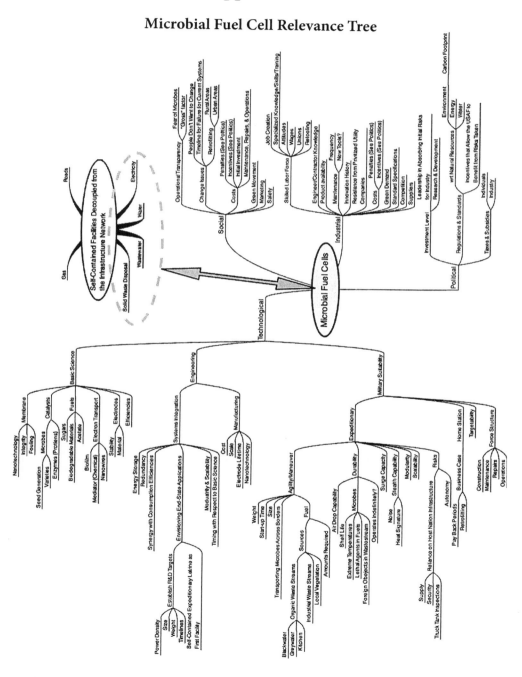

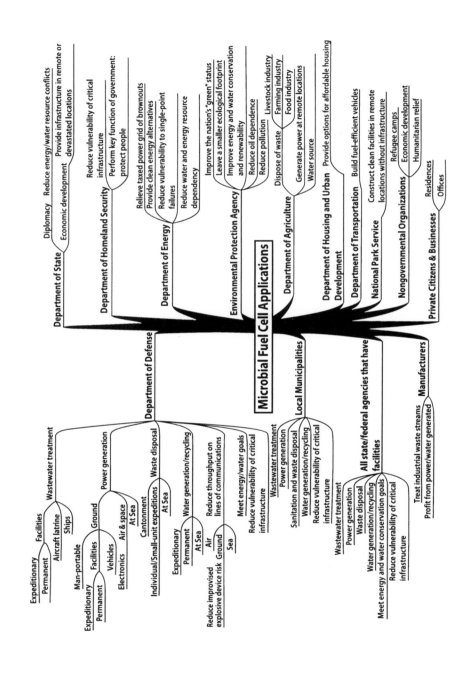

Microbial Fuel Cell Applications

Department of State
- Diplomacy
- Reduce energy/water resource conflicts
- Economic development
- Provide infrastructure in remote or devastated locations

Department of Homeland Security
- Reduce vulnerability of critical infrastructure
- Perform key function of government: protect people

Department of Energy
- Relieve taxed power grid of brownouts
- Provide clean energy alternatives
- Reduce vulnerability to single-point failures
- Reduce water and energy resource dependency

Environmental Protection Agency
- Improve the nation's "green" status
- Leave a smaller ecological footprint
- Improve energy and water conservation and renewability
- Reduce oil dependence
- Reduce pollution

Department of Agriculture
- Livestock industry
- Farming industry
- Food industry
- Dispose of waste
- Generate power at remote locations
- Water source

Department of Housing and Urban Development
- Provide options for affordable housing

Department of Transportation
- Build fuel-efficient vehicles

National Park Service
- Construct clean facilities in remote locations without infrastructure

Nongovernmental Organizations
- Refugee camps
- Economic development
- Humanitarian relief

Private Citizens & Businesses
- Residences
- Offices

Department of Defense
- Expeditionary
- Permanent
  - Facilities
  - Aircraft latrine
  - Ships
- Wastewater treatment
- Man-portable
- Expeditionary
- Permanent
  - Facilities
  - Vehicles
  - Ground
  - Electronics
  - Air & space
  - At Sea
- Power generation
- Cantonment
- Individual/Small-unit expeditions
  - At Sea
- Waste disposal
- Expeditionary
- Permanent
  - Air
  - Ground
  - Sea
- Water generation/recycling
- Reduce improvised explosive device risk
- Reduce throughput on lines of communications
- Meet energy/water goals
- Reduce vulnerability of critical infrastructure

Local Municipalities
- Wastewater treatment
- Power generation
- Sanitation and waste disposal
- Water generation/recycling
- Reduce vulnerability of critical infrastructure

All state/federal agencies that have facilities
- Wastewater treatment
- Power generation
- Waste disposal
- Water generation/recycling
- Meet energy and water conservation goals
- Reduce vulnerability of critical infrastructure

Manufacturers
- Treat industrial waste streams
- Profit from power/water generated

Appendix I

Competing and Complementary Microbial Fuel Cell Technologies Biofuels and Biomass

Microbial fuel cells (MFC) are not fed by biofuels or biomass. They can digest organic materials, some of which could be called biomass, but the primary purpose of an MFC is to treat wastewater and capture electrons as microbes digest the carbon-rich fuels. While tailored MFCs could probably digest harvested biomass, they are meant to dispose of organic waste rather than create demand for plant life to be used as fuels. In addition, unlike biofuels, MFCs do not convert biological material into synthetic fuels or gas to be used to fuel other systems such as vehicles. MFCs directly convert nuisance waste into useable power.

Hydrogen Fuel Cells

MFCs are not the same as hydrogen fuel cells, though the technologies have parallel components. The basic setup of hydrogen fuel cells and MFCs is the same, but the fuels and catalysts are different. Hydrogen fuel cells must have hydrogen fuel, which is costly to produce and uses more energy to create than the fuel cell can output. In hydrogen fuel cells, platinum (which is also expensive), rather than microbes, serves as a catalyst to split the molecule and harvest the electrons. Both technologies consume fuel, which differentiates them from batteries, but the consumable fuels and the reaction catalysts are different.

Protein-Based (or Enzyme-Based) Fuel Cells

MFCs are not protein- or enzyme-based fuel cells. Both are biological fuel cells, but enzyme-based fuel cells use purified enzymes from reduction and oxidation reactions, rather than complete microbial cells, as the catalysts. Both technologies have characteristics that allow them to fill different niches. The microbial catalysts in the MFC could theoretically be sustained forever as they regenerate themselves. Different organisms could also be combined to allow fuel flexibility, which would be highly valued for ground applications. Unlike microbes, enzymes could theoretically allow more complete electron harvesting since living microbes consume some of the chemical energy to survive and reproduce. Enzyme fuel cells, therefore, could potentially be a more dense power source more suitable to air and space vehicle applications.[1]

Solar Power

MFCs are not solar power. They do not use photovoltaics, space-based power vectoring, or solar thermal energy. MFCs are a good candidate, however, to couple with solar power to fill existing limitations. The USAF already has prototype expeditionary, flexible facilities with integrated photovoltaics.[2]

Wind Power

MFCs are obviously not wind power. MFCs, however, are a good candidate to couple with wind power to fill existing limitations.

Desalination Plants

MFCs are not desalination plants, and they do not replace the reverse osmosis water purification unit (ROWPU) that the USAF currently uses in expeditionary settings. MFCs can operate in salt water to produce energy (often called sediment batteries), but they will not convert salt water to potable water because the microbes metabolize carbon-based compounds, not salt.[3]

Notes

1. These ideas concerning differences and potential applications of the different types of biological fuels cells came from Maj Jennifer Gresham (Air Force Office of Scientific Research), phone interview with the author, 16 November 2007.
2. Keith, "BEAR Base Solar Power System."
3. Reimers et al., "Microbial Fuel Cell Energy."

Appendix J

Key Microbial Fuel Cell Capabilities and Challenges

Capabilities	*Challenges*
Within 48 hours, enables secure, basic ground services (water, electricity, and waste disposal) apart from the vulnerable infrastructure network, at both permanent and expeditionary locations, in a clean and efficient manner	Sufficient waste volumes
	Microbe vulnerability
	Social acceptance
	Reluctance to invest in facility technologies
Eliminates need for fuel and water to flow through LOCs (reduces risks/vulnerabilities/costs)	Resistance from utility and construction industry
Reduces water requirement by at least 70 percent	Timeline to convert homeland infrastructure
Sanitarily disposes of 100 percent of sewage and other carbon-rich waste	Must be coupled with demand-reducing technologies (energy and water
Reduces water requirement by at least 70 percent	
Generates 600+ W of power per person—25 percent of an expeditionary base power requirement	
For a 150,000-person deployment	
• Saves 2 million gallons/day of water	
• Saves 180,000 gallons/day of fuel	
• Saves $50 million/day in fuel operating costs (fuel price plus transport cost)	
Prevents natural resource conflicts	
Generates power with no heat/ noise	

PLATE 8

Appendix K

Basic Cost Analysis

This is a basic cost analysis for a 1,100-person expeditionary base and includes potential savings in both electrical power and water with implementation of efficient MFC systems.

Electrical Power

Table K.1. Organic power sources at 1,100-person expeditionary base

Potential Power Source	MMBTU[a]/day[b]	~kW[c]
Black/Gray Water	2+	30
Food Waste	4+	50
Paper/Cardboard	40	480
Wood	10	120
Total	56	680

[a] Million British thermal units

[b] Waste characterizations for "00-Staff, 50-Hospital Bed Bare Bases" were provided in tables labeled "Battelle Report" and "ACC/WMO Report" from Johnson and Diltz in discussion with author.

[c] Kilowatts

Mobile Expeditionary Power (MEP)-12A Generator[1]

Rated capacity: 750 kW
Actual output capacity: 625 kW
Fuel consumption rate: 1,320 gallons per day (568 watts [W]/gal/day)
Cost: $165,000
Weight: 25,000 pounds

Expeditionary Base Power Planning Factor

2.7 kW per person[2] (four MEP-12s/1,100 people)

MFCs, therefore, could supply about 25 percent of the required base power and replace one of the four MEP-12A generators at a 1,100-person location if 90 percent of the waste's potential energy could be captured.

Fuel Costs (per gallon)

Standard cost: $3.04[3]
Delivered cost via USAF tanker: $52.50[4]
Delivered cost (conservative) to remote operating location: $300[5]

Amount Saved Daily by Substituting an MFC for One MEP-12A

Standard cost: $3.04/gal x 1,320 gal/day = $4K/day
Cost for fuel delivered via USAF: $52.50 x 1,320 gal/day = $69K/day
Cost for fuel delivered to a remote operating location: $300 x 1,320 gal/day = $400K/day
Cost savings for 150,000-person deployment: $50M/day

Amount Saved Daily by Substituting Gray/Black Water Only for 30 kW of Power

Gallons of fuel saved: 30 kW ÷ 568 W/gal/day = 50 gal/day
Standard cost: $3.04/gal x 50 gal/day = $150/day
Cost for fuel delivered via USAF: $52.50 x 50 gal/day = $2.5K/day
Cost for fuel delivered to a remote operating location: $300 x 50 gal/day = $15K/day

Water

Water use planning factor (expeditionary): 20 gal/person/day[6]
Water use planning factor (permanent): 50 gal/person/day[7]
Wastewater planning factor: 14 gal/person/day[8]
The typical expeditionary plan calls for wastewater disposal via evaporation lagoons, so 14 gal/person/day is lost via evaporation that could be reclaimed with MFCs.
Water savings percentage: 14 gal/person/day ÷ 20 gal/person/day = 70 percent
Total water saved/day for a 1,100 person base: 14 gal/person/day x 1,100 people = 15K gal/day

Literature Estimates

Dr. Bruce Logan estimates that "this system would produce 51 kilowatts on the waste from 100,000 people."[9] Logan's calculation includes only gray water and black water, and he predicts 0.5 W/person.

Notes

1. Air Force Handbook 10-222, vol. 10, *Guide to Harvest Falcon*; and vol. 2, *Guide to Bare Base Assets*, 34.

2. Air Force Handbook 10-222, vol. 10, *Guide to Harvest Falcon*; and vol. 2, *Guide to Bare Base Assets*, 75.

3. Grant, "Surging Oil Prices."

4. The 2001 delivered fuel cost was "$17.50 per gallon for USAF worldwide tanker-delivered fuel." Since the standard cost of fuel tripled from 2001 to 2008, $17.50 x 3 = $52.50 is the 2008 delivered cost estimate. Defense Science Board Task Force on Improving Fuel Efficiency of Weapons Platforms, *More Capable Warfighting*, ES-3, 20. For additional validation of this estimate, see Col Elwood Amidon, briefing, subject: Needed Now, slide 22.

5. In 2001, the cost of delivered fuel was "hundreds of dollars per gallon for Army forces deep into the battlespace." Defense Science Board Task Force on Improving Fuel Efficiency of Weapons Platforms, *More Capable Warfighting*, ES-3. Other sources suggest this number could be as high as $600 per gallon. See Dimotakis, Grober, and Lewis, *Reducing DOD Fossil-Fuel Dependence*, 20.

6. Air Force Pamphlet 10-219, vol. 5, *Bare Base Conceptual Planning Guide*, 87.

7. Ibid., 86.

8. Ibid., 115.

9. Biever, "Plugging into the Power of Sewage."

Appendix L

Microbial Fuel Cells

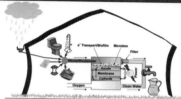

Blue Horizons 2008

OPERATIONS CONCEPT
- Phase 0-I: Provide water/energy to prevent conflicts and for economic stability/growth
- Phase 0-V: Build stealthy/maneuverable cities with no infrastructure/LOCs for power/water/waste
- Phase IV-V: Quickly provide water/power/ sanitation post-conflict to enable gov't legitimacy
- Post Natural Disaster: Provide essential services
- Homeland Security: Reduce physical/cyber infrastructure vulnerabilities

CAPABILITIES
- Enables remote facility operations
- Packaged system meets 100% ground power requirements with no heat/noise
- Meets 100% waste/sewage disposal requirements
- Provides a secure potable water source
- Daily savings for 150K-person deployment
  - $50M (fuel cost + transport)
  - 2M gallons H2O (70% reduction)
  - 180K gallons fuel (25% reduction)
- Reduces risk associated with critical vulnerabilities at infrastructure nodes & in LOCs

ENABLING TECHNOLOGIES
- Portable Autonomous Ground Power Systems (5.2.3.4)
- High Energy Density Fuel/Material – DC (4.2.2.6)
- High-capacity, multiple-cycle, distributed power storage technology
- Nanotechnology (membranes and nanowires)
- Biotechnology (microbe behavior and biofilms)

Microbial fuel cells quad chart. (Created by the author).

Appendix M

Tech Sheet

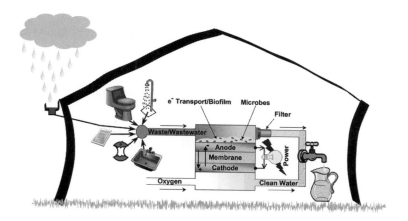

Microbial fuel cells (MFC) convert wastewater and organic material to clean water and electricity. MFCs are fed by sewage, gray water (shower and laundry water), storm water, industrial waste, kitchen scraps, paper, wood, or any other type of organic matter. Through anaerobic metabolism at the anode, microbes restore wastewater to a recyclable quality and produce electrons that can be captured for power. The byproduct of the reaction is potentially potable-quality water.

MFCs operate on principles similar to those of hydrogen fuel cells, but neither hydrogen nor a sealed cathode in an oxygen-pure environment is required. Power is not the only benefit; MFCs also sanitarily dispose of organic waste and produce clean water.

Possible Concept of Operations

MFCs should be coupled with other technologies to meet 100 percent of the power, water, wastewater, and solid waste disposal requirements autonomously and covertly—without sustainment support from LOCs or an infrastructure network.

- Phase 0–V (Shape, Deter, Seize Initiative, Dominate, Stabilize, Enable Civil Authority)

° Establish maneuverable bases that are light, transportable, and modular requiring no heavy equipment to build, no utilities infrastructure to support, and no fuels to sustain.

° Generate power without a heat signature or noise (flight line operations or facility power).

* Phase 0–1 (Shape, Deter)

° Prevent conflicts sparked by water and energy resource demand

° *National Security Strategy* (*NSS*): "Expand the circle of development by opening societies and building the infrastructure of democracy."[1]

° *NSS*: "Ignite a new era of global economic growth through free markets and free trade," which includes "secure, clean energy development."[2]

* Phase IV–V (Stabilize, Enable Civil Authority)

° Provide water, sanitation, and power postconflict or post–natural disaster.

° Provide essential services (remote or urban) without major construction or resources.

° Quickly give nascent government legitimacy by providing for the people's needs.

* Homeland Defense. Reduce/eliminate risk associated with critical nodes of vulnerability in both the physical and cyber realms by distributing the infrastructure network (power grid, water, and sewage); threat could be from enemy, natural disaster, or resource shortage.

Capabilities

* Within 48 hours, enables basic ground services (water, electricity, and waste disposal) apart from the vulnerable infrastructure network in a clean and efficient manner.

* Eliminates need for fuel and water to flow through LOCs (reduces risks/vulnerabilities/costs).

- Sanitarily disposes of 100 percent of sewage and other carbon-rich waste.

- Reduces water requirement by at least 70 percent.

- Generates 600+ W of power per person—25 percent of an expeditionary base power requirement.

- For a 150,000-person deployment
  - Saves 2 million gallons/day of water.
  - Saves 180,000 gallons/day of fuel.
  - Saves $50 million/day in fuel operating costs (fuel price plus transport cost).

Key Enabling Technologies

Enabling Technology	TRL	Maturity
Portable autonomous ground power systems (5.2.3.4)	3	2015
High-energy density fuel/material—DC (4.2.2.6)	5	2012
High-capacity, multiple-cycle, distributed power storage technology	3	2015
Nanotechnology (membranes and nanowires)	2	2018
Biotechnology (microbe behavior and biofilms)	2	2018
Microbial fuel cells	2	2020

Notes

1. Bush, *National Security Strategy*, 31.
2. Ibid., 30.

Abbreviations

3-D	three-dimensional
ABM	antiballistic missile
ACIA	Arctic Climate Impact Assessment
ACSC	Air Command and Staff College
AEPS	Arctic Environmental Protection Strategy
AFDD	Air Force doctrine document
AFOTTP	Air Force operational tactics, techniques, and procedures
AFRL	Air Force Research Lab
ANWR	Arctic National Wildlife Refuge
AOC	air operations center
AOC-WS	Air and Space Operations Center Weapon System
AON	Arctic Observation Network
ASAT	antisatellite
AU	Air University
BTL	biomass to liquid
C	Celsius
C2	command and control
C4ISR	command, control, communication, computer, intelligence, surveillance, and reconnaissance
CARA	Circum-Arctic Research Appraisal
CIA	Central Intelligence Agency
CLCS	Commission on the Limits of the Continental Shelf
cm	centimeter
CONOPS	concept of operations
COPUOS	Committee on the Peaceful Uses of Outer Space
CSIS	Center for Strategic and International Studies
CTL	coal to liquid
DARPA	Defense Advanced Research Projects Agency
DOD	Department of Defense
DODD	DOD directive
DOE	Department of Energy
DOS	Department of State
EBO	effects-based operations
EIA	Energy Information Administration

EMP	electromagnetic pulse
EO	Executive Outcomes
EU	European Union
F	Fahrenheit
FG07	Future Capabilities Game 2007
FID	foreign internal defense
FT	Fischer-Tropsch
FTR	Fuels Technical Review
GAO	Government Accountability Office
GBN	Global Business Network
GCC	geographic combatant commander
GDP	gross domestic product
GEO	geosynchronous Earth orbit/ Global Environment Outlook
GPS	Global Positioning System
GTL	gas to liquid
HSI	human-system interface
IADC	Inter-Agency Space Debris Coordination Committee
IMO	International Maritime Organization
IOP	instrument of power
IPCC	Intergovernmental Panel on Climate Change
IPY	International Polar Year
ISS	International Space Station
JAOC	joint air operations center
JFACC	joint forces air component commander
JP	joint publication
km	kilometer
LEO	low Earth orbit
LOC	line of communications
MEC	microbial electrolysis cell
MEO	medium Earth orbit
MEP	mobile electric power
MFC	microbial fuel cell
mm	millimeter
MRD	mission-related debris
MRI	magnetic resonance imaging
NaK	number of collisions
NAS	Naval Air Station
NASA	National Aeronautics and Space Administration

NCAR	National Center for Atmospheric Research
NDU	National Defense University
NGO	nongovernmental organization
nm	nautical mile
NMS	*National Military Strategy*
NORAD	North American Aerospace Defense Command
NSF	National Science Foundation
NSPD	national security presidential directive
NSS	National Security Strategy
OECD	Organization for Economic Cooperation and Development
OODA	observe, orient, decide, and act
PMC	private military company
PSD	private security detail
QDR	*Quadrennial Defense Review*
R&D	research and development
RF	radio frequency
RMA	revolution in military affairs
ROMO	range of military operations
RUF	Revolutionary United Front
SA	situational awareness
SAB	Scientific Advisory Board
SADF	South African Defense Force
SAF	Singapore Armed Forces
SAS	Special Air Service
SIPRI	Stockholm International Peace Research Institute
SOLE	special operations liaison element
SSN	Space Surveillance Network
SSTR	stability, security, transition, and reconstruction
TADMUS	Tactical Decision Making under Stress
TRA	Technology Readiness Assessment
TRL	technology readiness level
UN	United Nations
UNCLOS	UN Convention on the Law of the Sea
UNFCCC	UN Framework Convention on Climate Change
UNITA	National Union for the Total Independence of Angola
USAF	US Air Force
USAFR	US Air Force Reserve
USAID	US Agency for International Development

USARC	US Arctic Research Commission
USCENTCOM	US Central Command
USCGC	US Coast Guard Cutter
USG	US government
USGBC	United States Green Building Council
USGS	US Geological Survey
USSTRATCOM	US Strategic Command

Bibliography

Abbott, Chris, Paul Rogers, and John Sloboda. *Beyond Terror: The Truth about the Real Threats to Our World*. Berkshire, United Kingdom: Random House Group, 2007.

Ackerman, John T. "Climate Change, National Security, and the *Quadrennial Defense Review*: Avoiding the Perfect Storm." *Strategic Studies Quarterly* 2, no. 1 (Spring 2008): 56–96.

———. "Global Climate Change: Catalyst for International Relations Disequilibria?" PhD diss., University of Alabama, Department of Political Science, 2004.

Addison, Maj Milton J. Briefing. Subject: Air Force Facility Energy Center Program Management Review, December 2007.

Aelterman, Peter, Korneel Rabaey, Pham Hai The, Nico Boon, and Willy Verstraete. "Continuous Electricity Generation at High Voltages and Currents Using Stacked Microbial Fuel Cells." *Environmental Science and Technology* 40, no. 10 (2006): 3388–94.

Air Command and Staff College Space Research Electives Seminars. *AU-18: Space Primer*. Maxwell AFB, AL: Air University Press, 2009.

Air Force Doctrine Document 2. "Operations and Organization." Draft 9, December 2004.

———. *Organization and Employment of Aerospace Power*, 17 February 2000.

Air Force Doctrine Document 2-3. *Irregular Warfare*, 1 August 2007.

Air Force Doctrine Document 2-5. *Information Operations*, 11 January 2005.

Air Force Handbook 10-222. Vol. 2, *Guide to Bare Base Assets*, 1 April 2006.

———. Vol. 10, *Guide to Harvest Falcon Electrical System Installation*, 1 May 2000.

Air Force Operational Tactics, Techniques, and Procedures 2-3.2. *Air and Space Operations Center*, 13 December 2004.

Air Force Pamphlet 10-219. Vol. 5, *Bare Base Conceptual Planning Guide*, 1 June 1996.

Altman, Richard L., facilitator for Commercial Aircraft Alternate Fuels Initiative. "Global Climate Change and Energy Independence." Testimony before the Committee on Transportation and Infrastructure, House of Representatives 110th Cong., 1st sess., 16 May 2007.

Amidon, Col Elwood. Briefing. Subject: Needed Now: A National Energy Security Manhattan Project (original briefing to AF/A8PE; modified briefing by Dr. John Ackerman to ACSC Blue Horizons research class, 6 March 2006).

Amidon, Lt Col John M. "A 'Manhattan Project' for Energy." *Joint Force Quarterly* 39 (October 2005): 68–77.

Angenent, Lars. "Microbial Fuel Cells Turn on the Juice." *EurekAlert!*, 4 December 2007. http://www.eurekalert.org/pub_releases/2007-12/wuis-mfc120407.php.

Anselmo, Joe. "USAF Launches Major Biofuel Initiative." *Aviation Week*, Aerospace Daily and Defense Report, 30 January 2009. http://www.aviationweek.com.

Arctic Climate Impact Assessment (ACIA). *Impacts of a Warming Arctic*. Cambridge, UK: Cambridge University Press, 2004.

Arctic Council. "About Arctic Council." http://arctic-council.org/article/about.

———. "Norwegian, Danish, Swedish Common Objectives for Their Arctic Council Chairmanships 2006-2012," 27 November 2007. http://arctic-council.org/article/2007/11/common_priorities.

Arctic Environment Protection Strategy (AEPS). Roveniemi, Finland, 14 June 1991.

Ascher, William. *Forecasting: An Appraisal for Policy-Makers and Planners*. Baltimore: Johns Hopkins University Press, 1978.

Austin, Curtis, Ralph Borja, and Jeffery Phillips. "Operation Solar Eagle: A Study Examining Photovoltaic (PV) Solar Power as an Alternative for the Rebuilding of the Iraqi Electrical Power Generation Infrastructure." Master's thesis, Naval Postgraduate School, 2005.

Barich, William J., Brent L. Dessing, and Antonio B. Harley. "A Case Analysis of Energy Savings Performance Contract Projects and Photovoltaic Energy at Fort Bliss, El Paso, Texas." MBA professional report, Naval Postgraduate School, 2006.

Barnett, Tim P., and David W. Pierce. "When Will Lake Mead Go Dry?" *Water Resources Research* 44, no. 3 (29 March 2008): 1–10.

Biello, David. "Biofuels Are Bad for Feeding People and Combating Climate Change." *Scientific American*, 7 February 2008. http://www.sciam.com/article.cfm?id=biofuels-bad-for-people-and-climate.

Biever, Celeste. "Plugging into the Power of Sewage." *New Scientist*, 10 March 2004. http://www.newscientist.com/article/dn4761-plugging-into-the-power-of-sewage.html.

Biffinger, Justin C., Jeremy Pietron, Ricky Ray, Brenda Little, and Bradley R. Ringeisen. "A Biofilm Enhanced Miniature Microbial Fuel Cell Using *Shewanella Oneidensis DSP10* and Oxygen Reduction Cathodes." *Biosensors and Bioelectronics* 22, no. 8 (2007): 1672–79.

Biffinger, Justin C., Ricky Ray, Brenda Little, and Bradley R. Ringeisen. "Diversifying Biological Fuel Cell Designs by Use of Nanoporous Filters." *Environmental Science and Technology* 41, no. 4 (2007): 1444–49.

"Biofuels May Threaten Environment, U.N. Warns." *CNN.com*, 23 January 2008. http://www.cnn.com/2008/TECH/science/01/23/biofuels.fears .ap/index.html.

"Biomass-Fired Power Plant Starts Operation in NE China," *Xinhuanet*, 5 November 2007. http://news.xinhuanet.com/english/2007-11/05 /content_7014381.htm.

Black, Samuel, and Yousef Butt. "The Growing Threat of Space Debris." *Bulletin of the Atomic Scientists* 66, no. 2 (March 2010): 1–8.

Blackwater USA: Hearing before the Committee on Oversight and Government Reform, House of Representatives, 110th Congress, 1st. sess., 2 October 2007. Serial no. 110-89. Washington, DC: Government Printing Office (GPO), 2008. https://house.resource.org/110 /org.c-span.201290-1.1.pdf.

Booth, Barbara. "Arctic Meltdown: The Economic and Security Implications of Global Warming." *Foreign Affairs*, March/April 2008, 63–77.

———. "A Tiny but Powerful Microbial Fuel Cell." *Environmental Science and Technology* 40, no. 8 (April 2006): 2497–98.

———. "Runner-Up: Microbial Fuel Cells 101." *Environmental Science and Technology* 41, no. 7 (2007): 2087.

———. "Russia's Other Front." *Huffington Post*, 19 August 2008. http:// www.huffington post.com/scott-g-borgerson/russias-other-front _b_119946.html.

Boswell, Maj Randy L. "The Impact of Renewable Energy Sources on Forward Operating Bases." Research report. Maxwell AFB, AL: Air Command and Staff College, 2007.

Brearley, Andrew. "Faster Than a Speeding Bullet: Orbital Debris." *Astropolitics* 3, no. 1 (April 2005): 1–34. http://www.informaworld .com/smpp/section?content=a713727953&fulltext=713240928.

Brown, Lester R. "Draining Our Future: The Growing Shortage of Freshwater." *Futurist* 42, no. 3 (May–June 2008): 16–22.

Buchanan, Scott C. "Energy and Force Transformation." *Joint Force Quarterly* 42 (3d Quarter 2006): 51–54.

Builder, Carl H. *The Masks of War: American Military Styles in Strategy and Analysis.* Baltimore: Johns Hopkins University Press, 1989.

Bülow, Michael von. "The Countdown to Copenhagen." *en.cop15.dk*, 23 January 2009. http://en.cop15.dk/news/view+news?newsid=578.

Burge, Robert. "Effectiveness and Efficiencies in Private Military Companies." Master's thesis, Naval Postgraduate School, 2008.

Burrows, W. Dickinson. "Shower Water Recovery System: Criteria for Recycle of Gray Water for Shower Use." Medical Issues Information Paper No. IP 31-027, July 2001.

Bush, George W. Executive Order 13423. Strengthening Federal Environmental, Energy, and Transportation Management, 24 January 2007.

———. *National Security Presidential Directive/NSPD-66, Homeland Security Presidential Directive/HSPD-25: Arctic Region Policy.* Washington, DC: The White House, 12 January 2009.

———. *National Security Strategy of the United States of America.* Washington, DC: The White House, March 2006.

———. *National Strategy for Combating Terrorism.* Washington, DC: Executive Office of the President, 2006.

Byrne, Michael. "Cognitive Architecture." In *Human-Computer Interaction Handbook*, edited by Julie Jacko and Andrew Sears, 93–114. Mahwah, NJ: Lawrence Erlbaum Associates, 2003.

"CAAFI Emerges." *Aviation Week and Space Technology* 165, no. 17 (30 October 2006): 44.

Card, Stuart. "Information Visualization." In *Human-Computer Interaction Handbook*, edited by Julie Jacko and Andrew Sears, 509–44. Mahwah, NJ: Lawrence Erlbaum Associates, 2003.

Caruso, Lisa. "Carbon in the Skies." *National Journal* 40, no. 9 (March 2008): 15.

Catal, Tunc, Kaichang Li, Hakan Bermek, and Hong Liu. "Electricity Production from Twelve Monosaccharides Using Microbial Fuel Cells." *Journal of Power Sources* 175 (2008): 196–200.

Central Intelligence Agency (CIA). "Country Comparison: Total Fertility Rate." *The World Factbook* 2010. Washington, DC: CIA, 2010. https://www.cia.gov/library/publications/the-world-factbook/index.html.

———. *Long-Term Global Demographic Trends: Reshaping the Geo-political Landscape*. Washington, DC: CIA, July 2001. https://www.cia.gov/library/reports/general-reports-1/Demo_Trends_For_Web.pdf.

Chairman of the Joint Chiefs of Staff. *Joint Vision 2020*. Washington DC: GPO, June 2000.

Chandler, Jerome Greer. "Exotic No More." *Air Transport World* 45, no.1 (January 2008): 49–53.

———."Fueling the Future." *Air Transport World* 44, no. 5 (May 2007): 39–41.

Cheng, Shaoan, Hong Liu, and Bruce E. Logan. "Increased Performance of Single-Chamber Microbial Fuel Cells Using an Improved Cathode Structure." *Electrochemistry Communications* 8, no. 3 (2006): 489–94.

Cheng, Shaoan, and Bruce E. Logan. "Sustainable and Efficient Biohydrogen Production via Electrohydrogenesis." *Proceedings of the National Academy of Sciences of the United States of America* 104, no. 47 (2007).

———. "Power Densities Using Different Cathode Catalysts (Pt and CoTMPP) and Polymer Binders (Nation and PTFE) in Single Chamber Microbial Fuel Cells." *Environmental Science and Technology* 40, no. 1 (2006): 364–69.

Chipman, Susan F., and David E. Kieras. "Operator Centered Design of Ship Systems." Paper presented at the Engineering the Total Ship Symposium, Gaithersburg, MD, 17–18 March 2004.

Clinton, William J. *Presidential Decision Directive/NSC-26: United States Policy on the Arctic and Antarctic Regions*. Washington, DC: The White House, 10 June 1994.

Coates, Joseph F. "Future Innovations in Science and Technology." In *The International Handbook on Innovation*, edited by Larisa V. Shavinina, 1073–93. Amsterdam: Pergamon, 2003.

Cohen, Michael. "Russia and the European Union: An Outlook for Collaboration and Competition in European Natural Gas Markets." *Demokratizatsiya: The Journal of Post-Soviet Democratization* 15, no. 4 (September 2007): 379–89.

Collins, William, Robert Coleman, James Haywood, Martin R. Manning, and Philip Mote. "The Physical Science behind Climate Change." *Scientific American*, August 2007, 64–73.

Corn, M. Lynne, Michael Ratner, and Kristina Alexander. Arctic National Wildlife Refuge (ANWR): A Primer for the 112th Congress. Congressional Research Service (CRS) Report RL33872. Washington, DC: CRS, 14 February 2012.

Corporan, Edwin, Richard Reich, Orvin Monroig, Matthew J. DeWitt, Venus Larson, Ted Aulich, Michael Mann, and Wayne Seames. "Impacts of Biodiesel on Pollutant Emissions of a JP-8-Fueled Turbine Engine." *Journal of the Air and Waste Management Association* 55, no. 7 (July 2005): 940–49.

Corral, Oscar. "FIU, Military Create Instant Clinics." Miami Herald, 24 April 2008. http://www.miamiherald.com/548/story/507466.html.

"Crown Prince's Background: Expedition Sirius 2000." http://www .denmark.dk/en/menu/About-Denmark/Society/Royal-Denmark /The-Crown-Prince-Couple/The-Crown-Princes-Background /Expedition-Sirius-2000/.

Culver, Michael A. "20/20 by 2020": Transformation Vision Primer. Washington, DC: USAF, Office of the Civil Engineer, 2007.

Dalby, Simon. "Ecology, Security, and Change in the Anthropocene." Brown *Journal of World Affairs* 155, no. 13 (Spring-Summer 2007): 155–64.

"The Dark Side of Natural Resources." Global Policy Forum. http:// www.globalpolicy.org/security/docs/minindx.htm.

"DARPA Biofuels Program." Defense Advanced Research Projects Agency (DARPA) Information Paper, June 2008.

David, Leonard. "The Clutter Above." *Bulletin of the Atomic Scientists* 61, no. 4 (July/August 2005): 32–37.

The Defense Science Board Task Force on Improving Fuel Efficiency of Weapons Platforms. More Capable Warfighting through Reduced Fuel Burden. Washington, DC: Office of the Under Secretary of Defense for Acquisition, Technology and Logistics, January 2001.

The Definitive Guide to Bare Base Assets. Holloman AFB, NM: 49th Materiel Maintenance Squadron, February 2000.

Department of National Defence. Canada First Defence Strategy. Ottawa, ON: Office of the Prime Minister of Canada, May 2008.

Depczuk, D., and W. P. Schonberg. "Characterizing Debris Clouds Created in Oblique Orbital Debris Particle Impact." *Journal of Aerospace Engineering* 16, no. 4 (October 2003): 177–90.

Deputy Under Secretary of Defense for Science and Technology. *Technology Readiness Assessment (TRA) Deskbook*. Washington, DC: Department of Defense, May 2005.

Dew, Dr. Nicholas, and Lt Col Bryan Hudgens. "The Evolving Private Military Sector: A Survey." Paper presented at the Fifth Annual Acquisition Research Symposium. Naval Postgraduate School, Monterey, CA, 11 August 2008.

de Weck, Olivier L., Massachusetts Institute of Technology, Cambridge, MA. "Strategic Engineering: Designing Systems for an Uncertain Future." Lecture PowerPoint slides, 7 November 2006.

Dhanapala, Jayantha. "Arctic Security Problems—A Multilateral Perspective." Lecture. Burnaby, BC, Simon Fraser University, 12 March 2008.

Dimotakis, Paul, Robert Grober, and Nate Lewis. *Reducing DOD Fossil-Fuel Dependence*. McLean, VA: JASON, MITRE Corporation, September 2006.

DOD Directive 3000.05. *Military Support for Stability, Security, Transition, and Reconstruction (SSTR) Operations*, 28 November 2005.

Du, Zhuwei, Haoran Li, and Tingyue Gu. "A State of the Art Review on Microbial Fuel Cells: A Promising Technology for Wastewater Treatment and Bioenergy." *Biotechnology Advances* 25, no. 5 (2007): 464–82.

DuBois, Raymond F. *Defense Installations Strategic Plan*. Washington, DC, 2004.

Duke, James S. "Decision Analysis Using Value-Focused Thinking to Select Renewable Energy Sources." Research paper, Air Force Institute of Technology, 2004.

Eggers, Cdr Jeffrey W. "The Fuel Gauge of National Security." *Armed Forces Journal* 145, no. 10 (1 May 2008): 10–12.

Elleman, Bruce A. *Waves of Hope: The U.S. Navy's Response to the Tsunami in Northern Indonesia*. Newport Paper no. 28. Newport, RI: Naval War College Press, February 2007.

Elliot, Scott. "Air Force Rethinks Air Operations Centers." *Air Force Print News*, 26 February 2003.

Elsea, Jennifer, and Nina Serafino. *Private Security Contractors in Iraq: Background, Legal Status, and Other Issues*. CRS Report for Congress RL32419. Washington, DC: CRS, 11 July 2007.

Engelbrecht, Col Joseph A., Jr., Lt Col Robert L. Bivins, Maj Patrick M. Condray, Maj Merrily D. Fecteau, Maj John P. Geis II, and Maj Kevin C. Smith. *Alternate Futures for 2025: Security Planning to Avoid Surprise*. Maxwell AFB, AL: Air University, September 1996.

"Environment Pushes EU to Become Arctic Player." *Euractiv.com*, 4 December 2008. http://www.euractiv.com/en/energy/environment -pushes-eu-arctic-player/article-177438.

European Commission. "EU-Russia Energy Relations." http://ec.europa .eu/energy/international/bilateral_cooperation/russia/russia _en.htm.

European Policy Center. "The EU and the Arctic: Exploring Uncharted Territory?" Accessed 24 January 2009. http://www.epc .eu/en/er.asp?TYP=ER&LV=293&see=y&t=2&PG=ER/EN /detail&l=&AI=859.

ExxonMobil Aviation International Ltd., Technical Dept. *World Jet Fuel Specifications with Avgas Supplement*. Technical report. Leatherhead, UK: ExxonMobil Aviation, 2005.

"Fact Sheet: Increasing Our Energy Security and Confronting Climate Change through Investment in Renewable Technologies," 5 March 2008. http://www.whitehouse.gov/news/releases/2008 /03/20080305-2.html.

Fadok, Maj David S. "John Boyd and John Warden: Air Power's Quest for Strategic Paralysis." Maxwell AFB, AL: Air University, School of Advanced Airpower Studies, 1995.

Fan, Yanzhen, Hongqiang Hu, and Hong Liu. "Enhanced Coulombic Efficiency and Power Density of Air-Cathode Microbial Fuel Cells with an Improved Cell Configuration." *Journal of Power Sources* 171, no. 2 (2007): 348–54.

Farrar, Amy. *Global Warming*. Edina, MN: ABDO Publishing Co., 2008.

Flanders, Stephen N., Richard L. Schneider, Donald Fournier, Brian Deal, and Annette L. Stumpf. *Planning, Engineering, and Design of Sustainable Facilities and Infrastructure: An Assessment of the State of Practice*. Final report. Champaign, IL: US Army Corps of Engineers, Engineer Research and Development Center, March 2001.

Fomin, Pavel, Elizabeth Bostic, Christopher Bolton, Jonathan H. Cristiani, Scott Coombe, Terry DuBois, and J. J. Kowal. *Army Science Conference 2006: Technology Assessment of Soldier and Man Portable Fuel Cell Power*. Final technical report. Fort Belvoir, VA: US Army Communications-Electronics Research Development and Engineering Center, 2006.

Fontaine, Richard, and Dr. John Nagl. "Contractors in American Conflicts: Adapting to a New Reality." Working paper. Washington, DC: Center for a New American Security, December 2009.

Freguia, Stefano, Korneel Rabaey, Yuan Zhiguo, and Jurg Keller. "Electron and Carbon Balances in Microbial Fuel Cells Reveal Temporary Bacterial Storage Behavior during Electricity Generation." *Environmental Science and Technology* 41, no. 8 (April 2007): 2915–21.

Frey, Adam E. "Defense of Space Assets, a Legal Perspective." *Air and Space Power Journal* 22, no. 4 (Winter 2008): 75–84. http://www .airpower.maxwell.af.mil/airchronicles/apj/apj08/win08/frey.html.

"Fuel Cell Generates Electricity from Wastewater." *Membrane Technology* 2006, no. 12 (December 2006): 3.

The Futures Group International. "Relevance Tree and Morphological Analysis." In Jerome C. Glenn and Theodore J. Gordon, *Futures Research Methodology*.

Gaffney, Dennis. "Fly the Eco-Friendly Skies." *Popular Science* 272, no. 2 (February 2008): 40–46.

Galvin, Thomas P. "The Changing Face of Europe and Africa: The USEUCOM AOR in 25 Years." *Joint Force Quarterly* 45 (2nd Quarter 2007): 52–57.

Garrambone, Michael W., Michael S. Goodman, and Thomas Hughes. "Battle Control Center–Experimental, Training Performance Measurement System (TPMS)." Paper submitted to Air Force Research Lab. Dayton, OH: General Dynamics Advanced Information Systems, 30 April 2004.

Gawron, Valerie. *Human Performance Measures Handbook*. Mahwah, NJ: Lawrence Erlbaum Associates, 2000.

Geokas, Michael C. "The European Union and the Specter of Uncontrolled In-Migration." *Journal of Political and Military Sociology* 25 (Winter 1997): 353–62.

Geraghty, Tony. *Soldiers of Fortune: A History of the Mercenary in Modern Warfare*. New York: Pegasus Books, 2009.

Ghangrekar, M. M., and V. B. Shinde. "Microbial Fuel Cell: A New Approach of Wastewater Treatment with Power Generation." Paper presented at the International Workshop on R&D Frontiers in Water and Wastewater Management. Nagpur, India, 20–21 January 2006.

———. "Performance of Membrane-Less Microbial Fuel Cell Treating Wastewater and Effect of Electrode Distance and Area on Electricity Production." *Bioresource Technology* 98, no. 15 (November 2007): 2879–85.

————. "Wastewater Treatment in Microbial Fuel Cell and Electricity Generation: A Sustainable Approach." Paper presented at the 12th International Sustainable Development Research Conference. Hong Kong, 6–8 April 2006.

Gilovich, Thomas, Dale Griffin, and Daniel Kahneman, eds. *Heuristics and Biases.* Cambridge, UK: Cambridge University Press, 2002.

Gislason E. *A Brief History of Alaska Statehood, 1867–1959.* http:// xroads.virginia.edu/-CAP/ Bartlett/49state.html.

Glenn, Jerome C. "Introduction to the Futures Research Methods Series." In *2009 State of the Future,* edited by Jerome C. Glenn and Theodore J. Gordon. American Council for the United Nations (UN) University. The Millennium Project. Washington, DC: UN University, 2009.

————, ed. *Worldwide Emerging Environmental Issues Affecting the U.S. Military.* Washington, DC: American Council for the United Nations University, March 2007.

————, and Theodore J. Gordon. *2007 State of the Future.* Washington, DC: The Millennium Project, World Federation of United Nations Associations, 2007.

————, eds. *Futures Research Methodology.* CD-ROM, version 2.0. Washington, DC: American Council for the United Nations University, Millennium Project, 2003.

Global Business Network. "Why Scenarios?," n.d. http://www.gbn .com/about/scenario_planning.php.

Gorby, Yuri A. et al. "Electrically Conductive Bacterial Nanowires Produced by *Shewanella Oneidensis* Strain MR-1 and Other Microorganisms." *Proceedings of the National Academy of Sciences of the United States of America* 103, no. 30 (25 July 2006): 11358–63.

Gordon, Theodore J., and Jerome C. Glenn. "Environmental Scanning." In *Futures Research Methodology,* CD-ROM, version 3.0. The Millennium Project, 2009.

Gosnell, Mariana. "Top 100 Stories of 2008 #5: Nations Stake Their Claims to a Melting Arctic." *Discover,* January 2009, 26.

Grant, Greg. "Surging Oil Prices Send Military Costs Skyrocketing." *Government Executive.com,* 3 January 2008. http://www.govexec .com/dailyfed/0108/010308g1.htm.

Gray, Victor. "People Wars: Ruminations of Population and Security." *Parameters* 27, Summer 1997, 52–60.

Hall, G. E. "Space Debris–An Insurance Perspective." *Proceedings of the Institution of Mechanical Engineers, Part G: Journal of Aerospace Engineering* 221, no. 6 (December 2007): 915–24.

Hansen, Jim. "The Threat to the Planet." *New York Review of Books* 53, no. 12 (13 July 2006): 12–16. http://www.nybooks.com/articles/19131 .

Hansman, R. John, Christopher Magee, Richard de Neufville, Renee Robins, and Daniel Roos. "Research Agenda for an Integrated Approach to Infrastructure Planning, Design, and Management." *International Journal of Critical Infrastructures* 2, nos. 2–3 (2006): 146–59.

Harrabin, Roger. "EU Rethinks Biofuels Guidelines." *BBC News*, 14 January 2008. http://news.bbc.co.uk/2/hi/europe/7186380.stm.

Harrington, Caitlin. "F-15E Strike Eagle Flies on Synthetic Fuel Blend." *Jane's Defence Weekly* 45, no. 35 (27 August 2008): 7.

———. "USAF Conducts Flight Test Using Synthetic Fuel." *Jane's Defence Weekly* 45, no. 13 (26 March 2008): 10.

Hatcher, Patrick G. "New Sources of Biomass Feed Stocks: Algae and More." Lecture. Sierra Club, Old Dominion University, VA, 2 April 2008.

Hemighaus, Greg, Tracy Boval, John Bacha, Fred Barnes, Matt Franklin, Lew Gibbs, Nancy Hogue, Jacqueline Jones, David Lesnini, John Lind, and Jack Morris. *Aviation Fuels Technical Review.* Houston, TX: Chevron Global Aviation, 2006.

Hemighaus, Greg, Tracy Boval, Carol Bosley, Roger Organ, John Lind, Rosanne Brouette, Toni Thompson, Joanna Lynch, and Jacqueline Jones. *Alternative Jet Fuels.* Addendum 1 to *Aviation Fuels Technical Review* (FTR-3/A1). Houston, TX: Chevron Global Aviation, 2006.

Hester, R. E., and R. M. Harrison, eds. *Issues in Environmental Science and Technology: Sustainability and Environmental Impact of Renewable Energy Sources.* Cambridge, UK: Royal Society of Chemistry, 2003.

He, Zhen, and Largus T. Angenent. "Application of Bacterial Biocathodes in Microbial Fuel Cells." *Electroanalysis* 18, nos. 19–20 (2006): 2009–15.

"The History of Jet Fuel." Air BP website. http://www.bp.com/section genericarticle.do?categoryId=4503664&contentId=57733.

Hoagland, William. "Solar Energy." *Scientific American* 273, no. 3 (September 1995): 136–39.

Holcomb, Franklin H., Joseph Bush, James L. Knight, and Jason Whipple. "Energy Savings for Silent Camp™ Hybrid Technologies." *Journal of Fuel Cell Science and Technology* 4 (2007): 134–37.

Ilulissat Declaration. Arctic Ocean Conference. Ilulissat, Greenland, 27–29 May 2008.

Intergovernmental Panel on Climate Change Working Group II. Fourth Assessment Report. *Climate Change 2007: Synthesis Report—Summary for Policymakers*. Cambridge, UK: Cambridge University Press, 2007.

———. Technical Summary. *Climate Change 2007: Climate Change Impacts, Adaptation, and Vulnerability*. Cambridge, UK: Cambridge University Press, 2007.

———. Technical Summary. *Climate Change 2007: The Physical Science Basis—Summary for Policymakers*. Cambridge, UK: Cambridge University Press, 2007.

International Council for Science and World Meteorological Organization (WMO) Joint Committee for IPY 2007–2008. *The Scope of Science for the International Polar Year 2007–2008*. Geneva, Switzerland: WMO, February 2007.

International Ice Charting Working Group. "National Ice Services Advise of Continuing Navigation Hazards." *nsidc.org*. 24 October 2008. http://nsidc.org/noaa/iicwg/IICWG_2008/presentations/IICWG_IX_NEWS_RELEASE.pdf.

International Maritime Organization (IMO). "Introduction to IMO." http://www.imo.org/About/Pages/Default.aspx.

International Polar Year (IPY). "About IPY." http://www.ipy.org/index.php?/ipy/about/.

Iraqi Reconstruction: Reliance on Private Military Contractors and Status Report: Hearing before the Committee on Oversight and Government Reform. House of Representatives, 110th Congress, 1st sess., 7 February 2007. Serial no. 110-11. Washington, DC: GPO, 2007. http://www.gpo.gov/fdsys/pkg/CHRG-110hhrg36546/pdf/CHRG-110hhrg36546.pdf.

Isenberg, David. *Private Military Contractors and US Grand Strategy*. Report 1/2009. Oslo, Norway: International Peace Research Institute, 2009.

Jacko, Julie, and Andrew Sears, eds. *Human-Computer Interaction Handbook*. Mahwah, NJ: Lawrence Erlbaum Associates, 2003.

Jackson, Richard. *The Global Retirement Crisis: The Threat to World Stability and What to Do about It*. Washington, DC: Center for Strategic and International Studies (CSIS) and Citigroup, 2002.

———, and Neil Howe. *The Graying of the Great Powers: Demography and Geopolitics in the 21st Century*. Washington, DC: CSIS, May 2008.

———, and Rebecca Strauss. *The Geopolitics of World Population Change*. Washington, DC: CSIS, 10 July 2007.

James, Harold K. "Sierra Bravo: New Base Design Concept for the Air Force." Lecture. AF/A8X, Washington, DC, 26 July 2007.

Jennings, Gareth. "USAF Flies Boeing C-17 Using Synthetic Fuel Blend." *Jane's Defence Weekly* 44, no. 45 (07 November 2007): 12.

Johnson, Glenn R. "Fuel Cell Bioelectrode Development." Air Force Research Laboratory, Materials and Manufacturing Directorate (AFRL/ML) Biology Program White Paper, Wright-Patterson AFB, OH, 2007.

———. "Microbial Fuel Cell for Remote Power Generation and Waste Stream Treatment." AFRL/ML Biology Program White Paper, Wright-Patterson AFB, OH, 2007.

Joint Publication 1-02. *Department of Defense Dictionary of Military and Associated Terms*, 2 April 2001 (as amended through 26 August 2008).

Joint Publication 3-0. *Joint Operations*, 17 September 2006.

Joint Publication 3-30. *Command and Control for Joint Air Operations*, 5 June 2003.

Jones, Susanne. "What Is a Hybrid Vehicle?" http://www.helium.com/items/793791-prices-consumers-looking-driving.

Julian, Francois. "Europe Focuses on Green Engines." *Interavia Business and Technology* 691 (January 2008): 7.

Jumper, Gen John P., chief of staff, US Air Force. "Chief's Sight Picture: Technology-to-Warfighting: Delivering Advantages to Airmen," 17 July 2003.

———. "Future Force: Transforming Operations." Address. National Defense Industrial Association Convention, Arlington, VA, 1 April 2004.

Kauffman, Tim. "Pentagon's Plans to Use More Alternative Fuels Hit Turbulence." *Federal Times* 44, no. 4 (10 March 2008): 4.

Keenan, Rita, and Antigone Gikas. *Statistical Aspects of the Energy Economy in 2008*. Luxembourg: Eurostat, 2009.

Keith, Miriam, Air Force Research Laboratory, Airbase Technologies Division. "BEAR Base Solar Power System." Presentation. Joint Service Power Expo, Tampa, FL, 4 May 2005.

Kidwell, Deborah C. *Public War, Private Fight? The United States and Private Military Companies*. Occasional Paper 12. Fort Leavenworth, KS: Combat Studies Institute Press, 2005.

Kim, Byung Hong, In Seop Chang, and Geoffrey M. Gadd. "Challenges in Microbial Fuel Cell Development and Operation." *Applied Microbiology and Biotechnology* 76, no. 3 (September 2007): 485–94.

Ki-Moon, Ban, secretary-general, UN. Opening Statement to the High Level Segment of the UN Climate Change Conference. Poznan, Poland, 11 December 2008.

King, Angela G. "Research Advances." *Journal of Chemical Education* 84, no. 1 (2007): 10–14.

Kinsey, Christopher. *Corporate Soldiers and International Security: The Rise of Private Military Companies.* New York: Routledge, 2006.

Klare, Michael T. *Resource Wars: The New Landscape of Global Conflict.* New York: Metropolitan Books, 2001.

Kopp, Dr. Carlo. *The US Air Force Synthetic Fuels Program.* Technical Report APA-TR-2008-0102. Air Power Australia, Australia Air Defense Think Tank Paper, updated January 2008. http://www.ausairpower.net/APA-USAF-SynFuels.html.

Krahmann, Elle. "Controlling Private Military Companies: The United Kingdom and Germany." Presentation to the International Studies Association Annual Convention, Portland, OR, 24 February–1 March 2003.

Kraska, James. "The Law of the Sea Convention and the Northwest Passage." *The International Journal of Marine and Coastal Law* 22, no. 2 (2007): 257–81.

Krisko, Paula H. "The Predicted Growth of the Low-Earth Orbit Space Debris Environment—An Assessment of Future Risk for Spacecraft." *Proceedings of the Institution of Mechanical Engineers, Part G: Journal of Aerospace Engineering* 221, no. 6 (December 2007): 975–85.

Lambert, Christy. "Fuel Cells Help Make Noisy, Hot Generators a Thing of the Past." *EurekAlert!*, 11 December 2007. http://www.eurekalert.org/pub_ releases/ 2007-12/dnnl-fch121107.php#.

Lathrop, Coalter G., president, Sovereign Geographics, Inc. To the editor of *Foreign Affairs.* Letter, March/April 2008.

Lawton, Graham. "Pee-Cycling." *New Scientist*, 20 December 2006. http://technology.newscientist.com/article/mg19 225831.600.

Levin, Carl. "Opening Statement of Senator Carl Levin, Senate Armed Services Committee Hearing on Contracting in a Counterinsurgency: An Examination of the Blackwater-Paravant Contract and the Need for Oversight." Press release, 24 February 2010. http://levin .senate.gov/newsroom/release.cfm?id=322458.

Lindeburg, Michael R. *Mechanical Engineering Reference Manual for the PE [Professional Engineer] Exam.* 11th ed. Belmont, CA: Professional Publications, Inc., 2001.

Liou, Jer-Chyi, and Nicholas L. Johnson. "Risks in Space from Orbiting Debris." *Science* 311, no. 5759 (20 January 2006): 340–41.

Liu, H., R. Ramnarayanan, and B. E. Logan. "Production of Electricity during Wastewater Treatment Using a Single Chamber Microbial Fuel Cell." *Environmental Science and Technology* 38, no. 7 (2004): 2281–85.

Liu, Zhi-Dan, and Hao-Ran Li. "Effects of Bio- and Abio-Factors on Electricity Production in a Mediatorless Microbial Fuel Cell." *Biochemical Engineering Journal* 36, no. 3 (October 2007): 209–14.

Logan, B. E. "Energy Diversity Brings Stability." *Environmental Science and Technology* 40, no. 17 (September 2006): 5161.

———. "Generating Electricity from Wastewater Treatment." *Water Environment Research: A Research Publication of the Water Environment Federation* 77, no. 3 (2005): 211.

———. "Microbial Electrolysis Cell Research." Department of Civil and Environmental Engineering, Pennsylvania State University, University Park, PA, 19 December 2007. http://www.engr.psu .edu/ce/enve/beamr/beamr.htm.

———. "Simultaneous Wastewater Treatment and Biological Electricity Generation." *Water Science and Technology* 52, nos. 1–2 (2005): 31–37.

Logan, B. E., and John M. Regan. "Electricity-Producing Bacterial Communities in Microbial Fuel Cells." *Trends in Microbiology* 14, no. 12 (December 2006): 512–18.

———. "Microbial Fuel Cells—Challenges and Applications." *Environmental Science and Technology* 40, no. 17 (September 2006): 5172–80.

Logan, Bruce E., Bert Hamelers, René Rozendal, Uwe Schröder, Jürg Keller, Stefano Freguia, Peter Aelterman, Willy Verstraete, and Korneel Rabaey. "Microbial Fuel Cells: Methodology and Technology." *Environmental Science and Technology* 40, no. 17 (September 2006): 5181–92.

Logan, Bruce, Shaoan Cheng, Valerie Watson, and Garett Estadt. "Graphite Fiber Brush Anodes for Increased Power Production in Air-Cathode Microbial Fuel Cells." *Environmental Science and Technology* 41, no. 9 (May 2007): 3341–46.

"Logistics Fuel Reformer/Processor for Mobile Electric Power (MEP) Fuel Cells Power Generation." US Army Corps of Engineers, Engineer Research and Development Center, Research and Development Projects. http://dodfuelcell.cecer.army.mil/rd/Logistics(MEP).php.

"Loss of Andes Glaciers Threatens Water Supply." *CNN.com*, 26 November 2007. http://www.cnn.com/2007/TECH/science/11/26/andes.water.ap/index.html.

Loukacheva, Natalia. "Security Challenges and Legal Capacity of Greenland and Nunavut Jurisdictions." Toronto, ON: Munk Centre for International Studies, University of Toronto, 2004.

Lovley, Derek R. "Bug Juice: Harvesting Electricity with Microorganisms." *Nature Reviews Microbiology* 4, no. 10 (July 2006): 497–508.

———. "Microbial Energizers: Fuel Cells That Keep on Going." *Microbe* 1, no. 7 (2006): 323–29.

———. "Microbial Fuel Cells: Novel Microbial Physiologies and Engineering Approaches." *Current Opinion in Biotechnology* 17, no. 3 (June 2006): 327–32.

Lozano, Rodrigo. "Collaboration as a Pathway for Sustainability." *Sustainable Development* 15 (2007): 370–81.

Malik, Tario. "Debris Scare Sends Station Crew into Soyuz." *Space News* 20, no. 11 (16 March 2009): 12.

Mansfeld, Florian. "The Interaction of Bacteria and Metal Surfaces." *Electrochimica Acta* 52, no. 27 (October 2007): 7670–80.

Marks, Paul. "Network-Style Attack Could Reduce the Threat from Space Debris." *New Scientist*, 11 October 2008.

Martin, Gen Gregory S., commander Air Force Materiel Command (AFMC). Address. Air Force Association (AFA) 2004 Air Warfare Symposium, Lake Buena Vista, FL, 12 February 2004.

———. Address to the AFA Policy Forum, AFA National Symposium, Washington, DC, 16 September 2003.

———. Command briefing slides. Provided to author by AFMC/CAG.

Martino, Joseph P. "Technological Forecasting: An Introduction." *Futurist*, July–August 1993, 13–16.

Mayhew, Deborah J. "Requirements Specification within the Usability Engineering Life Cycle." In *Human-Computer Interaction Handbook*, edited by Julie Jacko and Andrew Sears, 917–26. Mahawah, NJ: Lawrence Erlbaum Associates, 2003.

McCarthy, Kevin F. *World Population Shifts: Boom or Doom?* Santa Monica, CA: RAND Corporation, 2001.

McFeely, Eugene. *Balancing Kinetic Effects of Airpower with Counterinsurgency Objectives in Afghanistan.* Strategy Research Project. Carlisle Barracks, PA: US Army War College, 29 January 2009.

McKenna, Ted. "Lost in Space: Could Space-Based Weapons Help Protect Military Satellite Capability?" *Journal of Electronic Defense* 28, no 1 (January 2005): 40.

McMillan, Robert. "CIA Says Hackers Have Cut Power Grid: Several Cities outside the U.S. Have Sustained Attacks on Utility Systems and Extortion Demands." *PCWorld*, 19 January 2008. http://www.pcworld.com/article/id,141564-pg,1/article.html.

Menicucci, Joseph, Haluk Beyenal, Enrico Marsili, Raajaraajan Angathevar Veluchamy, Goksel Demir, and Zbigniew Lewandowski. "Procedure for Determining Maximum Sustainable Power Generated by Microbial Fuel Cells." *Environmental Science and Technology* 40, no. 3 (February 2006): 1062–68.

Merholz, Peter. "Information Visualization: When the Visual Makes Us Smarter." In *Catalog of Tomorrow: Trends Shaping Your Future*, edited by Andrew Zolli. Indianapolis, IN: Que Publishing, 2003.

Meserve, Jeanne. "Sources: Staged Cyber Attack Reveals Vulnerability in Power Grid." *CNN.com*, 26 September 2007. http://www.cnn.com/2007/US/09/26/power.at.risk/index.html.

Miller, Nita Lewis, and Lawrence G. Shattuck. "A Process Model of Situated Cognition in Military Command and Control." Paper presented at the 2004 Command and Control Research and Technology Symposium: The Power of Information Age Concepts and Technologies. San Diego, CA, May 2004.

Mirmina, Steven A. "Reducing the Proliferation of Orbital Debris: Alternatives to a Legally Binding Instrument." *American Journal of International Law* 99, no. 3 (July 2005): 649–62.

Mitropoulos, Efthimios, secretary-general, International Maritime Organization. Opening Remarks, Jakarta meeting on Straits of Malacca and Singapore. Jakarta, Indonesia, 7 September 2005.

Moon, Hyunsoo, In Seop Chang, and Byung Hong Kim. "Continuous Electricity Production from Artificial Wastewater Using a Mediator-Less Microbial Fuel Cell." *Bioresource Technology* 97, no. 4 (March 2006): 621–27.

Moore, Ronald A., Janel H. Schermerhorn, Heather M. Oonk, and Jeffery G. Morrison. "Understanding and Improving Knowledge Transactions in Command and Control." Paper submitted to Space and Naval Warfare System Center–San Diego, n.d.

Morozan, A., L. Stamatin, F. Nastase, A. Dumitru, S. Vulpe, C. Nastase, I. Stamatin, and K. Scott. "The Biocompatibility Microorganisms-Carbon Nanostructures for Applications in Microbial Fuel Cells." *physica status solidi* 204, no. 6 (2007): 1797–803.

Morrison, Terri, and Wayne A. Conway. *Kiss, Bow or Shake Hands*. 2nd ed. Avon, MA: Adams Media, 1995.

Moseley, Gen T. Michael. *The Nation's Guardians: America's 21st Century Air Force*. Air Force chief of staff white paper. Washington, DC: United States Air Force, 29 December 2007.

Murawiec, Laurent, and David Adamson. *Demography and Security*. Santa Monica, CA: RAND Corporation, November 2000.

Myers, Gen Richard B. *The National Military Strategy of the United States of America*. Washington, DC: Pentagon, 2004.

Narihiro, Takashi, and Yuji Sekiguchi. "Microbial Communities in Anaerobic Digestion Processes for Waste and Wastewater Treatment: A Microbiological Update." *Current Opinion in Biotechnology* 18, no. 3 (June 2007): 273–78.

National Center for Atmospheric Research. "Arctic Ice Retreating More Quickly Than Computer Models Project." *UCAR.edu*. 30 April 2007. http://www.ucar.edu/news/releases/2007/seaice.shtml#mediaterms.

National Defense University. "The Arctic Circle: Development and Risk." Arctic Conference Report, 13–14 May 2008. http://www.ndu.edu/ctnsp/NCW_course/Arctic%20Summary,%20Approved.pdf.

National Energy Policy Group. *National Energy Policy: Report of the National Energy Policy Development Group*. Washington, DC: GPO, May 2001.

National Intelligence Council. *Global Trends 2025: A Transformed World*. Washington, DC: GPO, November 2008.

———. *Global Trends 2030: Alternative Worlds*. Washington, DC: GPO, December 2012.

National Oceanic and Atmospheric Administration. *Arctic Report Card 2008*. Washington, DC: Department of Commerce, October 2008.

National Science Foundation. "Factsheet: The Arctic Observation Network (AON)." http://www.nsf.gov/news/news_summ.jsp?cntn_id=109687.

National Snow and Ice Data Center. "Education Center: All about Sea Ice: Processes: Albedo." http://nsidc.org/seaice/processes/albedo.html.

Neustadt, Richard E., and Ernest R. May. *Thinking in Time*. New York: Free Press, 1986.

Nishida, Shin-Ichiro, Satomi Kawamato, Yasushi Okawa, Fuyuto Terui, and Shoji Kitamura. "Space Debris Removal System Using a Small Satellite." *Acta Astronautica* 65, no. 1–2 (July–August 2009): 95–102.

Norman, Donald A. *The Invisible Computer*. Cambridge, MA: MIT Press, 1998.

Norris, Guy. "Fueling Change." *Aviation Week and Space Technology* 169, no. 2 (14 July 2008): 58.

"North Pole May Belong to Denmark, Early Mapping Data Suggests." *Canadian Broadcast Company News*, 12 March 2009. http://www.cbc.ca/canada/north/story/2009/03/12/north-pole.html.

Norton, P., and C. Christensen. "A Cold-Climate Case Study for Affordable Zero Energy Homes." Paper presented at the Solar 2006 Conference. Denver, CO, 9–13 July 2006.

Norwegian Government. *The Norwegian Government's High North Strategy*. Oslo/Trosmø, Norway: Norwegian Ministry of Foreign Affairs, 1 December 2006.

Nye, Joseph S. *The Paradox of American Power: Why the World's Only Superpower Can't Go It Alone*. New York: Oxford University Press, 2002.

Obama, Barack. Inaugural Address. Washington, DC, 20 January 2009.

O'Brien, James M. "Private Military Companies: An Assessment." Master's thesis, Monterey, CA: Naval Postgraduate School, 2008.

O'Hanlon, Michael E. *Neither Space Wars nor Sanctuary: Constraining the Military Uses of Space*. Washington, DC: Brookings Institute Press, 2004.

Oh, Sang-Eun, and Bruce E. Logan. "Proton Exchange Membrane and Electrode Surface Areas as Factors That Affect Power Generation in Microbial Fuel Cells." *Applied Microbiology and Biotechnology* 70 (March 2006): 162–69.

———. "Voltage Reversal during Microbial Fuel Cell Stack Operation." *Journal of Power Sources* 167, no. 1 (May 2007): 11–17.

Ott, James. "Algae Advances." *Aviation Week and Space Technology* 168, no. 11 (17 March 2008): 66.

Østreng, Willy, ed. *National Security and International Environmental Cooperation in the Arctic–The Case of the Northern Sea Route.* Dordrecht: Kluwer Academic Publishers, 1999.

Packer, George. "Letter from Baghdad: War after the War: What Washington Doesn't See in Iraq." *New Yorker*, 24 November 2003. http://www.newyorker.com/archive/2003/11/24/031124fa_fact1.

Patterson, Emily, Emilie Roth, and David Woods. "Aiding the Intelligence Analyst in Situations of Data Overload: A Simulation Study of Computer-Supported Inferential Analysis under Data Overload." Interim Report. Columbus, OH: The Ohio State University, 1999.

Perez, Gonzalo, Robert Neathammer, Franklin H. Holcomb, Roch A. Ducey, Byung J. Kim, and Fred Louis. *Waste-to-Energy ECIP (Energy Conservation Investment Program) Project.* Vol. 1, *An Analysis of Hydrogen Infrastructure Fuel Cell Technology.* Technical report. Champaign, IL: US Army Corps of Engineers, Engineer Research and Development Center, April 2006.

Perlo-Freeman, Sam, and Elisabeth Skons. *The Private Military Services Industry.* Stockholm International Peace Research Institute, 2008.

Peterson, Peter G. "Gray Dawn: The Global Aging Crisis." *Foreign Affairs* 78, no. 1 (January/February 1999): 42–55.

Pham, T. H., K. Rabaey, P. Aelterman, P. Clauwaert, L. De Schamphelaire, N. Boon, and W. Verstraete. "Microbial Fuel Cells in Relation to Conventional Anaerobic Digestion Technology." *Engineering in Life Sciences* 6, no. 3 (2006): 285–92.

Pinker, Steven. *How the Mind Works.* New York: W. W. Norton and Co., 1997.

Plaza, John. "What's Right with Biofuels." *Business Week Online*, 8 May 2008, 6.

Population Reference Bureau. "World Population Highlights: Key Findings from PRB's 2008 World Population Data Sheet." *Population Bulletin* 63, no. 3 (September 2008). http://www.prb.org /pdf08/63.3highlights.pdf.

"Power Boosted 10-Fold in Microbial Fuel Cells." *Fuel Cells Bulletin* 2006, no. 7 (2006): 7.

Price, Catherine. "Flying the Coal-Fired Skies." *Popular Science*, 16 January 2009. Accessed 2 February 2009. http://www.popsci.com/node/31142.

Rabaey, K., J. Rodríguez, L. L. Blackall, J. Keller, D. J. Batstone, W. Verstraete, and K. H. Nealson. "Microbial Ecology Meets Electrochemistry: Electricity Driven and Driving Communities." *ISME Journal: Multidisciplinary Journal of Microbial Ecology* 1, no. 1 (May 2007): 9–18.

Rabaey, Korneel, Peter Clauwaert, Peter Aelterman, and Willy Verstraete. "Tubular Microbial Fuel Cells for Efficient Electricity Generation." *Environmental Science and Technology* 39, no. 20 (October 2005): 8077–82.

Rabaey, Korneel, Geert Lissens, Steven D. Siciliano, and Willy Verstraete. "A Microbial Fuel Cell Capable of Converting Glucose to Electricity at High Rate and Efficiency." *Biotechnology Letters* 25, no. 18 (September 2003): 1531–35.

Rabaey, Korneel, Geert Lissens, and Willy Verstraete. "Microbial Fuel Cells: Performances and Perspectives." In *Biofuels for Fuel Cells: Renewable Energy from Biomass Fermentation*, edited by Piet Lens, Peter Westermann, Marianne Haberbauer, and Angelo Moreno, 377–400. Integrated Environmental Technology Series. London: IWA Publishing, 2005.

Rabaey, Korneel, and Willy Verstraete. "Microbial Fuel Cells: Novel Biotechnology for Energy Generation." *Trends in Biotechnology* 23, no. 6 (June 2005): 291–98.

Redish, Janice, and Dennis Wixon. "Task Analysis." In *Human-Computer Interaction Handbook*, edited by Julie Jacko and Andrew Sears, 927–48. Mahwah, NJ: Lawrence Erlbaum, 2003.

Reguera, Gemma, Kevin D. McCarthy, Teena Mehta, Julie S. Nicoll, Mark T. Tuominen, and Derek R. Lovley. "Extracellular Electron Transfer via Microbial Nanowires." *Nature* 435, no. 7045 (2005): 1098–101.

Reichhardt, Tony. "Satellite Smashers." *Air and Space Smithsonian* 22, no. 6 (March 2008): 50.

Reimers, C. E., P. Girguis, H. A. Stecher III, L. M. Tender, N. Ryckelynck, and P. Whaling. "Microbial Fuel Cell Energy from an Ocean Cold Seep." *Geobiology* 4 (2006): 123–26.

Renner, Michael. *The Anatomy of Resource Wars.* Worldwatch Paper no. 162. Edited by Thomas Prugh, State of the World Library. Danvers, MA: Worldwatch Institute, 2002.

Renuart, Gen Victor E., commander, US Northern Command, Gen Norton A. Schwartz, commander, US Transportation Command, and Adm Timothy J. Keating, commander, US Pacific Command. To chairman, Joint Chiefs of Staff. Memorandum, n.d.

Resource Data Center. "Alaska's Oil and Gas Industry." http://www .akrdc.org/issues/ oilgas/overview.html.

Rezaei, Farzaneh, Tom L. Richard, Rachel A. Brennan, and Bruce E. Logan. "Substrate-Enhanced Microbial Fuel Cells for Improved Remote Power Generation from Sediment-Based Systems." *Environmental Science and Technology* 41, no. 11 (June 2007): 4053–58.

Richelson, Jeffrey T. "Scientists in Black." *Scientific American*, 3 February 1998, 48–55. http://jya.com/sib.htm.

Ries, Robert, Melissa Bilec, Nuri Mehmet Gokhan, and Kim LaScola Needy. "The Economic Benefits of Green Buildings: A Comprehensive Case Study." *Engineering Economist* 51, no. 3 (2006): 259–95.

Ringeisen, Bradley R., Emily Henderson, Peter K. Wu, Jeremy Pietron, Ricky Ray, Brenda Little, Justin C. Biffinger, and Joanne M. Jones-Meehan. "High Power Density from a Miniature Microbial Fuel Cell Using Shewanella Oneidensis DSP 10." *Environmental Science and Technology* 40, no. 8 (15 April 2006): 2629–34.

Ringeisen, Bradley R., Ricky Ray, and Brenda Little. "A Miniature Microbial Fuel Cell Operating with an Aerobic Anode Chamber." *Journal of Power Sources* 165, no. 2 (20 March 2007): 591–97.

Rittmann, Bruce E. "The Role of Biotechnology in Water and Wastewater Treatment." Tempe, AZ: Arizona State University, Center for Environmental Biotechnology, 2007.

———, Martina Hausner, Frank Löffler, Nancy G. Love, Gerard Muyzer, Satoshi Okabe, Daniel B. Oerther, Jordan Peccia, Lutgarde Raskin, and Michael Wagner. "A Vista for Microbial Ecology and Environmental Biotechnology." *Environmental Science and Technology* 40, no. 4 (February 2006): 1096–103.

Roberts, Paul. *The End of Oil: On the Edge of a Perilous New World.* New York: Houghton Mifflin Company, 2004.

———, "Tapped Out." *National Geographic* 213, no. 6 (June 2008): 86–91.

Robson, David. "Calling Occupants of Interplanetary Craft, Danger Ahead." *New Scientist* 199, no. 2673 (18 September 2008): 24–25.

Rodrigo, M. A., P. Cañizares, J. Lobato, R. Paz, C. Sáez, and J. J. Linares. "Production of Electricity from the Treatment of Urban Waste Water Using a Microbial Fuel Cell." *Journal of Power Sources* 169, no. 1 (2007): 198–204.

Rosenbaum, Miriam, Feng Zhao, Uwe Schröder, and Fritz Scholz. "Interfacing Electrocatalysis and Biocatalysis with Tungsten Carbide: A High-Performance, Noble-Metal-Free Microbial Fuel Cell." *Angewandte Chemie* 45, no. 40 (October 2006): 6658–61.

Rosenthal, Elizabeth. "Biofuels Deemed a Greenhouse Threat." *New York Times*, 8 February 2008. http://www.nytimes.com/2008/02/08/science/earth/08wbiofuels.html.

Rozendal, René, Hubertus V. M. Hamelers, Redmar J. Molenkamp, and Cees J. N. Buisman. "Performance of Single Chamber Bio-catalyzed Electrolysis with Different Types of Ion Exchange Membranes." *Water Research* 41, no. 9 (May 2007): 1984–94.

Rumsfeld, Donald H. *The National Defense Strategy of the United States of America*. Washington, DC: Department of Defense, March 2005.

———. *Quadrennial Defense Review Report*. Washington, DC: Department of Defense, February 2006.

Russell, Anthony L. "Carpe DIEM: Seizing Strategic Opportunity in the Arctic." *Joint Force Quarterly* 51 (4th Quarter 2008): 94–101.

Scahill, Jeremy. *Blackwater: The Rise of the World's Most Powerful Mercenary Army*. New York: Nation Books, 2007.

Scearce, Diana, Katherine Fulton, and the Global Business Network. *What If? The Art of Scenario Thinking for Nonprofits*. Emeryville, CA: Global Business Network, 2004.

Schanding, Gregory T. "A Value Focused Thinking Model for the Development and Selection of Electrical Energy Source Alternatives at Military Installations." Master's thesis, Air Force Institute of Technology, 2004.

Schanz, Marc V. "Strategic Alaska." *Air Force Magazine*, November 2008, 46–49.

Schnaars, Steven P. *Megamistakes: Forecasting and the Myth of Rapid Technological Change*. New York: Free Press, 1988.

Schrag, Joel. "First Impressions Matter: A Model of Confirmation Bias." *Quarterly Journal of Economics* 114, no. 1 (February 1999): 37–83.

Schwartz, Peter, and Doug Randall. *An Abrupt Climate Change Scenario and Its Implications for United States National Security*. Emeryville, CA: Global Business Network, 2003.

Sciubba, Jennifer. "The Defense Implications of Demographic Trends." *Joint Force Quarterly* 48 (1st Quarter 2008): 121–28.

Scott, K., C. Murano, and G. Rimbu. "A Tubular Microbial Fuel Cell." *Journal of Applied Electrochemistry* 37, no. 9 (2007): 1063–68.

Sendagorta, Fidel. "Jihad in Europe: The Wider Context." *Survival* 47, no. 3 (Autumn 2005): 63–72.

Shaud, John A. *Air Force Strategic Study 2020–2030*. Air Force Research Institute. Maxwell AFB, AL: Air University Press, 2011.

Siewiorek, Daniel P., and Asim Smailagic. "User-Centered Interdisciplinary Design of Wearable Computers." In *Human-Computer Interaction Handbook*, edited by Julie Jacko and Andrew Sears, 295–312. Mahwah, NJ: Lawrence Erlbaum Associates, 2003.

Simonite, Tom. "Dew-Harvesting 'Web' Conjures Water out of Thin Air." *New Scientist*, 15 November 2007. http://technology.newscientist.com/channeltechdn12923-dewharvesting-web-conjures-water-out-of-thin-air.html.

Simons, Suzanne. *Master of War: Blackwater USA's Erik Prince and the Business of War*. New York: Harper Collins, 2009.

Singer, Peter. *Corporate Warriors: The Rise of the Privatized Military Industry*. Ithaca, NY: Cornell University Press, 2003.

Skinner, Tony. "Pentagon Urges Effort to Address Space Debris Threat." *Jane's Defence Weekly* 46, no. 18 (6 May 2009): 7.

———. "Spatial Awareness." *Jane's Defence Weekly* 46, no. 29 (22 July 2009): 24.

Smith, Justin. "Biofuels: The Past, Present and Future." *Energy Current*, 2 February 2009. http://www.energycurrent.com.

Smith, Keith C. *Russian Energy Pressure Fails to Unite Europe*. Washington, DC: CSIS, 24 January 2007.

Smith, Phillip J., and Norman D. Geddes. "A Cognitive Systems Engineering Approach to the Design of Decision Support Systems." In *Human-Computer Interaction Handbook*, edited by Julie Jacko and Andrew Sears, 573–602. Mahwah, NJ: Lawrence Erbaum Associates, 2003.

"Sony Reports High Power Microbial Fuel Cell." *Fuel Cells Bulletin* 2007, no. 10 (2007): 10.

Space and Naval Warfare Systems Command. San Diego Knowledge Management and Decision Support programs. www.spawar.navy.mil/.

"Special Section: Microbial Fuel Cells." *Environmental Science and Technology* 40, no. 17 (September 2006): 5162.

Stams, Alfons J. M., Frank A. de Bok, Caroline Plugge, Miriam H. A. Van Eekert, Jan Dolfing, and Gosse Schraa. "Exocellular Electron Transfer in Anaerobic Microbial Communities." *Environmental Microbiology* 8, no. 3 (March 2006): 371–82.

Stanger, Allison. *One Nation under Contract: The Outsourcing of American Power and the Future of Foreign Policy.* New Haven & London: Yale University Press, 2009.

St. John, Mark, David A. Korbus, Jeffrey G. Morrison, and Dylan Schmorrow. "Overview of the DARPA Augmented Cognition Technical Integration Experiment." *International Journal of Human-Computer Interaction* 17, no. 2 (2004): 131–49.

Stern, Todd, and William Antholis. "A Changing Climate: The Road Ahead for the United States." *Washington Quarterly,* no. 31 (Winter 2007–2008): 175–88.

Ter Heijne, Annemiek, Hubertus V. M. Hamelers, and Cees J. N. Buisman. "Microbial Fuel Cell Operation with Continuous Biological Ferrous Iron Oxidation of the Catholyte." *Environmental Science and Technology* 41, no. 11 (June 2007): 4130–34.

Than, Ker. "Orbital Cleanup." *Popular Science* 273, no. 1 (July 2008): 30–31.

Tiboni, Frank, and Matthew French. "Blue Force Tracking Gains Ground." *Federal Computer Week,* 22 March 2004.

Tomczak, Matthias, and J. Stewart Godfrey. *Regional Oceanography: An Introduction.* Tarrytown, NY: Elsevier Science Inc, 1994. http://gyre.umeoce.maine.edu/physicalocean/Tomczak/regoc/pdffiles/colour/single/07P-Arctic.pdf.

Torrey, J. Michael, John F. Westerman, William R. Taylor, Franklin H. Holcomb, and Joseph Bush. *Detailed Fuel Cell Demonstration Site Summary Report: Naval Hospital at Marine Corps Air Ground Combat Center—Twenty-Nine Palms.* Technical report no. ERDC/CERL TR-06-17. Champaign, IL: US Army Engineer Research and Development Center, Construction Engineering Research Laboratory, June 2006.

Treadwell, Mead, chair, US Arctic Research Commission. *Is America Prepared for an Accessible Arctic?: Hearings before US Senate Commerce Committee.* Washington, DC, 24 June 2008.

Tsui, Eliza M., and Mark R. Wiesner. "Fast Proton Conducting Ceramic Membranes Derived from Ferroxane Nanoparticle-Precursors as Fuel Cell Electrolytes." *Journal of Membrane Science* 318, nos. 1–2 (June 2008): 79–83.

Tufte, Edward R. *Visual Explanations: Images and Quantities, Evidence and Narrative.* Cheshire, CT: Graphics Press, 1997.

"2008 Hybrids Certified as Tax Credit for Toyota and Lexus Comes to an End," 8 November 2007. Internal Revenue Service press release IR-2007-186.http://www.irs.gov/newsroom/article/0,,id=175518,00.html.

Tzu, Sun. *The Art of War.* Translated by Samuel B. Griffith. London: Oxford University Press, 1963.

UN, Department of Economic and Social Affairs. *World Population Prospects: The 2006 Revision.* New York: UN, 2007.

UN Environment Programme (UNEP). *Global Environment Outlook* (GEO⁴). UNEP, 2007.

UN General Assembly. Resolution 44/34. "International Convention against the Recruitment, Use, Financing and Training of Mercenaries." 4 December 1989. http://www.un.org/documents/ga/res/44/a44r034.htm.

Upson, Sandra. "U.S. Air Force Synthetic-Fuel Program in Limbo." *IEEE Spectrum*, September 2008. http://www.spectrum.ieee.org/sep08/6694.

US Air Force Scientific Advisory Board. *Report on Air Force Command and Control: The Path Ahead.* Vol. 1, *Summary.* Report no. SAB-TR-00-01. Washington, DC: Secretary of the Air Force, Chief of Staff, Pentagon, December 2000.

———. *Report on Air Force Command and Control: The Path Ahead.* Vol. 2, *Panel Reports.* Report no. SAB-TR-00-01. Washington, DC: Secretary of the Air Force, Chief of Staff, Pentagon, 2003.

US Air Force Space and C4ISR [Command, Control, Communications, Computers, Intelligence, Surveillance, and Reconnaissance] Capabilities CONOPS [Concept of Operations]. Peterson AFB, CO: Air Force Space Command, 29 September 2003.

US Arctic Research Commission. "Congress Hears Needs for New Icebreaker Vessels as White House Formulates Arctic Policy," 19 August 2008. www.arctic.gov/files/congress_hears_needs-20080819.doc.

US Department of Defense (DOD). *The Implementation of Network-Centric Warfare*. Washington, DC: Force Transformation, Office of the Secretary of Defense, 5 January 2005.

———. *National Defense Strategy of the United States*. Washington, DC: Office of the Secretary of Defense, June 2008.

———. *Quadrennial Defense Review Report*. Washington, DC: DOD, February 2010.

———. *The 21st Century Air Force: Irregular Warfare Strategy*. Washington, DC: DOD, January 2009.

———. *USCENTCOM 3rd Quarter Contractor Census Report*. Washington, DC: DOD, June 2009.

US Department of Energy. "Building America Research Is Leading the Way to Zero Energy Homes." Fact Sheet. United States Department of Energy, Energy Efficiency and Renewable Energy, June 2005.

———. *A National Vision of America's Transition to a Hydrogen Economy—to 2030 and Beyond*. Washington, DC: United States Department of Energy, February 2002.

———, and US Department of Transportation. *Hydrogen Posture Plan: An Integrated Research, Development and Demonstration Plan*. Washington, DC: US Depts. of Energy and Transportation, 2006.

US Department of State. Announcement of Appointment of Special Envoy for Climate Change, Todd Stern. Washington, DC, 26 January 2009.

———. "Barbary Wars, 1801–1805 and 1815–1816." http://www.state.gov/ r/pa/ho/time/jd/92068.htm (accessed 31 March 2009).

US Department of the Air Force. *The Air Force Handbook 2007*. Washington, DC: Department of the Air Force, 2007.

———. "U.S. Air Force Renewable Energy Program." Brochure. Tyndall AFB, FL: Air Force Civil Engineer Support Agency, 2006.

———. *US Air Force Transformation Flight Plan 2004*. Washington, DC: HAF/XP, November 2003.

US Department of the Navy. *FORCEnet: A Functional Concept for the 21st Century*. Washington, DC: Chief of Naval Operations and Commandant of the Marine Corps, 2005.

US Energy Information Administration. "Ethanol—A Renewable Fuel." EIA Energy Kid's website. Accessed 31 January 2009. http://www.eia.gov/kids/index.cfm.

———. *International Energy Outlook 2007*. Washington, DC: United States Department of Energy, Office of Integrated Analysis and Forecasting, May 2007.

———. "Petroleum Basic Statistics." Official energy statistics from the US government, reviewed September 2008. http://www.eia.doe .gov/basics/quickoil.html.

———. "US Imports of Crude Oil." Accessed 6 February 2009. http:// tonto.eia.doe.gov/dnav/pet/hist/mcrimus1m.htm.

———. "World Estimated Recoverable Coal." Official energy statistics from the US government, reviewed 13 June 2005. http://www.eia .doe.gov/fuelcoal.html.

US Geological Survey. *Circum-Arctic Resource Appraisal: Estimates of Undiscovered Oil and Gas North of the Arctic Circle*. Washington, DC: Department of the Interior, May 2008.

US Green Building Council. *Building Momentum: National Trends and Prospects for High-Performance Green Buildings*. Washington, DC: US Green Building Council, February 2003.

US Joint Forces Command (USJFCOM). *The Joint Operating Environment (JOE) 2008: Challenges and Implications for the Future Joint Force*. Norfolk, VA: USJFCOM, 2008.

———. *The Joint Operating Environment (JOE) 2010*. Norfolk, VA: USJFCOM, 2010.

———. *The JOE 2010: Joint Operating Environment*. Suffolk, VA: Joint Futures Group, February 2010.

US Senate. *Secretary of State Confirmation of Hillary Clinton: Hearings before the Foreign Relations Committee*. 111th Cong., 1st sess., January 2009.

Vendura, George J., Patrick Malone, and Larry Crawford Jr. *A Novel, Light Weight Solar Array: Comparison with Conventional Systems*. Technical report. Tustin, CA: L'Garde, 2006.

Von Stackelberg, Peter. "The Future of Universal Water." *Nanotechnology Now*, February 2008. http://www.nano tech-now.com /news.cgi?story_id=28193.

Walker, Charles W., Jr., and Alyssa L. Walker. *Biological Fuel Cell Functional as an Active or Reserve Power Source*. Adelphia, MD: US Army Research Laboratory, June 2006.

Warnke, David M. "Making the Business Case for Sustainable Design in the Department of Defense." Master's thesis, Air Force Institute of Technology, 2004.

Warwick, Graham. "Fuel for Jet A Debate." *Aviation Week and Space Technology* 168, no. 22 (2 June 2008): 38.

Westly, Erica. "Arctic Land Grabs Could Cause Eco-Disaster." *Discover*, August 2007.

Wheeler, Howard. *A Mission to Clear Dangerous Debris from Space.* Guildford, UK: University of Surrey, 2010. http://www2.surrey ac.uk/mediacentre/press/2010/26099_a_mission_to_clear _dangerous_debris_from_space.htm.

White, Melissa K., Scott M. Lux, James L. Knight, Michael J. Binder, Franklin H. Holcomb, and Nicolas M. Josefik. *DOD Residential Proton Exchange Membrane (PEM) Fuel Cell Demonstration Program.* Vol. 2, *Summary of Fiscal Years 2001–2003 Projects.* Final report. Champaign, IL: Engineer Research and Development Center, September 2005.

White House. "The Agenda: Energy & Environment." http://www .whitehouse.gov/agenda/energy_and_environment/ (accessed 26 January 2009).

Whole Building Design Guide (WBDG) Sustainable Committee. "Optimize Energy Use," 13 October 2008. http://www.wbdg.org /design/minimize_consumption.php.

Wickens, Christopher D., John Lee, Yii Liu, and Sallie Gordon Becker. *An Introduction to Human Factors Engineering.* 2nd ed. Upper Saddle River, NJ: Pearson Prentice Hall, 2004.

——, and Justin G. Hollands. *Engineering Psychology and Human Performance.* 3rd ed. Upper Saddle River, NJ: Prentice Hall, 2000.

Williams, Huw. "Military Planners Explore Options for Reducing Reliance on Oil-Based Energy." *Jane's International Defence Review,* 6 January 2009. http://idr.janes.com/public/idr/features/shtml.

Williamson, Ray A. "The Growing Hazard of Orbiting Debris." *Science and Technology* 8, no. 1 (Fall 1991): 77–82.

Wulf, Herbert. *Internationalizing and Privatizing War and Peace.* Houndmills, United Kingdom: Palgrave Macmillan, 2005.

Yoffe, Shira B. "Basins at Risk: Conflict and Cooperation over International Freshwater Resources." PhD diss., Oregon State University, 2001.

Yokoyama, Hiroshi, Hideyuki Ohmori, Mitsuyoshi Ishida, Miyoko Waki, and Yasuo Tanaka. "Treatment of Cow-Waste Slurry by a Microbial Fuel Cell and the Properties of the Treated Slurry as a Liquid Manure." *Animal Science Journal* 77, no. 6 (December 2006): 634–38.

Yoshikawa, Hidekazu. "Modeling Humans in Human-Computer Interaction." In *Human-Computer Interaction Handbook*, edited by Julie Jacko and Andrew Sears, 118–46. Mahwah, NJ: Lawrence Erlbaum Associates, 2003.

You, Shijie, Qingliang Zhao, Jinna Zhang, Junqiu Jiang, and Shiqi Zhao. "A Microbial Fuel Cell Using Permanganate as the Cathodic Electron Acceptor." *Journal of Power Sources* 162, no. 2 (November 2006): 1409–15.

———. "Sustainable Approach for Leachate Treatment: Electricity Generation in Microbial Fuel Cell." *Journal of Environmental Science and Health, Part A: Toxic/Hazardous Substances and Environmental Engineering* 41, no. 12 (2006): 2721–34.

Yusoff, Mohd Nasir. "Eye-in-the-Sky over Malacca Straits from Sept 13." *Bernama.com*, 8 September 2005. http://www.bernama.com/bernama/v3/news_lite.php?id=154485.

Zhiyong, Ren, Thomas E. Ward, and John M. Regan. "Electricity Production from Cellulose in a Microbia Fuel Cell Using a Defined Binary Culture." *Environmental Science and Technology* 41, no. 13 (July 2007): 4781–86.

Index